Love Ledgers

Confessions of a Plain Jane Accountant

Connie Lukey

For 'Mr. Wonderful'

Choose not your friends
By outward show
The feather floats,

While pearls lie low.

— Unknown

1

THE TOP TWELVE reasons for becoming an accountant, according to Jane Parker, CPA, on this day of April 30, 1999:

12. All of the openings in mortician school were filled.
11. Random people on the street stop to ask you what the square root of 2,065 is.
10. You get to express sympathy for people who paid more in taxes this year than you will earn over the course of your lifetime.
9. You find new and creative ways to claim your cat as a dependent.
8. At parties, you can regale your friends with those fascinating work stories.
7. You own the Mercedes Benz of calculators.
6. You love those rockin' tunes they play while you're on hold with the Canada Revenue Agency.
5. Ever since the television show *Freaks and Geeks* aired, it's become cool to be a nerd.

4. When funerals arise unexpectedly, you don't have to rush out and buy a dark suit.

3. From March 1 to April 30 you have the perfect excuse to avoid visiting your mother-in-law.

2. You never get stuck in rush hour traffic, because by the time you leave the office everyone else has gone home.

And the number-one reason for becoming an accountant:

1. Even in the deepest and darkest of recessions, you will never have to worry about being unemployed. Because, let's face it, no one else would ever want your job.

2

IT'S SEVERAL MINUTES before sunrise when my dachshund, Wanker, begins bleating along with the clock radio by my bed. Ignoring him, I snuggle deeper beneath the warm blankets, waking slowly to the patter of the early-morning DJ. One more song—then I'll get up.

It's my first day off in fifty-seven days, and I've looked forward to sleeping in, but I'm slowly accepting that this is not what fate has in store for me. Now the piercing ring of the cordless phone joins the din. My right hand emerges from the covers and feels about the bedside table.

"Is this Jane who is thirty-nine today?" a joyful, game show announcer–like voice booms into my ear.

Wanker lets out a playful growl. He considers it his job to wake me each morning and is affronted by this interloper intruding on our routine.

"Am I on the radio?" I ask the disembodied voice.

"Thaaaaaaat's right, Jane. How does it feel to be thirty-nine today?"

"You must have the wrong Jane."

"I don't think so. There's only one Jane Parker in Grey County who is turning thirty-nine today."

"Do you think you could say that one more time?"

"I sure can. Congratulations, Jane. You are thirty-nine today."

And so begins the first day of May 1999, the anniversary of my thirty-ninth year on this planet. It's actually a double celebration, because, for accountants, May 1 is the real New Year's Day, April 30 being the final day of Canadian tax season. Every year at this time, like big old bears after a long winter's hibernation, we lumber forth from our cubicle caves and office dens, stretching and yawning, our tired eyes blinking in the sun, to join civilization once again.

I pull on workout shorts and a sports bra, pour some kibble in Wanker's dish, thumb through my alphabetized collection of VHS exercise tapes and slide a step aerobics routine into my VCR. Since my physical assets have a tendency to grow exponentially with hours logged on a computer, I combat fat by working out every morning. For me there's a thin line between voluptuous and voluminous; I work hard to stay on the light side of it.

"Why do they say 'Keep your spine neutral,'" I ask Wanker as we finish off with hamstring stretches. "Are they worried your spine is going to take up with an insurgent group and attack Serbia or something?"

Wanker tilts his head as if deep in thought, his soulful brown eyes trained on mine, forehead furrowed in concentration.

"I bet the Swiss have no problem with this one."

But my thoughts only confuse the little dachshund, who is German and fails to make the connection.

After forty-two minutes of high-impact step aerobics, I shower, mix up some yogurt and granola with berries, and have breakfast on my rec room couch in front of the television.

Normally it takes forever to blow-dry my shoulder-length blonde hair into the power bob that frames my heart-shaped face and blue–grey eyes. But today is not an office day, so I just pull it through an old ball cap in a ponytail. I put on jeans and a Tshirt from my wardrobe, meticulously organized according to the FIFO (first-in, first-out) inventory method in order to negate outfit duplication. Then I drive downtown with Wanker riding shotgun.

We go for a walk beside the bay before I buy an ice cream cone and sit on a bench overlooking Owen Sound Harbour. After the months I spent holed up in front of a computer screen, the sun feels good on my back and shoulders.

At the far end of the harbour there's a flurry of activity aboard the MS Chi-Cheemaun, the Manitoulin Island ferry that's been docked here all winter. Chi-Cheemaun is the Ojibwa word for "Big Canoe," but today it looks as pretty as a cruise ship, all spiffed up for its annual voyage to Tobermory, where it'll spend the summer shuttling passengers between there and South Baymouth. Without the usual load of vehicles, the ferry sits high in the water.

Other pleasure crafts bob and weave in the surf. Sailboats, motor boats and jet skis bounce through the choppy waters of Georgian Bay. An ear-piercing blast from the Chi-Cheemaun notifies them that it is pulling out into the channel, leaving the small boats to fight through its wake. I wondered how many of these trips the ferry's made in its lifetime.

Taking in the scene helps me set aside the stress of the last two months and take a moment to calm my harried head. Birthdays always put me in a reflective mood.

The smell of fresh lake water mingles with vinegar and deep-fried potatoes from a nearby chip truck. On Monday I'll return to the office and face the heap of files that got shoved aside in the race to finish tax season, but today I just want to breathe in the beauty that is Georgian Bay in May.

Later in the afternoon I go to my parents' place for my family birthday party. My folks live on a small hobby farm in the Georgian Bluffs region, just north of Balmy Beach. My sister Shelly, brother-in-law Steve and their two children are coming up from Meaford for it, so they pick me up on their way through town and we ride out together.

My dad has just finished cutting the large front lawn on his riding mower and is edging around the trees with a weed whacker when we drive up. He shuts off the motor and greets me with a big bear hug as I clamber out of the van, his face sweaty under a faded red cap. We head toward the house, where my mother has set the table and ordered pizza for everyone.

It's a little early for dinner, and the kids are dying to go for a ride. Next to his family, my father's three great loves are horses, trucks and dogs. He keeps a chestnut Quarter Horse for trail rides and a fat bay Newfoundland pony for the kids in the small barn at the end of the driveway. I saddle up Newfie and take turns leading him around the front yard with Shelly's kids, Maddison and Billy.

When they're finished with the pony, I slip a hackamore on the old Quarter Horse, Roy, and we go for a quick bare-back gallop around the field's perimeter. I clamp my thighs tight against Roy's withers and hold onto his mane with my left hand. There's nothing quite so exhilarating as a thousand pounds on thundering hooves charging around a field, and it leaves me a bit breathless.

Upon returning to the house, Mom takes one look at my sweaty horse-hair-coated backside and demands that I change clothes before coming in contact with her furniture. I've donned the spare pair of jeans I have in the car just as my grandparents arrive with the pizza. A feeding frenzy ensues as the kids fight to see who can eat the most slices. When they're finally full, Mom places a birthday cake with three lit candles in front of me. She uses one candle for each decade. Next year, I will have four.

My overexcited niece and nephew crowd in beside me.

"Don't spit on the cake," my sister warns three-year-old Billy after we sing "Happy Birthday."

I take a deep breath, make my perennial wish for Prince Charming to show up so we can start our family, and blow out the candles.

"Aunt Jane," says Billy, eating cake with his mouth open. "Do you have a dad?"

I point to my father at the end of the table. "Grandpa James is my dad."

"No, I mean a dad that you take home with you."

I shake my head and stick a fork in the creamy white icing.

Mom and Dad give me a one-hundred-dollar bill for my birthday, and the kids present a Tshirt with a dachshund on it. My sister gives me a book entitled *Lonely No More: How to Meet Your Soulmate in Less than a Year*. It's the kind of book I always look at in the self-help aisles of our local bookstore but am too embarrassed to purchase.

"Thanks, Shelly. I can use all the help I get. I don't want to be single and alone when I turn forty."

"But forty is the new thirty," she says.

"My ovaries didn't get the memo."

"You should make a pact. No more dating Mr. Right Now; give yourself a deadline to find Mr. Right before you turn forty," Shelly tells me.

"But I haven't been dating anyone, Mr. Right or otherwise. There are no single men of a suitable age left in Grey County. They all either married or left town in their thirties. It's not that I haven't been looking."

"Then you may have to expand your parameters," Mom says.

"I asked Nana to marry me when I was sixteen," Grandpa Alf says.

I'd love to find a man and have a family, and I know my mother is getting anxious, her world revolving around her grandchildren as it does. But sometimes I feel like nothing I do will ever be good enough. If I discover a cure for cancer or become the first woman to walk on the moon, to my family I'll still be Jane – The One Who Never Got Married.

When I get home I dive right into the book. My younger self would have made fun of anyone who'd read something like this, but thirty-nine-year-old single me can't put it down.

The first chapter is titled "You Deserve to be Loved."

Interesting… do most people who buy this book believe they don't deserve to be loved? Surely that's not my problem. It's true there were many times over the years when I was overweight and unhappy and didn't see how anyone could possibly find me attractive. But those days disappeared a year ago when I lost eighty pounds and could fit comfortably into a size six. Of course I deserve to be loved.

I know my childbearing years are dwindling, and I really want to find a partner, but it should be an exciting adventure, not an act of loneliness and desperation. Life is a journey and all that.

The time has come to be proactive. With tax season over, there are no excuses for not getting out more.

Meet Your Soulmate recommends walking your dog as great way to meet people.

"Get ready to be my man magnet, Wank," I say, hoisting his small sausage body in the air so he can look me in the eye.

The book also advocates telling friends and acquaintances you're looking to meet someone, so they can set you up with men they think might be right for you. When my friend Kristen calls to wish me a happy birthday, I enlist her support.

My answering machine has languished in the closet since the last time I gained weight. I pull it out, dust it off and hook it back it into my phone, its red light a glowing beacon in my living room.

In bed I'm too worked up to sleep, anticipating my exciting year. It feels good to have my friends and family pulling for me. We're all in this together.

3

I WAKE UP the next morning excited to launch right into the first day of my Find a Man Before I'm Forty project. My weight is down, tax season is over, and spring is in the air. I'm ready.

I love my little one-and-a-half-storey house just off 6th Avenue East. In Owen Sound all of the streets names are numbers, with streets running east and west, avenues north and south. Unimaginative, perhaps, but it makes it easy to get where you're going; you just have to find your place on the grid.

I bought the house from a carpenter who had done a beautiful job renovating it from top to bottom. An oak staircase descends from the main floor to a cozy pine-panelled rec room complete with an oak bar. The bathroom houses a whirlpool soaker tub and skylight. There's a tidy, newly refurbished kitchen, and I can watch the goldfish swim in their pond from a large deck off the back of the house. I scoured Owen Sound for four years before I finally found it. My dad calls it the doll's house.

When I bought it last December, I was sick of wasting my money on rent and having nothing to show for it. It's hard enough getting by on one not overly substantial income, and, since the accounting firm I work for doesn't have a pension plan, I knew I should be investing for my future. Plus, I love having my own personal space. I'm proud to be an independent woman of the nineties, owning a home on my own.

My mother, on the other hand, viewed buying a house as giving up on finding a husband and was convinced things would go terribly wrong. She was sure any house I could afford would be high-maintenance and, therefore, she would be called upon for maintenance or to bail me out financially. I've been supporting myself on a shoestring for the better part of two decades, but Mom has always had a strong man to look after her, and the idea of me doing things in such a non-traditional way makes her uncomfortable.

Mom isn't the only one who struggled with the concept. When I finally took the plunge and signed the mortgage, our office farm-tax accountant, Larry, asked, "Why would you buy a house with stairs; isn't it going to be hard getting up and down them when you're old?"

"There was a waiting list at the retirement villa or I would have moved there directly," I told him.

I work at Fielding Austin Cooper Keyes LLP, or FACK for short. My childhood dream was to either follow in the footsteps of Olympic figure skating champion Dorothy Hamill or be a cashier at Woolco. Although my thick blonde hair was perfectly suited to Dorothy's signature wedge cut, an intense dislike of being cold combined with an inability to skate thwarted my path to the podium. My second choice ended with Woolco's untimely demise.

The office of Fielding Austin Cooper Keyes LLP is in a beautiful century-old red brick mansion on 1st Avenue West, overlooking the Sydenham River.

Originally built for one of Owen Sound's wealthiest families, the house was converted to an office over fifty years ago. On the main floor the former living room is our reception area, and the dining room has been converted into a large boardroom. Two large partner offices are situated at the north and south corners of the house on both floors. My office is at the back of the second floor. Although the tall chimney still stands on the outside of the building, the ancient fireplace was covered over with drywall decades ago. Early this spring a pregnant raccoon decided the chimney was the perfect place for a nest. On the nights when I work late, I can hear the raccoon family scraping away inside the walls, giving the place an eerie, haunted-house feeling.

Old client files are stored in the blue-shingled attic on the third floor. Back when I was an articling student, or grunt, as we're known in public accounting, cleaning out the attic was one of my summer jobs. Spider webs, mouse droppings and working papers mouldy from years of being dripped on by the ancient leaky roof were some of the treasures I uncovered in the archived files. A small blue turret with a brass weathervane houses our library of accounting and tax manuals.

It's my first day back after tax season, so I take a moment to assess the damages. Our busy season begins in January, when all our clients with December year-ends start pouring in. It's a paper spring runoff that doesn't stop until the riverbanks are full to overflowing. As a result, accountants are rarely allowed to take time off from January to June; and asking for a day off in April is the equivalent of Santa Claus wanting a vacation day on Christmas Eve.

Essentially, in January we leave the harbour and begin navigating the rapids; RSPs, T4s, and T5s have to be out by the end of February. Personal tax season in March and April takes us right over the falls. Just when we think the worst is over and we can breathe again, the June 30 deadline for all those December year-end corporations comes along and sucks us back into the whirlpool.

All of the jobs that came in during the last three weeks of April and were pushed aside for personal tax returns are now scattered haphazardly in piles around my office. I begin the job of sifting through the rubble, figuring out the pecking order by taking notes on who's been waiting the longest, who has the most urgent deadlines and who has the biggest mess to clean up.

Sam Austin, one of the four partners I work for at FACK, strides briskly into my office, running his fingers through what little remains of his hair. For years Sam sported a traditional middle-aged-man comb-over, but his wife has recently convinced him to keep it closely cropped. If only she could get him to nix the floods.

What Sam may lack in fashion sense he makes up for in devotion to detail. Whether the client is large or small, Sam puts hours into every job, rewriting the notes to the financial statements and rewriting them again.

Sam is a good man who truly cares about his clients. But working for a perfectionist can drive even the most conscientious of staff to the brink of insanity. The competing pressures of bringing a file in under budget and meeting Sam's exacting standards are incredibly stressful. The only way to satisfy both goals is to work additional hours and not record your time. This is the practice of almost every accountant, but few will admit to it.

"I had hair like Lyle Lovett before I got Perry as a client," he says.

Perry is a client who recently purchased a chain of laundromats in Grey County called Laundramada, which, as a surprise to no one, is not doing very well.

"How far along are you on his year-end? The bank is threatening to pull the plug on his line of credit if we don't get financial statements to them stat."

Sam is addicted to the television show *ER* and has recently started tossing medical jargon around. I envision a team of accountants in scrubs rushing toward the Laundramada financial statements with defibrillation paddles in an effort to jump-start its weakening vital statistics.

"I got about halfway through it, then I called his new bookkeeper Cassie to go over some things I need clarification on. She hasn't gotten back to me yet."

"How is it so far?"

"Let's just say Cassie's bookkeeping is far from stellar."

"That's a cosmic understatement."

"Way to milk it, Sam."

I sigh and tell him I'll move Perry to the top of the pile and get on it right away. Then I dig in and focus for the rest of the morning.

At noon I attend a luncheon hosted by a local human relations group. *Meet Your Soulmate* encourages readers to view all such gatherings as an opportunity to connect with potential partners, so in an effort to put my best self out there I've dressed in a tight-fitting black pencil skirt and a red silk shirt.

Unfortunately, I have the time wrong. When I show up twenty minutes late, everyone is already eating. A nice man instructs me to go downstairs and hang up my coat.

From the coat room I notice the door to the adjoining bathroom is open and walk in. Performing a last-minute hair and make-up check, I glance in the mirror and see there are urinals on the wall. Has it finally come to this? Am I so desperate to meet a man that I'm magnetically pulled into men's washrooms?

Luckily I slip out unnoticed, join my table and get through the meal without further embarrassment. I scan the room but don't see any promising prospects—at least none without rings on their fingers.

Back at the office there are several urgent messages from Sam, Perry, and Perry's bookkeeper. My butt has barely hit my chair when the phone rings yet again.

This time it's our receptionist/office administrator, Fiona, calling me from the front desk.

"Jane, you should look behind you."

Twisting in my chair, I strain to see my backside.

In the centre of my skirt there's a gaping red hole, as if I'm waving a red flag at a bull with my behind. I'd worn my brightest red panties. I must have forgotten to do up the zip at the back of my skirt. It had been undone for the entire luncheon. Sam, the other FACK partners and a large portion of Owen Sound's most prominent business professionals had been in attendance.

I push the incident out of my mind and continue to plough through the Laundramada file so I can submit it for review before I go home. I get it all done except for a couple of simple questions I need answers from Sam on. But every

time I walk down to his office at the south corner of the second floor he's on the phone.

In desperation I send an email to Collette, whose cubicle
is just outside his office. Collette and Anne are two staff
members I refer to collectively as the negativity sisters due
to their great love of gossiping about everyone in the office.
Collette is prone to talking for hours; I have no idea what
she puts on her timesheet. She has long brown hair and her
eyeballs protrude slightly, like the actor Marty Feldman's
or an exotic goldfish's. Four years older than me, Collette
has retained every piece of clothing she ever purchased.
She files them in her closet in order of wear date and cycles
through them regularly. Today she is wearing a thin violet
chiffon frock festooned with satin ribbons around its ruf-
fled collar. I remember wearing a similar one to my cousin's
wedding in 1982.

It's almost five now. In a hurry to get going, I dash off the
following to Collette:

> To: PartnerSam@FACK.ca
> "HELLO COLLETTE!!!! CAN YOU PLEASE LET
> ME KNOW IF SIR CHATS-A-LOT EVER STOPS
> YACKING AND GETS OFF THE PHONE SO I CAN
> ASK HIM A QUESTION?"

For added emphasis, I attach a clipart picture of a mammoth
telephone and hit Send.

I've barely clicked my mouse when an instantaneous
roar of laughter emanates from Sam's office. I realize I've
sent the email to Sam instead of Collette.

Thank god Sam has a sense of humour. He prints off my errant email and pins it to the bulletin board behind his desk. If I'd sent it to FACK's other partners, Dean, Joe, or Frank, I'd be in deep trouble.

It's almost seven by the time I finally get the information I need from Sam, finish the file, and leave it on his desk for review.

4

I WAS BORN in Owen Sound General Hospital in the spring of 1960. My mother, Catherine MacDougall, had been a secretary for the municipality of Grey County, but she was asked to quit her job when her pregnancy began to show. It was what women did back then.

My mother was considered an attractive woman. Every night before bed she coated her face with a thin layer of Vaseline petroleum jelly; she'd read Doris Day did the same in order to maintain her eternal youth. When I was very young Mom taught me that tucking your shirt tails into your underpants was the secret to looking neat and pulled together. I followed her advice until the eighth grade, when Vinnie Vlchek pointed out that the waistband of my pastel days-of-the-week underpants said it was only Tuesday when, in fact, it was Friday already.

My parents met at work.

My dad, Jim Parker, was also a Grey County employee. His job was operating heavy equipment for the roads department. He drove bulldozers and backhoes in the summer, snowploughs in the winter. My father worked hard to support his family, never turning down a chance for overtime shifts. And there was no shortage of opportunity to work extra hours in the winter, when the Lake Huron streamers deposited blankets of snow all over the Bruce Peninsula.

I was the first child. Our quiet lives were shattered two years after my birth by the arrival of Shelly, who entered the world screaming and has yet to calm herself. After three years of trying to get her to take an afternoon nap, my mother gave up and relinquished control forever. My earliest memories are of being continuously shushed when Dad returned from a long shift and my sister had finally fallen asleep.

Both my parents had grown up on farms, and we lived on a seven-acre lot one side road over from my grandparents' farm in Georgian Bluffs. When I was six my father bought me a fat Shetland pony named Tank and tied him to a cement block in our backyard, since the pasture wasn't fenced yet.

My grandparents, Betty 'Nana' and Alfred 'Alf' MacDougall, still live on their hundred-acre soybean farm, although Alf rents it out these days. His day job had him travelling all over as a cow inseminator for a company out of Guelph and caused him to be known as the man responsible for more pregnancies than anyone in Grey County.

"Can you please move the bull semen out of the trunk, Alf?" my grandma would say every Thursday when she needed to drive into town for groceries.

It was a simpler time. Our phone was on a party line, our television had an antenna, and on days when it wasn't windy we could get two Canadian and three American stations. Our telephone ring was two longs and a short. If there was nothing good on television you could always listen in on your neighbours' phone conversations.

As the eldest child in our family, I assumed the role of responsible good girl who always did as she was told. According to Mom, I slept peacefully through the entire night from my first day home from the hospital, leading her to believe that childrearing was simple and she would have a big family. Shelly quickly debunked this mythology; she woke up eight times during her first night at home. If my sister was going to be the squeaky wheel that got the grease, I would be the well-oiled machine that required no attention whatsoever.

My attempts to keep peace in the family did nothing to appease Shelly, who thrived on belittling me every chance she got. What little self-confidence I was born with plummeted under the barrage of her continuous criticism.

But life on the farm provided fond memories, too. I loved the country life; the trees, the rocks, the beauty of the Bruce Peninsula. I cherished time spent reading, drawing, watching television, riding horses and hanging out with my best friend, Angie, who lived around the corner on Highway 40. At school I worked hard and did well academically.

The one area of my life I couldn't control was my relationship with food. High-calorie treats were my downfall, and I frequently hid stashes in my room, a squirrel hoarding nuts for winter. Luckily my mother, who ate the same breakfast of dry whole-wheat toast, half a grapefruit with a teaspoon of sugar, and black coffee every day for seventeen years, did not believe in keeping such decadent delights around the house. Since we lived in the country and I had no access to convenience stores, I maintained a healthy weight for my entire childhood.

Every morning Shelly and I waited at the end of our lane for our ancient bus driver, Mrs. Thoob, who drove us in to Keppel-Sarawak Public School at forty miles an hour. She wore a polka-dot kerchief tied around her head to hold her rollers in place. It was at Keppel-Sarawak that I first met Angie. Even at six years old she was a super-energized flurry of non-stop action, the perfect foil for my quiet bookishness. On many occasions I stopped Angie from leaping off a cliff, while she pulled me out of my shell.

Although tall, dark, Amazonian, Angie had the complete opposite of my gentle spirit, we did share a love of fashion, or what we could find of it in Grey County. Angie liked to sew her own clothes, although she often rushed, resulting in some early wardrobe malfunctions.

Angie had great ideas and was an enthusiastic speaker. I was quieter but more industrious and enjoyed putting in the work required to get the job done. Together we made a great team, and I knew we would be best friends forever.

5

"HEY, JANE. WHY don't you come out for a drink with Doug and me on Friday?" Anne asks. "He's golfing with his friend Ed."

Anne is the other negativity sister. When I moved back to Owen Sound eight years ago, Collette and Anne were two thirty-something singles in the office, and they'd welcomed me as the third; we were a tightknit group. But now Anne and Collette are married, making me the odd woman out in a firm that prides itself on balance.

Anne is three years younger; we had both attended West Hill Secondary School in Owen Sound but travelled in different circles. My friends were geeks; she hung out with the preppy kids. Despite the fact that I'd had better marks than Anne in high school, she is a chartered accountant to my CGA and never misses an opportunity to pull rank. Luckily her specialty is auditing, which I abhor and sidestep as much as possible, so for the most part I'm able to avoid working with her.

Anne never exercises but maintains a slim figure due to her distaste for most food. She has no muscle tone whatsoever and her large breasts flop almost to her belly, like half-filled hot-water bottles. She can be very attractive when wearing a smile and a push-up bra; however, these two occurrences rarely happen simultaneously.

Ed is a friend of her husband, Doug, and I had met him briefly when we sat a CGA exam together a few years ago. He seemed reasonably good-looking and funny, and I appreciate Anne's efforts to set me up. As it says in my new bible, *Meet Your Soulmate*, "Never turn down a blind date; sometimes your friends know what you need better than you do."

Wanker looks on as I spend forty-five minutes working on my hair and make-up then test-drive seven outfits before arriving at what I hope looks naturally beautiful and not as though I'm trying too hard. I drive up along the lake to meet Anne at the Owen Sound Golf and Country Club.

"Ed couldn't make it," she announces as I pull out one of the club's creaky wooden tapestry hard-backed chairs and sit down beside her.

This isn't the first time Ed has pulled a runner. Back in February Anne planned to host a Super Bowl party, telling me her grand plan was to invite both Ed and I. This fell through at the last minute when Ed cancelled, claiming he wasn't feeling well.

Sitting at the big window, we watch as the golfers roll in over the hill of the eighteenth green.

"Anne, one cancellation could be coincidence, but two is a pattern. Ed is making it clear he's not interested in me."

Anne appears to accept this.

"Well, there is one member here who is single," she tells me.

"In the whole Owen Sound golf club there's only one single male?" No wonder I can't seem to meet anyone.

"Actually there are three, but two are in their twenties and the other is forty-three."

"How do you know this?"

"I looked it up when I was doing the revenue test on the membership fees." Anne is in charge of the golf club audit.

"And there's only one single male over thirty?"

"Yes. He's an engineer and he golfs in the Friday-afternoon league. According to my calculations he should be coming over the hill at any moment."

"I know that feeling."

Sure enough, several minutes and two beers later the sole single guy's threesome crests the hill.

"That's him." Anne points to a tall, dark and plain-looking gentleman trudging over the hill pulling a golf cart.

"He works at Tenneco and he's an automotive engineer. We're going to pair you off with him at the next charity scramble tournament."

I find him neither attractive nor unattractive. He is just a man I know nothing about, but apparently he is the only remaining option, so I must take him or leave him.

"How do you know he doesn't have a girlfriend?"

"Look at those pants. Do you think a girlfriend would allow him out of the house dressed like that?"

That evening Shelly calls to ask if I want to spend the night at her place. Steve is out of town and she says she wants some adult company, but I know she's afraid to stay in the house alone.

I play with the kids to the point of exhaustion—mine, not theirs—then collapse on the couch for the night.

At dawn I'm woken by Billy yelling in my ear. "Jay, Buzz, Jay, Buzz."

Assuming he's pretending to be an alarm clock, I press gently on his soft baby hair, hoping he'll play along and commence imitating the snooze button. He disappears and I close my eyes.

Seconds later he reappears with a videotape of *Toy Story* clutched to his tiny toddler chest.

"Oh, you meant that Buzz," I say. He nods.

I pop the tape into the VCR and we snuggle under the blankets while the rest of the household sleeps.

6

ON MY LUNCH hour I like to follow the pink brick path along the bank of the Sydenham down to the harbour so I can enjoy the sunshine and clear my head while I eat. Straw hanging baskets overflowing with vibrant pink and purple fuchsia and sweet alyssum dangle from the old-fashioned iron street lamps that welcome me to the rusty red groyne at the water's edge. The sun's rays playing on the ripples in the harbour like strings of white twinkle lights are so engaging I don't notice I've wandered smack dab into the middle of a group of senior citizens waiting for a midafternoon cruise. Tied to a bollard just behind them is an old boat called *The Drake*. A gallant gentleman in his seventies is trying his best to round up more passengers.

"We've still got lots of room, miss; would you like to come aboard?" His smile is charming, and I beam a broad one right back to him.

"I'd love to, but I have to go back to the office."

"It's a beautiful day, and you get free sandwiches."

"A very tempting offer, but no, thank you."

I've always had a bit of a thing for older men but am not quite ready for a seniors' cruise. As I look to make my exit politely, one rolls right up beside me on roller blades: a familiar face wearing a backwards red ball cap. A helmet would be the more appropriate headgear for such activities, I think.

"What is this tempting offer you are tempted with?" Mr. Rollerblades asks in a heavy Russian accent.

I stare at the man in front of me, sure I've seen him somewhere before, but I'm unable to place his face.

He looks puzzled too, then holds out his hand and smiles. "I am Kaz."

Then I remember. I prepared some tax returns for him several years ago, when I was just starting out at FACK.

"Yes, I remember you. I prepared the tax returns for you and your wife."

"This would be my ex-wife now; we are divorced."

Lifting my hand, he inspects my naked fingers. "You are divorced also?"

"No, I was never married."

"Pretty girl like you; how come you never married?"

"I'm just lucky, I guess."

It's my standard reply.

"Lucky for me," says Kaz.

"Do you have any children?" I ask.

"I have three kids, but they are all grown up. I live in the Harbourfront condos and I'm on holidays."

"Are you going anywhere?"

"These guys I work with have a timeshare in Galveston, Texas. I can go there and stay for free. Why don't you come with me?"

It is a day for temptation.

"I'd love to, but I have to be back to work by one-thirty."

"You should come by my place; I would love to see you again."

These types of open-ended invitations are useless, I think. I would never just drop in uninvited to the condo of a man I barely know.

"It was nice bumping into you. Enjoy the rest of your holidays," I say as I reluctantly change direction and head back toward the office.

It's been a long time since I've been hit on, and it cheers me up immensely. Kaz is quite cute, and I do love a man with an accent.

Back at the office the negativity sisters are at my desk, whispering and giggling.

Claudette is bursting with news. "Anne was walking by Frank's office, and she heard this clipping sound."

"I looked in, and he'd removed his shoes and socks and was clipping his toenails at his desk." Anne finishes her story and the two of them snort with laughter.

Frances Keyes is FACK's eccentric chain-smoking, hard-drinking tax partner. Brilliant, he scored second in Canada on the tax portion of his Uniform Final Examination. Unfortunately, his people skills are not as finely honed as his academic skills, and he holds all staff members who don't specialize in tax in disdain.

It was never part of the FACK plan for Frank to become a partner. When the previous partner retired in the mid-eighties, FACK's long-standing managing partner, Dean Fielding, advertised the position and was slightly shocked when William Murray, a prominent tax expert from one of the big-eight accounting firms, expressed interest. No one could figure out why a famous Canadian tax expert who'd conducted seminars nationwide would want to move to little old Owen Sound.

Seven months after his arrival, the mystery was solved when William and FACK's senior tax manager, Laura Robins, flew together to Toronto to start their own accounting firm, leaving their respective spouses behind. Apparently they'd met and fallen in love at a tax seminar two years earlier. Having lost his two senior tax people literally overnight, Dean had no choice but to promote Frank to tax partner immediately.

Frank has extremely sensitive skin and often wears his shirts and sweaters inside-out to prevent the seams from giving him a rash. Rumour has it he once chucked a dot-matrix printer out the second-floor window after it shredded thirty-two prenumbered, preprinted T4 forms that refused to align with its plastic tractor feed arms. He can, however, solve complicated tax problems that no one else in our office understands. When sober, Frank is a witty speaker, keeping his audience engaged through even the most mind-numbing material. He has a great affinity for classic rock from the sixties and seventies and is particularly partial to Bob Dylan and the Beatles.

Frank has always scared me a little, so when I need help with a tax problem I seek out Katie, his long-suffering senior tax manager.

"Frank was trimming his toes and tapping them to the beat of the Traveling Wilburys," Anne says.

I may not be brilliant like Frank, but I do share his love of music, and I'm about to enrol in a rock 'n' roll fantasy of my own. I've just signed up for music lessons with Owen Sound's legendary rocker, Chet 'The Fret' Dunn. Learning to play the bass guitar has been on my bucket list for years, and I've decided there's no time like the present. Being an accountant may pay my bills but it does not fill my soul. That's what hobbies are for.

Not one of my family members, friends or, especially, co-workers is allowed to know I'm taking bass lessons. The term "creative accountant" is a derogatory one, often associated with disciplinary action and/or prison sentences. In the financial world, calling someone a creative accountant is like telling a military man "Your mother wears army boots." There's no way I am letting anyone, especially the negativity sisters, in on my secret.

My instructor is an Owen Sound-born bassist who is semi-famous for playing with the seventies rock group the Spastic Colons. Chet stayed with the Spastics until they descended into obscurity in 1982 after releasing half a dozen albums. He went on to record with the Afterlife and others and toured with bands like the Boneheads and Chewy Nuggets. He left the world of rock in 1985 when he returned to Owen Sound, got married and settled down.

He still gets royalty cheques for "New Resolutions," the 1976 song he co-wrote and sang with the Spastics. In the early 1990s Chet had joined his former band for a reunion tour.

Since returning to Owen Sound, he spends most of his time teaching lessons, parenting his five-year-old son Matthew and recording music in the backyard studio he calls the Rumpus Room.

On Wednesday night after work I'm beyond excited as I drive past Kelso Beach and out 3rd Avenue West. Chet's house is not one of the fancy places that look out over Georgian Bay. It's on the non-beachfront side of the road, an ordinary if well-maintained grey brick bungalow set a fair way back from the road.

I drive by it by mistake and am several miles out of town before I realize my error and turn around. I hate being late and try not to panic as I drive slowly back into town, checking the house numbers as I go. I'm relieved when I finally find Chet's place and turn into the driveway. I'm thirteen minutes late for my first lesson.

Chet is livid.

I jump out of my car and head to the house. But before I can darken his doorstep, Chet cuts me off at the pass, grabs my elbow and frogmarches me to the Rumpus Room, situated above his garage. He's so angry he doesn't bother to introduce himself.

Chet shows me how to strap on the old black-and-red Fender four-string he uses for his students to practice on. He plays a vintage Horner violin-shaped bass with a pearl pickguard, like the one Paul McCartney played in the Beatles.

Most of the lesson is Chet showing me the different parts of the bass and the correct hand positions for holding it. It's a thrill to feel the thick leather strap around my shoulders for the first time; the old guitar is lighter than I'd imagined it would be, or maybe my shoulders are just getting stronger from all those morning workouts. My fingers feel strange and awkward at the back of its neck, pressing down on the frets; clearly this is a lot harder than it looks on TV. My left hand, right hand and fingers seem to have all joined dissenting groups and are refusing to work together.

As our hour together passes, Chet, like the strings on his instrument, begins to loosen up.

I think he likes me.

After years of instructing ten-year-old boys who refuse to practice and leave peanut butter smudges on his cherished collection of vintage basses, a serious thirty-nine-year-old lady accountant comes as a refreshing change.

After my first half hour, I manage to pluck out oom, pah, oom, pah to the beat of his foot tapping in four-four time, over and over.

He beams at me. "See, just like you're in a band."

"Yeah, right." I roll my eyes and he laughs, my earlier tardy transgression forgiven.

He doesn't look anything like the man I remember from the album cover of *Passing Gas* or *A Mighty Spectrum of Spenkters*, the Spastic recording that went platinum in 1974. Back then he posed flashing a peace sign, his thick brown hair hanging down to his nipples, and wore purple flared bell-bottoms, shirtless under a suede vest with plastic beads on each fringe. No one would guess the man standing before me sporting plastic-rimmed glasses and short snow-white hair is the same person. He's wearing an old Spastic Colons Tshirt under a faded plaid flannel shirt. His jeans have holes in the knees. Not the kind you buy with holes already in them as a fashion statement—real holes.

But there are still faint traces of enigma about him, and by the end of the lesson I am completely hooked. I make a pact to practice for half an hour every day, and already I'm looking forward to next Wednesday.

7

AFTER OUR CHANCE meeting on Monday, I take my lunch to eat on the same bench beside the harbour every day in hopes of seeing Kaz again. After our third such "coincidental" encounter, he asks if I'd like to have a real lunch date in a restaurant with him.

It's my first date in eons. Beyond excited, I agree to meet him at the Boot and Blade.

Our date starts out great; there's chemistry between us. I love his accent and the way he talks adoringly about his two kids.

Would he want more of them?

"I came here from Russia at seventeen not knowing a word of English. I moved to Toronto, where it took me six months of studying before I could communicate with anyone," he tells me.

He looks good in a crisp white collarless shirt and khakis. He speaks loudly and gets right to the point. Without his signature ball cap, I notice his curls are starting to recede and strands of grey thread through them.

Everything is going swimmingly until he pulls out his glasses to get a closer look at the menu.

That's when I see them.

Those telltale square windows at the bottom of the lenses, exactly like ones in the big bifocals Grandpa Alf wears.

"Um, Kaz? How old are you?" I ask.

"Sixty-four" he announces proudly. "Next year, I will retire."

And with that one little number, my sky-high hopes abandon their jubilant highwire dance and splatter over the ground. How is it possible this youthful rollerblader will soon start collecting the old-age pension?

Outwardly I remain calm, but Kaz sees the disappointment in my eyes. We don't speak of it again, but a cloud hovers over us as we quietly finish our lunch.

"When can I see you again?" he asks as we walk to my car.

Better to do this quickly, I say to myself. *Like ripping off a bandage.*

"I really like you, Kaz, but you're the same age as my dad."

"Well, we could never get married," he says, driving any further doubt from my mind for good.

And with those final words my foray back into the dating world ends as abruptly as it began.

That would have been the end of it, except that someone from the office must have spotted the two of us having lunch together. When I get back to my desk, the negativity sisters are on the case.

The harassment is relentless: phone calls, emails and ongoing interrogation. Who is he, how did you meet him, how old is he, when are you going out again, is it serious, ad nauseam. Between anticipating my date, getting over my date, and dealing with the inquisition that follows, I don't have many chargeable hours that week.

Right about then, Larry, the farm-tax accountant who inhabits the office next to mine, notices the fracas and wanders over to investigate. Larry illustrates the stereotyped nerdy accountant more than anyone I know. He is short and bald with a fringe of black hair that rings his scalp; he wears thick glasses and shirtsleeves with a pen-protector pocket. If they still made green visors, Larry would be wearing one.

After being debriefed on the situation by the negativity sisters, he offers up a relative to the cause.

"Jane, I have a single brother-in-law who would be perfect for you. He's coming into Owen Sound to watch me play in the Fighting FACK tournament on Saturday. You should come out Saturday night to watch us and I'll introduce you to him."

The Fighting FACK is our men's softball team. They've been playing for four years and have yet to win a game, although they did once tie the Volunteer Firefighters when most of their heavy hitters were called out to a bush fire in Leith.

I really just want to go to home, rent every romantic comedy from Video Town and snuggle on the couch under my fuzzy blanket. But *Meet Your Soulmate* says you should never turn down a blind date, so I tell Larry I'll be there, and Anne promises to come with me for moral support.

For the rest of the week I avoid the harbour so I won't bump into Kaz again. It still hurts. I liked him a lot, but I know it was the right thing to do. In my head I have a vision of Battleship 40, once so far away on the horizon, cutting stealthily across the lake where it will soon slide into port. I feel as though I'm headed straight for dry dock and there's nothing I can do about it. Following the rules as set out in *Meet Your Soulmate*, I've adopted a three-date maximum. I cannot waste time on dead-end relationships.

I'm a romantic; I've always believed in love at first sight. But, according to the book, every potential soulmate should be given three chances. On the first date he may be nervous, or having a bad day or just the sort of person who doesn't always make a good first impression but turns out to be absolutely lovely once you get to know them.

So, once again, Saturday afternoon finds me making up, trying on outfits, getting my nails done and stealing my nerve to meet Larry's highly touted still single brother-in-law at the ball diamond.

Half an hour before show time, Anne phones.

"Hey, Jane. I've decided to go clubbing with Doug and some of his friends instead. Why don't you come with us? I still want to introduce you to his friend Ed."

Scared to watch the Fighting FACKs alone, I agree to meet her at Norma Jean's Bistro instead. One of Anne's old boyfriends shows up in a neon-green muscle shirt and a tight curly perm. He looks like Richard Simmons on acid. If he reflects her taste in men, perhaps I shouldn't be letting her fix me up.

We wait until midnight, but once again the phantom Ed does not make an appearance. I drive by the ball diamond on the way home, but all the lights are off and everyone is long gone.

Larry doesn't mention it at work on Monday, but he seems a little quieter than usual.

8

ALMOST ALL OF my old high school friends from West Hill Secondary School are either married or have long since left town. The remaining singletons I know of are Mark White and Ian Tookesbury, whom I rarely hear from. Many of the married couples get together now and then for social events, but as the last single woman standing I'm something of a pariah and am rarely included. Angie mentioned a few months ago that Ian is engaged, so it looks like it's down to just me and Mark.

Mark is a sweet if somewhat nerdy guy. We'd all thought he'd be the first to get married. At twenty-three he'd traded his flashy Fierro for a Ford Taurus, settled into a high-paying job at Magna International and put a down payment on a bungalow while we were still going to keg parties and writing mid-terms. But Princess Right has yet to alight on his lily pad.

I hadn't heard from Mark in ages when he calls out of the blue.

"Hey, Jane. I heard you weren't invited to Ian's wedding. Do you want to go with me?"

"You sure know how to make a girl feel special, Mark."

With an offer like that, how can I say no? Ian apparently is tying the knot this Saturday; no doubt I'm a last-minute choice.

The occasion calls for an emergency shopping trip to Waterloo, where I locate an adorable little black dress reminiscent of the one Audrey Hepburn wore in *Breakfast at Tiffany's*. I buy a matching black jacket, and Mom lends me a hammered-silver necklace that matches it perfectly. I can't wait to wear it.

I also pick up the CD *Retrospective Colonoscopy: Greatest Hits of the Spastic Colons* and immediately start listening to it. I can't believe the bassist from this group is genuinely excited about teaching me to play.

I listen to all the tracks several times, but of course my favourite is "New Resolution," the only hit single Chet co-wrote and sang. I can't get the first few lines out of my head:

> *January seems to start off just fine*
> *February sees a little decline*
> *March is marching to the beat of my heart*
> *April, April it just all falls apart.*
> *These new resolutions are messing with my mind*
> *And a new constitution is what I need to find.*

Last night was my second lesson. I'd practiced working on a simple two-note baseline every night for two weeks until

I had it down perfectly. When it comes time to do one for Chet, I can't get my hands and fingers to work together.

Chet doesn't seem to notice and talks nonstop until I agree to a six-month commitment.

"I'm playing with this sax player at the Harb next weekend. You should come out and see us," he says.

His enthusiasm is contagious; I daydream about quitting this accountant gig, getting my grove on and touring with a rock band. I buy a third-hand Yamaha bass and keep running my hands reverently across the strings.

A flurry of activity blows in on Monday morning as the initial stages of the FACK/Montgomery Lawrence merger officially begin. Three former Montgomery Lawrence staff and new partner Ken Lawrence close up their old shop and move into our office. A corner office has been cleared out for Ken on the second floor, across from Sam, but office renovations for the new staff are nowhere near completion. Cindy Walsh, a forty-three-year-old woman who's worked loyally for Ken for over fifteen years, is asked to bunk in with me until her office is ready. I'm delighted she'll be joining us, as this means I will lose my status as the only single woman in the office.

Cindy doesn't appreciate being single any more than I do and has no qualms about notifying everyone in the office that she's looking for a man. I admire her honesty and directness, and the two of us hit it off.

Her candour pays dividends when Kim sets her up on a blind date with Bart, an old friend of hers from high school. Bart calls Cindy right away; the next morning she dances into work, over the moon with excitement.

Something about Bart's name sounds familiar. I begin checking on our personal tax files. It turns out he is known around town for borrowing money and bouncing cheques. He's been married before and has two kids, but both his marriage and mortgage had become overextended.

I'm a little hurt that Kim hasn't fixed me up. I've known her since I arrived at FACK in 1991, and she's been a good friend. Immediately I began overthinking this. *Couldn't she have fixed me up with anybody? Is there something wrong with me?*

I decide to go all out and get a manicure and pedicure so I'll look my best in my hot new dress. My regular hairdresser is on maternity leave, so I get an appointment with Jenn, who's covering Jackie's clients until she comes back. It's last minute and she's already booked, but she graciously agrees to take me at seven thirty Saturday morning, before the shop opens.

Jenn is my age and, miraculously, also single. Growing up I'd been vaguely aware of her, since everyone in this town knows everyone, but she went to OSCVI and I to West Hill, so our paths had never really crossed.

An attractive girl with a throaty laugh and voluptuous body, Jenn loves to party and is very outgoing. I wonder why she's still single.

We're alone in the salon. Jenn is wearing tight ripped jeans and a skin-tight black lace top. She cranks her hairdresser chair up so that her breasts are level with my face. The studio lights are dim, and in the background I hear Sade singing "The Sweetest Taboo." To trim my bangs, Jenn moves in even closer and straddles my knee.

I freeze in the chair, not certain what to do.

"Which side do you part it on?" she asks me.

"The right."

She frowns. "It keeps wanting to go to the left."

"I know the feeling."

It's difficult not to stare at Jenn's breasts, right at eye level. I have to admit they are magnificent.

Mark hasn't seen me since I'd lost over eighty pounds the previous year. When he picks me up I greet him all done up in my sexy new dress.

He doesn't appear to notice.

At the reception he and I are the only unmarried couple. Everyone dances with their spouse, but Mark had pulled a muscle in his back, so we can't dance.

It's good to see Ian and his new bride so happy, though. I decide to focus on the positive and share in the joy of the occasion. If Ian can meet someone and get married at thirty-nine, so can I. Even though I'm starting to feel frustrated, I don't want to get jaded.

● ● ●

I'm walking down the long hall to my office Monday morning when I hear voices coming from Frank's office. This surprises me, as I haven't heard anyone else go in there.

"He just got one of those new computers that talks to you," says Cindy, who's already at her desk in my office. "He's been chatting away to it all morning. Did you hear Katie had to cover for him at a client meeting on Friday when he showed up with booze on his breath?"

Katie, Frank's long-suffering tax manager, is short, sweet and full of energy. A red-headed spark plug, she has to eat every two hours to maintain her monster energy levels.

"That happens more often than you'd think," I tell her.

"What's going on with his hair?" Cindy asks me.

"He likes to just let it grow for as long as possible, then he gets a brush cut and starts over from scratch. Last year he let it go so long he looked like the offspring of Kramer from *Seinfeld* and the bride of Frankenstein. John Jamieson—you know, the Audit and Assurance manager, who runs the office football pool—takes bets on when he'll shave it all off. I put ten dollars on July 7; I think the heat will start to get to him around then. But enough about Frank already; I'm dying to know how it went with Blind Date Bart."

"It was the blind date from hell, possibly the worst date I've ever been on."

"Really? That terrible?" I say, feeling bad for Cindy but a little relieved, now, that Kim hadn't set me up with Bart after all.

"When I got to the Barking Frog he'd already had a few beers. Then he chugged four more, so I had to drive us to the restaurant for dinner."

"Okay, not a good start."

"Then all through dinner I had to ask all the questions; he didn't ask me a single thing. By the end of the evening we'd talked about his ex-wife, his kids, his parents, his neigh-bours, his brothers, sisters and cousins. I knew his entire life story, and he knew that I am a blonde woman who works at Kim's office. I could write a book about him."

"*The Book of Bart.*" I smile at my own joke.

"More like *The Bore of Bart*."

"Is he recently divorced? Maybe he needs a refresher course on dating."

"Or social skills of any kind. And get this: when I told Ken I was going out with Bart he said 'Not that loser from Springmount.'"

"Ken knows him?"

"Yes. We did a financial forecast for him on a new business he wanted to start a couple of years ago, and he skipped out on paying our bill."

I remember my research into Bart's personal files. Apparently his financial situation has not improved.

"You didn't remember him?"

"I was so enamoured with him on the phone that my brain just let Ken's remark float by. But as soon as I sat down across from him on Friday night it came back to me. After dinner he asked me what I'd like to do next, and I was ready to call it a night. But he insisted we go to a movie."

"Well, at least you got a movie out of it."

"He picked this horrible horror flick, dozed off during the opening credits and slept through the entire movie."

"Yikes."

"I don't know which was worse—having to watch that awful movie or being glared at by everyone in the theatre. Bart's snores were louder than the murderer's chainsaw in the movie. No matter how hard I poked and prodded, I couldn't rouse him from his alcohol-induced coma."

"I'd have walked out and just left him there."

"I couldn't. We drove over in his car. When he finally woke up, he had the nerve to ask if he could come back to my place. When I said no, he got all huffy."

Oh my god. I've never gone on a blind date in my life. This is not encouraging. Surely the author of *Meet Your Soulmate* has never had to endure an experience like this.

"Seriously, Cindy. That is possibly the worst blind-date story I have ever heard. But don't let it discourage you. We have a common goal," I say, telling her about my birthday pact and the soulmate book.

"Can you lend it to me?" she asks. "You know, I think if we're serious, we may need to extend our search beyond the borders of Grey County."

I nod.

"Absolutely. It's time to start thinking outside the Bart."

9

DUE TO THE craziness of tax season, I haven't had my niece or nephew for a sleepover since early March, and Madison is clamouring for her turn. Early Saturday morning Shelly drops her off with her wheelie Barbie suitcase and enough pink clothes, pink accessories and assorted girlie accoutrements to last her for a week in the Hamptons.

Our visit goes the way of all previous visits; she trashes my house, asks me to buy her stuff, never utters the words "Thank you" and demands constant attention. Perhaps I am not cut out to be a mother, I think. I can't get anything done with one child around; how does one manage with a whole crew of them? No wonder Shelly has such a hard time losing weight. When would she ever have time to exercise?

No cheap date for Madison. I take her to a nice restaurant and, instead of ordering from the kid's menu, she selects lobster.

Then we go to Video Town to rent a movie.

The longest relationship I've had with a man since moving back to Owen Sound is with the cute twenty-five-year-old clerk who works there. We see each other almost every weekend.

I take Maddie through his checkout because I figure she should meet the one man who's always been there for me.

"Auntie Jane don't have a boyfriend," Maddie informs him. "She gots a winkie and a condom."

"That's a wiener dog and a Honda," I correct her.

We watch the Spice Girls movie twice, dancing along to all the songs. After a full day of fun with Aunt Jane, I'm exhausted and Maddie's still going strong. I tuck her into my bed, put on my super comfy baby-blue flannel jammies with the floating fried eggs on them, brew myself a caramel herbal tea and pop the romantic comedy I'd rented for myself into the VCR.

Would I be a good mother, I wonder. Do I have the patience the position requires? And if parenthood is such a joyful experience, why are all parents constantly recruiting volunteer babysitters?

I've just gotten comfortable when I hear small feet padding down the stairs. Madison's blonde curls pop through the doorway.

"Aunt Jane, I want to go home," she says in a small shaky voice. Her forlorn face is fraught. She's got a bad case of homesickness and is missing her own bed.

I give her a hug and my best warm, reassuring auntie look.

"Sure, Madison. I'll take you home. Just give me a minute to change out of my PJs."

"Okee dokee," she says, sounding more like her confident self.

"You know, I'm really going to miss you tomorrow when I'm having breakfast at McDonald's all by myself."

Her sadness evaporates and she snuggles in beside me under the blanket, falling asleep almost immediately.

I used to think having kids would be just like babysitting—except you don't get paid and no one ever comes to take you back home at the end of the night. But looking at Maddie's perfect angel face, her golden curls spilling over the pillow, I forget my tiredness, the money and the mess.

I could get used to this.

10

IT'S THE FIRST week of June and things are heating up at work again. We're driving toward the last big deadline of the year, June 30, the day all corporations with a December fiscal year end must file their corporate tax returns.

I find myself buried under a mountain of queries.

At FACK, we have a detailed process for every company year-end we prepare. When a file arrives, it gets assigned to an accountant, such as myself, "the preparer." I organize all the information needed to put the financial statements together into a file then draft the financial statements and prepare the corporate tax return. Once this is completed, I hand the file to a manager. The manager reviews the file, writes out a detailed list of any questions—the query sheet—and delivers everything back to me. Query sheets have two columns: one where the reviewer writes out their questions, and the other where the preparer responds. I can say why my work is correct or make an adjustment and write out how I fixed it.

For most preparers, getting queries, especially a long detailed list of them, is a painful and humiliating experience. Kim and I refer to query sheets as "the fuck-up lists." A reviewer is trying to convey "Here's where I think you fucked up."

Some of my favourite queries over the years have included the following:

1. Is the American bank account in US funds?
2. Why were there so many waffles in the inventory at year end?
3. Can you assess the reasonableness of the movements in the tax account?

My answer: movements appear reasonable.

The much more humane approach, in my thinking, would be for the manager to simply meet with the preparer and talk about questions that have come up during the review and work together to fix them.

But accountants are not social workers, and a direct approach wouldn't cost the client nearly as much. At FACK my time is billed out at about a hundred dollars an hour; the manager reviewing the file is at around one hundred and seventy-five an hour. We pass the files back and forth with query sheets, merrily charging the client by the hour for our handwritten banter.

After the queries are cleared to the manager's satisfaction, the file is passed to a tax specialist who reviews the tax return and the parts of the file that support it. This generates more query sheets, which are given back to the preparer. And when those queries are cleared, the whole mess gets passed on to a partner for final review at upwards of three hundred dollars per hour. At this point the partner generally remembers something they forgot to tell the preparer from the initial meeting, and the file has to be changed by the preparer then reviewed again by the manager, tax manager and partner.

When the partner is finally satisfied, they give the statements to one of their administrative assistants, which in our case is either Fiona or Betty, who prints and binds multiple copies of the financial statements, corporate tax returns and various other forms as necessary.

The Montgomery Lawrence merger is already starting to show signs of strain as the new partnership struggles with the layers of forms and procedures FACK goes through on every engagement. Before merging with FACK, Ken had a thriving practice. Clients came in and Cindy or one of his other staff accountants prepped the files. Either Ken or his partner, Jerry, looked them over and made any changes as necessary. Often they could complete a small file for a thousand dollars or less.

This had all worked fabulously, until fifty-four-year-old Jerry dropped dead of a heart attack while beating his drums in the Georgian Bay Caledonia pipe band in the annual Kiwanis Owen Sound Santa Claus parade. With no one available to step into Jerry's ghillie brogues, Ken accepted FACK's offer of a merger, which he'd been dodging for over a decade.

FACK's convoluted system of queries and questionnaires results in invoices averaging four to five times higher than the old Montgomery Lawrence clients are accustomed. Many of them are balking at the new charges and, since Ken's income depends on his share of the profits from his clients, he is not entirely satisfied with the way things are working out.

Cindy and the other staffers who've come over from ML seem happy enough, though. That Wednesday night they invite me to attend Owen Sound's first ever Bachelor Auction with them. Just as I'm heading out the door, Shelly phones.

"Have a good night at the auction. Maybe I'll send my kids with you and see how much they go for," she says when I tell her what I'm up to.

Why do parents continuously complain about their kids to me when I would give everything in my possession just to have one of my own?

I go to the auction with high hopes. Since I seem to have failed at obtaining a man in the conventional manner, I figure I might just as well go ahead and purchase one. To an accountant it seems like a reasonable transaction.

Many of the bachelors sell for over three hundred dollars, however, which is way out of my price range. Economically, it proves once again that the man shortage in Owen Sound has reached crisis proportions. I might have considered buying a bachelor if he came with a warranty. Lonely and desperate as I am, I still can't imagine paying that kind of money for a date with a stranger.

In an effort to promote themselves before the bidding started, the bachelors had come out into the crowd and mingled with prospective buyers.

The Cowboy, a rather obnoxious fellow in western wear, hovered around our table and wouldn't go away no matter how hard we hinted. Five minutes with him felt like an eternity.

When it comes time for him to strut his stuff he sells for two hundred and twenty-five.

I really like one bachelor. He is thirty-five and has white, white hair. The girls at my table say he reminds them of Steve Martin.

A pamphlet had been distributed before the show in which each bachelor described the date he had planned for his lovely lady purchaser. On my attractive bachelor's bio there'd been a typo: instead of a romantic dinner by firelight, his bio proffered a romantic dinner with firefighters. So, he's making his rounds, issuing a disclaimer.

Unfortunately, my funny bachelor sells for one hundred and ninety-five dollars and I still can't afford him.

A sixty-two-year-old bachelor who pledged to take his date ice-fishing sells for $350.

"You'd have to pay *me* $350 to park my butt on a frozen lake waiting for a large-mouth bass to bite," I tell Cindy.

"It's because he's older, Jane. The older ladies are willing to shell out big time."

I get a vision of myself in my late sixties paying five hundred dollars to sit on a frozen pond hooking worms with a widowed octogenarian, and a chill runs down my spine. I need to get my situation rectified.

Halfway through the auction Kim drops in. She's just come from the Barking Frog and wants us to stop by the bar for a drink after the auction wraps up.

Cindy bows out, but I'm up for a change of venue. Kim's already inside when I pull into the parking lot.

Staring inside through the big windows of the bar I have the awed expression of a child at Marineland's Beluga observation tank.

The bar is flanked at one end by two pool tables and an antique jukebox holds court in the opposing corner. Neon signs for beer and framed portraits of famous NASCAR drivers adorn the wood-panelled walls. Televisions are strategically positioned so everyone in the house gets a front-row seat for whatever big game is in progress. On Friday nights a crown and anchor board is wheeled in to facilitate the raffling of raw meat to hungry carnivores.

At centre stage is a polished oak bar, manned by a bartender and two tiny waitresses. Their uniforms consist of tight blue jeans and Tshirts; "The Barking Frog Bar and Grill" is emblazoned across their chests. Drunks gaze blearily at the servers' breasts as if an impromptu quiz-show game of "Spell That Bar" might break out at any moment and serious preparation is required.

Patrons belly up to the bar literally; many appear impregnated from years of consuming Budweiser, whiskey and deep-fried cuisine. Lit cigarettes, scattered randomly like fireflies, produce an invisible smoke cloak that will cling to the clothes, hair and pores of every patron. A Toby Keith tune is barely audible over the buzz of a dozen conversations.

Aha, I think. I've finally hit the fatherlode: the den where the men of Owen Sound come to hide out. Could this bastion of testosterone prove to be my Holy Grail?

I suck in my stomach, pop a piece of winterfresh gum in my mouth and reach for the brass door handle with shaky fingers.

The first person I recognize is Cindy's blind-date bozo, Bart, sitting barside with a buddy who introduces himself as Gord.

At the auction Cindy told me that Bart had called her earlier in the week and asked if she was free for another date this weekend. She'd told him truthfully that she was visiting her sister in Toronto but was free and clear for the next weekend. He'd gotten huffy, said "Okay, goodbye," and hung up on her.

This man is a clueless Neanderthal of immense proportions. And what on earth, I wonder, is Cindy thinking, agreeing to go out with him again next weekend after their disastrous first date. Is she that desperate?

"Did you buy a bachelor?" Gord asks.

"No, they were too expensive. I'm hoping they'll have an end-of-season clearance sale in August."

"Perhaps if you wait long enough, you could cash in on some returns and exchanges."

"Well, *I'm* not waiting anymore." Bart continues on his path down the pity trail. "It took me two weeks to get up the nerve to call Cindy again and she shot me down."

I probably should keep quiet, but I've had one too many screwdrivers by this time and am on a mission to defend my friend.

I explain how the phone call had gone from Cindy's point of view.

Poor Kim, however, is dealt the blame for everything, and Bart keeps referring to Cindy as "Miss Rude."

I feel bad for Kim. It never pays to play matchmaker. When it doesn't work out, which would seem to be the case about 99 per cent of the time, the matchmaker takes the flak from both sides.

"Bart, you fell asleep on your first date with her," I remind him.

"I was married for a long time. I'm only recently divorced, and I don't know all the rules of dating."

"Bart, you watch hockey a lot, right?"

"My son plays for the Barrie Colts."

"Tell me some hockey rules."

Bart holds up a hand and ticks them off on his fingers. "No hooking, slashing, checking, icing, interference, high sticking, kneeing, elbowing, roughing, unsportsmanlike conduct, and you can never have more than six men on the ice."

"Is there a rule that all six players must be awake?"

"No, that would be too obvious."

"She shoots, she scores," Gord says.

Both physically and intellectually, Gord appears to be Bart's opposite. Bart is big and beefy; Gord, short and wiry. Bart is fond of monosyllabic answers; Gord, witty and intelligent.

Gord's sandy-brown hair is peppered with silver and the corners of his eyes wrinkle when he smiles. I quickly unearth his vital statistics; forty-three years old, divorced, two teenage boys.

Under the D, 43. Bingo!

Every woman has one thing about a potential partner that does it for her. For some it's washboard abs, blue eyes, a warm heart, a big bank account or a high-profile job. I've always been a sucker for men who are funny. And by funny I don't necessarily mean a man who tells jokes so much as

a man who can see the humour in life's ever-more-compli-
cated situations. I find myself more attracted to Gord with
each new wry observation he makes.

"I took my son to London for a hockey tournament and
got lost in a mall last weekend," he informs us.

"You got lost in a mall? How is that possible?"

"The mall was like a big, dark maze with a roof. I kept
walking around in circles. I passed the lady at the help desk
four times."

"So how come you didn't ask her for help?"

"Because men don't ask for directions."

Yes, the joke is so old it should be dusted for dinosaur
dung, but the way Gord tells it is innately hilarious.

As the night wears on Bart gets drunker and drunker.
Perhaps this is a trend with him.

"Kim told me there were two girls at the office she
could fix me up with: Cindy and Jane. I didn't know you, and
I picked Cindy. If I had've known you were Jane, I would have
picked Jane."

I have no response to this.

"Do you want to come to the Harb with me on Friday?
They've got some really good bands playing next weekend."

Why couldn't Gord ask me? I'm one of those people who
hate to say no. I hate hurting someone's feelings unnecessarily. But I just can't bring myself to go out with Bart after
everything Cindy has told me.

"I can't. I'm bowling on Friday."

"Can't you get a spare?"

"No. I can barely keep my ball out of the gutter."

"I meant a spare as in someone who can fill in for you."

"No. You have to let them know by Tuesday."

It's a lame excuse. I decide it's a good time to make my exit.

"I saw you in here with Kim a few months ago," Gord says as I zip up my coat. "I was hoping to meet you then."

I haven't stopped thinking about him.

11

TWICE A YEAR I drive through the old stone gates of
Greenwood Cemetery in the south end of town. Today I
stop for a moment in the little church on the grounds and
read the inscription on the beautiful stained glass windows.
"Abide with me, fast falls the eventide."

It feels strange walking without my constant companion, Wanker. In the far corner of the cemetery a group of history buffs searches for Billy Bishop's grave. My hero rests in
the opposite corner, under a flowering crab apple tree. His
artistic sensibilities, I know, would appreciate the beauty of
the spot.

Grade 11 was a year that would change my life forever. It
was the year I discovered my three great loves: art, fashion
and Christopher Graham.

I did not find fashion in Owen Sound. It came to me
through my new bible, *Seventeen* magazine. My sister would
pick up the latest issue on her weekly trip to town with
Mom for groceries. I'd wait impatiently as she took her time

thumbing through its glossy pages. When she was finally finished she would sell it to me for twice its cover price of one dollar.

The cable-knit sweaters, plaid shirts and dingo boots sported in the big September back-to-school issue may have been trendy, but they also made good sense when the winter streamers came whipping across the bay to Snowin Sound. I took every quiz on what boys liked and bought Bonnie Belle 10-0-6 lotion for my spotty teenage complexion.

At sixteen years old, I'd had crushes before. There was Kevin Hart, the quiet Harrison Ford look-alike who won all the West Hill track meets and got to represent our high school at OFSA. Mr. Rowan, my curly-haired eighth-grade teacher, who always wore the most incredible sandalwood aftershave. Hawkeye Pierce from the television show M*A*S*H.

But Christopher was different—he was the real thing. For years my mother's mantra had been "Don't fall for the first boy who sweeps you off your feet. Go to university, travel, have a career, then fall in love. Do something with your life."

My mother had married at eighteen and had me when she was nineteen. When she'd asked old Dr. Brayer, the only family doctor in Wiarton, to prescribe an IUD for her, his response had been "What on earth would you need one of those things for, missy?"

As a result, I was born exactly ten months after my parents' wedding day. Two years later my mother found a doctor in Owen Sound who not only prescribed IUDs but also had this great new contraceptive called "the pill."

"Mom actually wanted me," Shelly was fond of announcing when she figured out the logistics after taking sex education in Grade 9 phys ed class.

When I met Chris I knew with utmost certainty there would never be another boy for me. There was no one like him, before or since.

We met in art class. The art room had seagulls painted on its cement block walls and the words "Beauty is its own excuse for being" stenciled in calligraphy above the big sink where we washed out our paint brushes.

One day, Chris peered over my shoulder as I sketched a hand cracking open an egg with my self-portrait in its yoke.

"What does it mean?" he asked.

I tried to come up with a thoughtful, whimsical, intelligent answer that would give him a glimpse into the complicated inner workings of my deep and beautiful soul.

"I don't know," I said.

And with that wittiest of exchanges he sat down beside me and we shared the same table for the rest of the semester.

Chris was not breathtakingly handsome in the broad-shouldered, classical cleft-chin kind of way. He stood about two inches taller than my dainty five foot three, and, though he wasn't overweight, there was a softness about his body. He had mild acne, bushy eyebrows, defiant sandy-brown curls and eyes as blue as Georgian Bay.

What attracted me most to Chris was his manner, an easy warm humour that lit up any room he walked into. To me he was simply beautiful. From the first moment we met, I knew what it meant to be lightning struck by love.

While the other boys at West Hill dressed as though they rolled out of bed every morning and pulled on the first discarded, wrinkled Tshirt and jeans in their line of vision, Chris actually cared how he looked. No buying his clothes at Woolco and getting his hair cut at the Wayne Mills barbershop for him. His unruly curls were kept in check with regular visits to a salon on 2nd Avenue. He wore Lee painter pants with navy and red or green-striped rugby shirts. He was the first male in Grey County to wear velour and look good in it.

Although I found Chris incredibly physically attractive, it was loving him that taught me the value of a man who sees the humour in life. As far as I was concerned, we were the perfect match. He was the extrovert to my introvert, *The Goodbye Girl*'s Elliot to my Paula.

Chris was ambitious and mature for his age. Born in January, he was the first of us to get his licence. When I was still babysitting to earn extra cash, he'd taken an after-school job at a bakery.

It was fitting that we bonded in art class; while most of the boys from Owen Sound idolized Bobby Orr or the rock band Rush, Chris's hero was Tom Thomson. One evening he volunteered to paint some posters for the school's team, the Raiders, and I offered to help.

We rolled out several lengths of brown kraft paper on the floor and mixed a batch of baby blue and gold paint. We were able to work in the empty hallways, everyone having long since left for home. I loved the quiet with just the two of us. Chris chatted comfortably as we painted our big signs "Remember to support the Raiders," "Don't forget to support the Raiders," and "Remember, don't forget to support the Raiders."

On the last day of school before Christmas vacation I showed up to a quiet homeroom. Most students traditionally ditched classes and skipped the final day, but I couldn't bring myself to for fear of getting in trouble. Peeking through the window of my homeroom door, I realized I was going to be the only one in class. Even the teacher had yet to arrive. Unsure what my next move should be, I lingered in the hallway.

Right about then Chris came strolling down the hall. I could not believe my luck.

A smile lit up his face when he saw me. "Hey, Jane! Why don't we take off and do something together?"

And just like that, what had looked like a long, boring day turned into my best day ever.

We headed downtown. It was a perfect pre-Christmas day. Snow falling on the century-old store fronts transformed 2nd Avenue into a real-life version of ceramic Christmas villages with cotton-batting snow and lit-up pine trees. Lots of other kids were milling about, but I had eyes only for Chris.

We had lunch at a little diner called Scopis. We sat beside each other in a leather-clad booth at the back of the restaurant. Every time his sleeve brushed mine I felt my heart flutter.

Angie came in hauling a brightly coloured plastic bowling set she'd just purchased at Woolworths. I tried to warn her away with a look, but she sat down with us.

As we were leaving the building we ran into Itchy Bill, who was doing his regular patrol of 2nd Avenue East.

Itchy Bill is something of a legend in Owen Sound. He's been walking up and down the streets of downtown in his pearl-button western shirt, cowboy hat and boots for as long as I can remember. Bill made me nervous. It's not that I didn't like him; he was actually a sweet, simple man who went out of his way to be friendly. It's just that I never knew what he might do. Like the time he caused a traffic jam when he took an afternoon nap in the middle of 2nd Avenue.

Chris, however, had no such qualms and spoke easily to him, completely comfortable. Bill nodded and smiled, finally tipping his cowboy hat to us before he walked away scratching his backside.

They don't call him Itchy Bill for nothing.

Continuing on our way, we walked past Centre Theatre. Chris noticed a movie poster for *The Wiz* and grabbed my hand. "I really want to see that; do you want to see it with me over the holidays?"

It would be my first date. This amazing boy was asking me out on my first date. I thought I might float away on a cloud and never come down.

When we finally got back to West Hill, he walked me to the sparsely filled yellow school buses lined up in the driveway and asked me to write out my phone number for him. He would check to see when his parents would let him borrow their car and give me a call over Christmas break.

It was a wondrous holiday. He called on Christmas Eve and we went to see the movie on Boxing Day. After the show he took me to a new donut shop he liked called Tim Hortons on 10th Street. I had a strawberry-jelly donut and got sugary white powder all over my wide-wale chocolate-brown cords. So much for first impressions.

Chris didn't hold my hand during the movie or kiss me at the end of the night, but I felt the strong connection between us. He invited me to spend New Year's Eve at a family party at his big old red-brick home on 9th Street West, and I welcomed in the new year with great anticipation.

Our love was pure and innocent. I longed to be with him every hour of the day and night. Logistically, this proved somewhat difficult since I lived on a farm in Georgian Bluffs and didn't drive, and he was a townie without a car of his own; but we made the most of the precious hours we could carve out for ourselves.

We saw each other at school every day. In addition to art class, we ate lunch together in the cafeteria, Chris easily fitting in with my friends, who all knew and liked him. On Thursday nights when my mom drove to town for groceries she'd drop me at his house and we'd watch *Mork and Mindy*. We both loved the off-the-wall comedy of Robin Williams, whose sandy curls and blue eyes reminded so much of Chris that I bought him rainbow-striped suspenders.

We snuggled under the crocheted brown-, orange- and yellow-zigzagged afghan on his parents' flowery couch to watch *Dallas*, and we were both shocked when JR got shot. Chris thought the culprit was weaselly Cliff Barnes, but I knew it could only be Kirstin. Hell hath no fury and whatnot.

On Saturday nights Dad would drive Shelly and me to Roller Villa, where Chris and I held hands as the wheels of our roller skates glided across the red rubber floor under the rotating lights of the disco ball. I adorned my skates with sparkly laces and pink fuzzy dice. Chris bought soft rabbit fur for his. If we had enough money we'd go to a movie at

Centre Theatre. Chris liked the serious films; we saw *Norma Rae* and *The China Syndrome*. Both inspired long conversations about how lucky we were to be artists. We would never be abused by such a corrupt and greedy corporate world.

We both loved the coming-of-age movie *Breaking Away*, which inspired us to ride our wobbly 10-speeds down the hot side roads of Grey County. One afternoon my skinny front tire hit a piece of gravel the wrong way and spun out. I did a header into the metal bar of my bike, knocking out my two front teeth and splitting my lip, which necessitated a trip to the Owen Sound emergency ward and several stitches. I still have the scar.

We talked about our future and made plans to go to university in Toronto together. He would be a great artist; I would achieve stardom as a fashion designer.

Chris was the first boy I kissed. His lips were sweet and tentative. I cherished every kiss, replaying them over and over in my head until the next one came along.

One hot summer night in late June we were kissing goodbye in my doorway. It was just past midnight on a school night, and everyone in the house had gone to bed, but we just couldn't seem to say goodbye. Not wanting the moment to end I reached for his hand and guided it gently from its resting place on my hip up under the buttons of my soft flannel shirt.

His eyes widened, and it was one of those magical first moments as his palm brushed lightly across my breasts. Then the sound of a door creaking upstairs startled us both and I jumped, afraid my parents or Shelly had woken up and might come downstairs to discover us.

We quickly said goodnight. Chris got into his father's big old station wagon and drove home.

The next week we had final exams and were busy studying. All too soon Chris had to leave for his summer job at a Boy Scout camp near Grand Bend.

It was the longest summer of my life. Chris promised to write often, but I got only two brief cards from the camp store and a hasty call from a pay phone in Port Franks.

On Labour Day weekend he called to tell me he was finally home, and of course I couldn't wait to see him. He picked me up in his dad's station wagon and we drove to Kelso Beach. I noticed he looked a little different, his hair bleached lighter from the sun, his light skin freckled and peeling.

After two months of longing I was wild with anticipation, thinking of the things we could do in that big old car. I slid over close to him on the vinyl seat and wrapped my arms around him.

"Oh my god. I missed you so much, Chris."

He looked into my eyes. I'd just gotten the stitches out of my lips, and he touched the scar gently with his forefinger.

"I missed you too, Jane, but there's something I need to tell you." He paused for a minute and swallowed, then took a deep breath and looked at me.

"Jane, I met somebody when I was at camp."

"Sure, you probably met lots of people at camp."

"Yes, but this was someone special."

I wasn't following him. I was the special person in his life. There wasn't room for two special people.

"What are you trying to say? Aren't we special?"

"You know how much I like you, Jane, but this was different."

And that's when I knew. He'd met another girl.

"Oh my god. Who is she?"

"It doesn't matter. She... she's not from around here."

"What do you mean, she's not from here? Where is she from? Is she your new girlfriend? Is she moving here?"

I felt shaky and sick. I extracted myself from his arms and attempted to get out of the car, but the old metal handles were stuck and wouldn't budge.

"Jane, it's okay. We can still be friends. We can talk about this."

But I couldn't even look at him. He was my one and only, the only person on this planet other than my dad and Angie who'd ever really 'got' me. I couldn't talk about an ending when we were just beginning.

In desperation, I shoulder-checked the car door so violently I broke its rusty hinges. It dropped off like a severed appendage in the sand. Freed at last and wanting more than anything in the world just to get away from this tragedy, I stepped over the broken door and began walking down the beach. It was cold and deserted. Everybody'd gone home for the summer.

Chris got out of the car and ran after me.

He put his hand on my arm and pulled me around to face him.

"I'm sorry, Jane. I didn't plan for this to happen."

And I couldn't stop myself from reaching for his hands. I looked down at the dark hairs on his wrist.

"I love you, Christopher. I've never loved anyone the way I love you."

He put his arms around me, and I snuggled in close for the last time, breathing in his musky smell and telling myself this would all work out.

• • •

I place a vase of dried sunflowers mixed with cattails and corn husks—colours he would have loved to paint—beside his grave. His father's stone is beside him now, and it gives me some comfort to think he's no longer alone. There's a fresh wreath on a little tripod between the two of them. Mrs. Graham must have been here recently. I must stop by and visit her soon; it's been a while.

I kneel in front of the marble slab and gently trace the letters of his name. It's quiet now. The historians have left and a cool breeze rises up through the maple trees. "I still miss you, Chris."

I pull my jacket tighter around me and walk quickly back to my car.

12

EVERYONE SEEMS TO think the worst of busy season is over once we get past April 30, but June can be even worse. Since all incorporated companies have six months to file their tax returns, the returns for all our clients with December year ends have to be filed by June 30. After a short respite at the beginning of May, we are plunged once more unto the breach, dear friends, for another six weeks of stress.

Today I have an audit to finish, three bingo audits to complete, and I can't get the Marbud receivables to balance.

Desperate times call for desperate measures. I decide it's time to check out the one and only Owen Sound Singles Club.

The club has met every Thursday night at a table in the back corner of the Harrison Park Inn Restaurant for almost two decades. I've always thought such organizations were for losers, but my birthday pact and *Meet Your Soulmate* encourage participation in such gatherings. And nothing I've done so far is working. Logic dictates that if I want a different result, I am going to have to try different tactics.

I look up the ad for the singles club in the *Sun Times* and get a phone number for Cathy, the club president. On the phone she is warm and friendly. "We get together every Thursday at seven. It's very informal. You just drop in to the restaurant and tell the hostess you're here to see Cathy."

Not wanting to appear too eager, I walk into the Harrison Park Inn on Thursday at 7:15. I pull open the heavy restaurant doors and timidly approach the hostess station.

"I'm here to meet Cathy," I whisper discreetly to the hostess.

"Who's Cathy?" she bellows.

"Well, there's this group that meets here and Cathy told me just to ask for her and you'd take me to it."

"Oh, you mean the singles club," she announces in a booming voice likely audible on Manitoulin Island.

She leads me across the dining room to a table of ten women in their sixties and two smiling geriatric men.

Oh my god, I think. What if someone I know sees me? If the negativity sisters get wind of this, they will harass me until the end of time.

Then I notice a younger man, not sitting at the table with the group but hovering close behind it. He's fortyish, blue-eyed and blond with chiseled features. He reminds me of Robert Redford in his fifties: tanned, weather-beaten and extremely attractive.

He looks at me and introduces himself with a lazy smile. "I'm Sean."

Sean joins us at the table for dinner. We chat a bit and he asks if I'll be his partner for euchre.

At first I'm nervous and make some stupid moves. But once we get rolling I pull myself together and we win two of four games.

"Do you want to get a coffee, Tim Hortons, after the game?" Sean asks me.

Of course I do.

We have a great time. He's funny in an old-fashioned way. I enjoy his company and the evening flies by. By the end of the night, I know quite a bit about him. I can't help but be reminded of Cindy's train wreck blind date, but I quickly reason the similarity away—suave Shawn bares no resemblance to that beer-guzzling buffoon Cindy went out with.

A passionate gardener, he's divorced and lives alone in a cute brown brick house with a huge backyard only a few blocks from me on 8th Avenue A East. Once a big drinker, he's been sober for eight years. He has a son he barely knows from a woman he dated briefly in his early twenties.

But the surprising news is that years ago he dated Kim, my fellow FACK accountant friend. They dated for three years when she was in college and they're still friends after all these years. This town, I've found, is so small that every-one is connected somehow.

He refuses to reveal his age.

"You're pretty, and I like that you don't smoke. Would you like to go for breakfast down by the harbour sometime?"

I'm trying to remain cautiously optimistic, but I can feel my long-suffering hormones jumping and skipping in a happy dance of anticipation.

On Monday morning I arrive at work to find Anne planted in my office. It's 8:30, and I immediately sense something must be up, because:

a) Lazy, last-minute Anne can barely haul herself into the office by nine, and
b) As I'm a bubbly morning person, I have been ordered never to speak to her until after ten, when she's started on her second coffee.

"What's up?" I ask.

She puts her hands on her hips and clears her throat as though holding a press conference to address the League of Nations. "Doug and I"—she pauses for effect—"are trying."

I decide to have some fun with this.

"Trying what?"

"You know. We're ter-rye-ing." She pronounces each syllable as though speaking to a mentally challenged child whose first language is not English.

Yes, Anne. You are very trying.

Over the years several women have shared this sort of procreation revelation with me and I've yet to discern the proper response. I struggle with such situations, because:

a) Afterward, every time I encounter the aforementioned couple, I can't help wondering if they've just been coupling, and
b) Doesn't making announcements of this nature put performance pressure on all concerned?

People tell you they're trying; it can get awkward if several months pass and no news is forthcoming. What is the protocol in this situation? I'm quite sure enquiring as to why things aren't happening is inappropriate.

Maybe I should slap Anne on the back and say, "Go get 'em, tiger. You work those eggs. Go, sperm, go!"

I settle for "Congratulations, Anne. That's wonderful news."

"Thanks, Jane." With that she's off to spread the impending news.

I wonder how the partners will react when she gets pregnant. Every time a FACK staffer gets married, the partners give her "the timing talk."

Our busy season runs from the first of January until June 30, the last big deadline of the year. Since maternity leaves in Ontario are six months long, the partners want all female staff members to take their time off from July to December, when it's not as busy. Every time a FACK girl announces her engagement, Sam, Dean or Joe meet with her to make sure she knows the rules. It comes down to a bunch of old men telling a young woman when she should have sex in order to have her children at a time that would be the least disruptive for the firm. Male staff are spared 'the timing talk.' Although they'd been legally permitted to take parental leave since 1990, it simply never occurs to FACK's uber traditional partners that a man might take time off to bond with his newborn offspring.

Since I'm single, I've been spared this talk, but I know it exists because both Katie and Kim have been subjected to it.

"I'm feeling kind of tired. I'll think I'll take the afternoon off," I overhear Anne tell Fiona.

Oh, gross. She's going home to have sex.

That evening Shelly joins me for dinner at Kelsey's. We both flirt and joke with Glen, our friendly waiter. After he picks up our payment she says to me, "He was nice."

"Yes, he was," I sigh.

"Well, I'm glad you liked him, because I wrote your phone number and 'Call Me' on the back of our bill."

"Oh my god, you didn't." I am mortified.

"Oh yes, I did," she smiles wickedly.

Embarrassed, we both sprint from the restaurant before he returns to our table. Now I'll never be able to eat there again.

Sean hasn't called since our memorable first meeting, and the ominous waiting-for-the-phone-to-ring game is on. He wanted me to go back and see his garden after our date, but I had to work on my due-June-30 rush jobs. When I told Kristen about him she said that his garden is amazing and has been featured in the Georgian Bay Garden Club's annual garden tour. Maybe he's bummed that I blew off his offer of a personal tour.

Adding to my angst over Sean, I'm also missing Chet. I look forward to our weekly Wednesday-night lessons, but he's been up north on a fishing trip for the last three weeks.

We've skipped way ahead in my *Big Book of Bass* to learn shuffle beats.

"Your shuffle beats aren't shuffly enough, Jane," he told me.

At our last lesson he was trying to teach me country bass lines.

"Do you ever go to country bars?"

"Sometimes."

"You should go to a bar and sit in with us."

He picked up his guitar and began strumming along with me. What a thrill to play bass with this legendary rocker. It may just be the coolest thing I've ever done.

Goodbye to Plain Jane Accountant.

13

AFTER CHRISTOPHER GRAHAM broke up with me on Labour Day weekend, Grade 12 felt like the darkest year of my life. Chris and I had no classes together and our paths rarely crossed. I never got to meet the infamous girl-friend who'd ended our relationship, but I heard through the grapevine that she lived in Waterloo and they didn't get to see each other often.

I missed everything about him and longed for those nights when we couldn't hang up the phone; the sound of his voice was the last thing I heard before drifting off to sleep. When the stabbing pain diminished to mere heart-ache, I considered asking if maybe we could be friends. But in my heart I knew that I loved him too much to settle for a platonic relationship.

It wasn't that I wasn't capable of having friends who were boys. Kyle Jackson and I had been friends since he moved to our neighborhood the summer before sixth grade. A city dweller until his parents had moved to Georgian Bluffs, Kyle was different from the country kids I'd grown up with. His dad owned a television-repair shop in Owen Sound and his mom was a wunderkind homemaker, seamstress and cook. They'd bought a big old clapboard farmhouse with ten acres just down the road from Angie's place on Highway 40.

Kyle was tall and gangly, his face dominated by braces, wire-framed glasses and a big, dopey grin. His grooming routine consisted of pulling a ball cap over his freshly show-ered hair every morning in an attempt to flatten his dirty-blonde curls. This procedure struck me as grossly unjust, as I was forking out over thirty-five dollars of my hard-earned babysitting money on perms for my stick-straight hair. Kyle's daily uniform consisted of Levis, a Tshirt, sneakers and a two-tone taupe-and-tan Adidas bag for transporting home-work to and from West Hill Secondary School on the bus.

"Adidas stands for 'All day I dream about sex,'" Angie informed me dreamily.

"This may explain why your grades were so bad last semester."

"When are you going to snap out of it already?" Angie'd been putting up with my moody funk over Chris for months. She'd been patient and comforting in the beginning but was now urging me to move on.

Because of his dad's business, Kyle's house was always spilling over with the latest in electronic gadgetry. He had a big reel-to-reel tape-recording machine in his bedroom, and various vintages of television sets were scattered throughout the house. The Jacksons were the first folks in our neighborhood to own a microwave oven. Kyle made a point never to stand in front of it when it was turned on, because rumour had it that microwaves could make a man sterile.

Despite Kyle's intelligence and easy-going charm, it never occurred to me to find him attractive. Angie had a crush on Kyle almost from the moment they met. Thus, as the object of my best friend's desire, Kyle was automatically verboten.

When I'd attended the Grey County 4-H Club's Christmas party in the eighth grade, Santa pulled a small gift box from under the tree. My mother had brought the presents she'd wrapped for Santa to give Shelly and me, but I hadn't noticed this one. Shelly knew perfectly well that our parents played the role of Santa, but, as the youngest sibling, she continued to feign belief lest Santa's bountiful generosity ended once they realized the jig was up.

When I unwrapped the box I found a silver mood ring, its glass oval set in something resembling a silver-plated band. I tried it on, and the glassy stone slowly turned green, much like my finger would after wearing the ring for two or three days. Green, according to the little colour chart that came with it, meant I was calm, relaxed and loveable. The tag inside the box said "From A Secret Admirer" in neat printing. I looked up to see Shelly smirking and knew she was the culprit. But I decided to enjoy the ring anyway. I'd always wanted one.

Angie was so anxious to start university that she fast-tracked enough high school courses to graduate half a year ahead of us. She got early acceptance to the University of Windsor and moved into residence that winter, leaving me to finish Grade 13 without my best friend and constant companion.

By the end of Grade 12 I'd grown out my perm to flaunt a feathered, winged hairstyle courtesy of *Charlie's Angels*. This look could be achieved only by painstakingly curling back several diagonally cut layers of the hair that framed my face. I used an electric wand called a curling iron, which I plugged into an outlet in the bathroom every morning. Shelly and I were forever forgetting to unplug it when we were finally finished the process, and it was often left on all day while we were at school, causing my dad to dub it "our little electric bathroom heater."

Angie's need for excitement was quickly fulfilled when she fell madly in love with her thirty-five-year-old anthropology professor, Xavier Lavoie, who was possibly the sexiest man alive. Xavier was from Montreal but had lived all over the world. His French accent, the forelock of dark brown hair that perpetually flopped over his forehead, along with his hint of stubble, café au lait skin and six-pack abs caused many an adoring pupil to stare at him dumbfounded for entire lectures. By the end of the first semester Angie had moved all of her earthly possessions from the student residence in Laurier Hall to Xavier's spacious condo on Riverside Drive.

Angie's parents had an equal and opposite reaction to Xavier. The first thing they noticed was not his off-the-charts hotness but the fact that he was seventeen years older than Ang and came complete with two ex-wives and three children of assorted parentage.

Most parents of a girl in Angie's situation might have initially ranted and raved but eventually surrendered to the power of love. Angie's parents were determined to rectify the situation and find her a more suitable suitor.

They promptly dispatched me to Windsor on a reconnaissance mission. My job was to suss out the situation and report back.

"You've always been the sensible one, Jane. Go down there and talk some sense into her," Angie's mom, Lynn, said, giving me money for a bus ticket.

Years ago my mother had sent me over to our new neighbour's farm when our four-month-old Australian shepherd pup began getting frisky with their equally immature collie. Neither party had gotten around to getting the dogs spayed or neutered; we'd foolishly thought they were too young for silly reindeer games.

"Just try to pull them apart, Jane," my mother had urged.

I'd turned the hose on them, which put a damper on the proceedings, but three months later the collie produced seven of the ugliest pups I'd ever seen, their traditional butterscotch coats splotched with blue-grey patches and their eyeballs white with different-coloured pupils.

I resigned myself to my current assignment, which had an equal likelihood of success.

Xav and Angie met me at the bus station. I knew I would fail before I even stepped off the bus. Xav was simply one of the sexiest men I had ever met.

Had he been a sixties film star, he would have been wearing a fedora and holding a cigarette. Instead, he wore Air Jordans and chewed gum.

"Would you like a stick?" he said, proffering a pack of yellow Juicy Fruit.

"What do you think of him?" Angie whispered the second he left to use the men's room.

"He had me at 'Bonjour.'"

"I know."

We sighed simultaneously.

14

CHET'S BAND IS one of the acts scheduled to play
in Owen Sound's Canada Day celebrations. I drive out to
the Harrison Park band shell to see him only to discover
he's actually playing at Kelso Beach. By the time I get back
through the holiday traffic, I've missed him.

Disappointed, I wander through the park checking out
the vendors, the smell of deep-fried elephant ears and
chocolate bars tempting me at every turn. I settle for a hot
dog and eat it at a picnic table with a young couple, their
toddler and infant girl. The toddler stares at me as I bite into
the wiener.

"Ot gog, ot gog," he says, pointing a curious finger at it.

"Drink your juice, Max," his mom, who looks about
twenty-three, says, handing him a violet sippy cut with a
green top.

I take another bite, and a splash of red ketchup drips
onto the new red-and-white Tshirt I'm wearing to commem-
orate my country's birth.

"Ouchy," the little boy says, pointing at the blood-red drip.

"It's okay," I tell him. "It's only a condiment."

His mom graciously hands me a wet wipe from her diaper bag.

It's our family tradition to watch the fireworks at Owen Sound Bay together. Sitting on an itchy grey wool blanket flanked by my niece and nephew, the fireworks remind me of dozens of wriggly sperm. Launched with great power, they streak purposefully across the sky toward their hidden target in the clouds. A moment of complete silence occurs, then a flash of light is followed by a sonic boom that echoes across the water, signaling mission completed. The crowd never gets tired of this, uttering their orgasmic "Oohs" and "Ahhs" in sync with each new explosion.

I'm waiting for the big finale and thinking about how I might get to my car before everyone tries to leave the parking lot when I spot Kyle and his family stretched out on a blanket just below us. Kyle catches my eye, then Kiley Junior clouts him over the head with a neon-green glow stick and he turns around to deal with him.

• • •

Canada Day falls on a Thursday this year, so I decide to take Friday off as well and make it a long weekend. As usual, I'm unable to sleep in on Friday morning.

I can't stop worrying about why Sean hasn't called, but the phone finally rings on Friday night and we make plans to have breakfast together the next morning.

He's waiting for me outside the restaurant when I arrive, looking dashing in new jeans and a crisp white shirt. But after the hostess seats us on the patio, our conversation grows strained and there are several awkward pauses. We talk mostly about him, and I can't help remembering Cindy's date from hell with boorish Bart.

"Ask me something else. Women don't like it when you ask them too many personal questions," Sean says.

Maybe he's just trying to be polite, but isn't he even a little curious about me?

Afterward we go for a walk by the water.

"It's a beautiful morning," I say.

"And you make it more beautiful. We should be holding hands."

But we don't.

That night I wake up to the sound of a baby crying.

I sit up in bed, ears tuned to the sound like a hunting dog scenting its prey. According to the red numbers on my alarm clock, it's just past 3 a.m.

The crying is not the "I'm wet," "I'm hungry," or "Come play with me" fussing that is music to maternal ears. This baby's cry says "I'm frightened."

My feet hit the floor and I begin walking down a long corridor lined with doors. I pull open the first door, but the room is empty.

The crying intensifies.

I increase my pace down the hall, pulling each door open as I go. It stretches on forever, and panic descends as each door reveals yet another empty room.

I finally reach a small room at the end. The crying is so loud now, she must be in there.

I fling open the door to a bright white room with gleaming hardwood floors. A small antique crib is rocking gently in the corner, the tinkling notes of "Brahms's Lullaby" floating from the octopus arms of a mobile of tiny baby angels rotates over it. A cold breeze blows in through an open window, forcing the sheer white curtains to billow and stretch their long white fingers in an attempt to clutch the cradle.

I run to the crib and yank off a white crocheted baby blanket, but there are only clean white sheets under the covers. The crying stops just as the chill air from the open window hits my sweat-soaked body.

I wake up shivering in my bed.

I must have forgotten to shut my bedroom window; the cold air is blowing in on me. I yank it down with a bang and dive back under the duvet, pulling it tight around me. Sleepy Wanker yawns, sensing my distress, and snuggles in close to me.

But there will be no going back to sleep now.

15

LARRY INVITES ANNE and me to go golfing with him in Chatsworth on Sunday afternoon.

I'm not a golf aficionado but I go along anyway, thinking that, since many males congregate on golf courses, it's a good place for me to be. But eighteen holes on a demanding course in the heat prove disastrous. I can't hit the ball off the tee or onto the green if my life depends on it. Hot, frustrated and not seeing any men besides old married Larry, I begin to understand Mark Twain's point: golf is "a good walk spoiled." How much nicer it would be to hike in the shady woods, then read a good book in a hammock with a cold drink.

Larry's golf shirtsleeves reveal a white strip of farmer tan on each of his forearms. I wonder if he also wears his pocket protector with mechanical pencils as he drives his tractor. Anne, having recently taken golf lessons, is turned out in peach culottes with a matching peach golf shirt. Glossy new white-and-brown polyurethane cleated golf shoes complete the perfect ensemble.

Anne assumes the role of stroke coach. She has several things to say every time I take a swing. I am averaging thirty to thirty-three strokes per hole. Doing the math, I figure this comes to approximately five hundred ninety-four tips imparted during one extremely long, hot afternoon.

"Jane, don't use that club." "Jane, don't take your eyes off the ball." "Jane, bend your knees," and on and on.

"Hell," I mutter under my breath, "thy name is golf."

"Focus, Jane, focus."

Meanwhile, Larry's treating the whole excursion as if he's on a date with us. Stopping at the clubhouse for refreshments after nine holes, he says, "My wife and I don't really talk anymore."

"Are you not getting along, Larry?" Anne, who's always hungry for good gossip, is not about to let this opportunity pass her by.

"I guess it's just that after two kids and twenty-seven years of marriage, we don't have much left to say."

I sip my beer, tune them out and think about my bass guitar waiting for me in its case at home. Maybe someday I can be a bassist in an alternative-rock band. I'll meet thousands of charming music-minded single men while playing gigs on weekends and never have to set foot on a golf course again.

With my hands under the table I begin practising the finger positions for the bass line to "Another One Bites the Dust."

"How did Fiona let the office know she was separated?" Larry's voice pierces my reverie.

Fiona, our angelic receptionist, had recently split from her husband when he publicly announced his plan to pursue a sex-change operation.

"She just stopped wearing her ring and people started speculating and asking questions," Anne says.

"Maybe we should play as a scramble for the last nine holes?" Larry suggests. "We just hit one ball and each of us takes a turn."

"That would be awesome," I say, remembering the two large hills we have to climb and the noon sun getting hotter every minute.

"And what would we learn from that?" asks Anne, looking pointedly in my direction.

We haul our golf bags back out into the thirty-two-degree heat.

Anne resumes her hitting-coach duties as I slash my way uphill. When I can't stand it any longer I pick up my ball and trudge to the green, where I plunk it down seven centimetres from the hole.

"Jane, what are you doing?" Anne huffs, her agitated bosom bouncing beneath her peach shirt as she advances on me.

Just then a ball sails between us, missing Anne's nose by inches.

Startled, she jumps sideways and lands squarely in a fresh pile of poo cleverly hidden at the side of the green by a loose Canada goose. The encounter leaves a smeary brown smudge on her shiny new golf shoes.

"Saved by the ball," I mutter under my breath.

"Fore!" Anne hollers, waving her club at the frustrated foursome waiting impatiently on the hole behind us. "You're supposed to yell 'Fore!'"

I look back with interest, straining to see if any of men in this group aren't wearing wedding rings. Am I finally about to meet some guys on the golf course? It is, after all, the only reason I'm subjecting myself to these rounds of torture in the first place.

But the four-letter 'F' word they holler back is not in accordance with Golf Canada's guide to rules and etiquette for the game. I miss the putt, tuck the ball in my pocket and walk off the green.

When it's finally over we head to our cars. I notice Larry sports a thin strip of untanned skin on his newly naked ring finger. It matches well with his farmer-tan arm bands.

I discover a gardener's tan is much more attractive on Tuesday night when I meet Sean for dinner at Pizza Hut. Wearing a brown Tshirt and faded white Levis, his tanned skin looks awesome.

In a playful mood, he teases me and our waitress mercilessly.

"Are you ever going to tell me how old you are?" I ask him.

"I'm fifty-five, and I'm five years away from retirement. Anything else you need to know?"

"How many times have you been married?"

"Just once; once was enough."

"And you have a son?"

"Yes, but I didn't have him with my wife; she already had two children from her first marriage when we got married. My son was raised by his mother; I didn't even get to know him until he was in his twenties. He got married last year and invited me to the wedding. He seems like a good kid."

"Are you a grandpa yet?"

He looks amused. "No, but I suppose it could happen any day."

We return to his house and I finally get a tour of his garden.

His pride and joy, it is a magical mini park growing in his backyard. There are annuals, perennials, trees, shrubs in every colour imaginable.

He doesn't know what to do next, so I suggest coffee, thinking we could just go in the house and have one, but he insists on Tim Hortons.

"I liked you from the minute I saw you at the singles club. You're so pretty and educated. I tried to make eye contact with you all night. I just wanted to take you and hug you and kiss you."

I'm speechless.

"Does it bother you when I tell you you're pretty?"

"No, but I have a confession to make."

"What's that?"

"I think you're pretty, too."

Neither of us wants the evening to end. We drive down to the lake for a walk. Being peak tourist season, it's crowded with people.

We make an attractive couple, the sun, hanging low as it sinks toward the water, shining on our matching blonde hair.

We bump into several people he knows. I see Collette and Bob, which means that by Monday my secret will be public knowledge.

I don't care.

We walk all the way out to the grain elevators, where I nearly step on a cast-off condom hidden in the grass. Luckily Sean doesn't notice. I'd bought a pack of Tic Tacs for my purse, and it shakes like a baby's rattle with each step I take.

"Let me hold your hand now," he says. "It's dark and no one can see us."

"I don't care if anyone sees us."

It feels good and natural. He doesn't let go until we reach the car.

"I had a really good time tonight," he says as we pull up in front of my house. "It's the best date I've had in a long time."

I get my keys out.

"Just let me kiss you on the cheek," he says.

I kiss his lips anyway and we end up in each other's arms. For a few brief moments he holds me close. It all feels so good. My head pressed against his chest, I can hear the soft thud of his heart.

"Good night," I whisper. He lets go too fast.

"Do you want to come with me to an auction tomorrow?"

"I can't. I have this family thing. But call me, okay?"

And for once there's no doubt in my mind that he will.

16

I'VE BEEN BUYING rudimentary learn-to-play-the-bass books and practising religiously. I'm eager to show Chet my new skills at my lesson on Wednesday night and proudly pluck out "Row, Row, Row Your Boat" and the A&W root beer theme song on my bass.

He's impressed.

"Soon we'll have you moving on up to 'Turkey in the Straw.'"

"Now, that will be a day of celebration."

"In my younger days I used to be a big partier."

"But you've settled down now?"

"A wife and kid tend to have that effect on you," he says. He tells me he has a five-year-old son, Matthew. I wonder why he's had only one child.

Friday after work Kim invites me out to the Barking Frog for a meat raffle.

Kim's charity group, BG Kids, hosts meat raffles at the bar every Friday night to raise money for their foundation. My motives are not entirely charitable in nature. The blue-collar bar has about a six-to-one male-to-female ratio, so, in keeping with my birthday resolutions, it's a good place to be.

I wonder if I should tell Kim I've been seeing her ex-boyfriend Sean, but it feels weird to think we've kissed the same boy. I decide to wait until I see where the relationship is going.

Even though Sean occupies my thoughts for most of my waking hours, I find myself wondering if Gord will be here tonight. But Bart is all by his lonesome for once. Cindy doesn't show up, either, and I feel some sympathy for him. Even a doofus can get his heart broken.

Kim's long-time buddy Paula is sitting with us. She mentions that the organization she works for, Haven House, is also going to start doing meat raffles at the Harrison Park Inn.

Kim leans over to me. "Isn't that where they have the singles cards on Thursday nights?"

Interesting. Has Sean talked to her about me? He told me they are still friends and keep in touch.

"Yes, I went there once. It's a great place to meet seventy-year-old widowed ladies."

We laugh and Bart stops gazing into his beer and comes over. "I had my first date in three years and I fell asleep. You can't have a worse date than that."

Cindy and Bart's blind date took place two months ago. Is Bart just figuring this out now?

I don't have the heart to tell him their dating debacle hasn't slowed Cindy down. She is out on yet another visually impaired rendezvous this very evening.

• • •

First thing Monday morning, Cindy is just about to debrief me on her date when we are interrupted by Frank, who appears to be arguing rather loudly with himself in his corner office.

Cindy looks at me quizzically. "He's been doing that all morning. I looked in his office when I came in this morning and there was no one in there with him."

"Frank is always talking to himself," I say. "Enough with the suspense already. How was your blind date?"

"It was amazing." She pauses for effect. "He was super nice and we had a wonderful time. We talked for four hours straight and didn't have a single awkward moment."

"So, are you going out again?"

"Yes, he's going to call me."

She continues about her day, floating through the office radiating happiness and singing her new love's praises to every staff member who crosses her path.

I admire Cindy's openness and positive attitude. I never share my romantic escapades with anyone from the office. It's bad enough having to get through these things with the help of close friends and many pints of Häagen-Dazs. Having co-workers be privy to the depths of my humiliation would be too much.

Also, the negativity sisters would have a field day.

"My total business income from a non-related Canadian-controlled private corporation was $54,782.83," I hear Frank say loudly to no one in particular.

Overwhelmed by curiosity, I tiptoe down the hallway to his office and sidle over a few steps so I can nonchalantly peek through his open door. He's wearing a headset and giving it commands in the manner of a football coach relaying messages to his team on the field.

And his computer answers him back.

"You owe $4,006 in federal tax and $2,269 in Ontar-ee-ooh tax. Please make your cheque or money order payable to the Receiver General of Can-ah-da."

"The partners thought clients were getting weirded out by Frank's constant talking to himself," Katie informs me as she heads into his office with a stack of orange files. "They figured if they could find a computer that actually talked back to him it wouldn't seem quite so strange."

"Do you think they could find me a computer that would like a wife and kids?"

• • •

I get up early Sunday morning for yet another breakfast date with Sean. What is wrong with dinner, I wonder. Why does he always want to go out for breakfast?

We meet at his place and drive to Inn on the Bay together. He's wearing these incredibly sexy olive cotton pants with a blue-green polyester shirt that could have come directly from Grandpa Alf's closet.

After a lovely meal the waitress brings our bill. "Would you like to charge this to your room?"

"Only if my mom says it's okay," Sean quips.

He gets us iced cappuccinos to go and we drink them with straws in the little tree house he's built at the back of his massive garden. I'm sucking away madly at the last chocolate bubbles when he leans over to give me an impulsive peck on the cheek. We talk about what we have to do that afternoon.

"I'll just give you a quick tour of the house before you go."

His house is exquisite. A small brown brick two-storey filled with antiques, comfy overstuffed couches, TVs and gleaming hardwood floors. He has a refurbished claw-foot tub and a vintage Jackson Bell radio that actually works.

All too soon we are back at the front door, but before I can say goodbye he pulls me to him and starts kissing me.

These are nothing like his kisses from Wednesday night. His mouth is open and his tongue is everywhere. He kisses my mouth, cheek and ears. He seems especially fond of kiss-ing ears, so that his tongue makes extremely loud slurping sounds that echo as though inside a cavern.

I kiss him back with equal passion and run my hands over his strong back. My fingers go through his silky blond hair.

"Are you scared?" he whispers.

"You're too old for me."

"I know."

We keep on kissing.

Finally, I pull away and we walk to my car. I say goodbye and am sitting in the car when he sits on the edge of the door frame and rests his head against my legs.

"That can't be comfortable," I say, looking down at him.

"Don't go. I just want to neck with you for an hour."

Yeah, then I'll put on a poodle skirt and we'll jive on down to the sock hop for a soda.

He takes my hand and leads me back into the house, my heart beating in the wild way only a person who hasn't had sex in over six years can know.

He takes me to a little room upstairs. We sit down on a couch in front of a big bay window that provides yet another spectacular view of the garden below.

We get back to business.

"Let's go lie down on my bed," he suggests.

"I thought you just wanted to neck?"

"I just want to kiss and cuddle you lying down. It's much more comfortable."

So I clamber onto his beautiful antique bed.

He pulls me on top of him and I can feel how hard he is.

"I want to take you to a secluded cabin and make love for days."

"I didn't know men over fifty still had sex."

"I don't have sex; I make love."

Naked, up close and personal, he has the best body I've ever seen. Buff biceps, a light sprinkle of blond hair scattered across a strong chest that tapers down to a tummy so taut you could bounce a quarter off it. Who knew gardening could make a man so fit?

Unable to control myself, I begin unbuttoning his ugly blue-green grandpa shirt.

"I hate this shirt. Let's get it off you."

"How do you feel about my pants?"

With the flourish of a magician pulling a rabbit from his hat, he whips off his belt and his pants drop onto the gleaming hardwood floorboards. He stands naked before me, beaming proudly.

It is a moment of shock and awe, like none I've ever experienced.

Rearing up to meet me stallion-style is the most enormous penis I have ever seen.

We hustle back to his bed.

"Do you have a condom?" I ask, wondering if a regular-sized one will fit.

And then he looks at me with those movie-star blue eyes and says, "I don't know if we should have sex right now, because it changes everything between two people."

It's like pouring a bucket of ice water on a troop of Bonobos monkeys.

Why would a man get me out of my car as I am about to leave, get me naked in his bed, then announce that maybe now isn't such a good time for him? Is that magnificent member just for show? Perhaps his earlier tongue action has damaged the inner workings of my ear and I've heard him incorrectly.

"What?" I say, seeking clarification.

"I don't think this is a good idea."

"You're a big tease." I hop out of bed and struggle to get dressed, trying my hardest to be graceful in this graceless situation.

"I won't be able to concentrate on my work now. I'll be thinking about you all day," he says.

I drive home in a daze, trying to get a handle on what's just happened. Was it a dream? Have I imagined the whole thing? Is it some cruel joke; have the negativity sisters hired a gorgeous gigolo to torment my poor sex-starved self?

At home there's a message from Shelly. "Come on out; we're taking the kids to the beach."

Maybe a swim will cool me down. I drive to Meaford to meet them at Steve's shop. When I get there he's busy hooking a trailer with one of the shop's demo jet skis onto the van. I climb into the back seat with the kids, stepping over assorted action figures, pink hair accessories, fast-food wrappers, juice boxes and a rotting apple core.

On arrival at Memorial Beach, Shell, Madison and I slip into our bathing suits in the back of the van.

I'm just pulling on my Speedo when Maddie lets out a squeal.

"Aunt Jane, what happened?" She's pointing at my naked breasts.

Puzzled, I gaze down, only to be met with two of the biggest, ugliest black-and-yellow hickeys I have ever seen. Threatening to spill the secret of my early-morning sexcapades, their stripes circle my nipples like the rings of a bullseye.

Words escape me; I stammer incoherently. Shell puts her hand over her mouth to stifle her laughter.

"Did somebody beat you up?" Madison has the tenacity of a bulldog with a bone. Nothing will stop her now.

I'm still speechless.

Shell jumps to the rescue. "It was Wanker. Wanker bit her."

"Why Aunt Jane? Why did he bite you?" she says, like little Cindy Lou Who asking the Grinch why he was taking all the Whos's presents.

The wheels in my mind turn furiously as I try to construct a reasonable scenario in which my docile little dachshund might suddenly attack my breasts.

"I fell into some peanut butter, and he was trying to lick it off."

Madison nods, completely satisfied with this explanation. I breathe a sigh of relief.

Shelly, however, has practically doubled over in an attempt to contain herself. "That's one feisty fifty-five-year-old you got nibbling on you, Jane."

I whip my bathing suit up just as Steven opens the back door and appraises the situation.

"How was your date this morning?"

Shell looks at me, and I look down at my toes.

"It sucked," Shell says, in full-on hysterics now.

I throw a sand pail at her.

The lake looks as moody as I feel, a palette of blues, greys and browns. At the beach the water is almost translucent, revealing a sandy bottom and grey granite rocks as it laps the shore. Normally Georgian Bay would be way too cold for me this early in July, but the heatwave has gotten to me and I wade out with the kids to a pair of gigantic boulders that jut up out of the water like breasts.

Billy climbs onto the west side of the rock formation. Maddie and I cross the rocky bridge that joins the two rocks and stretch out to sun ourselves on the flat eastern rock.

These rocks, called "The Sisters," have been around for as long as I can remember. Legend has it that many years ago two little girls ignored their parents' warnings and swam out into Georgian Bay. The current caught them. They couldn't swim back to shore and drowned out there together. Immediately afterward, the two granite boulders emerged from the depths of the Bay, holding hands, where they stand side by side to this day.

Steven sets about launching the jet ski, edging it carefully out past the rocks in the shallow water before turning it loose, driving fast, spinning in circles and jumping over the wake.

We take turns going for rides until we are sunburned and exhausted. When it's finally time to load the water-craft back onto the trailer, a good-looking guy walking on the beach stops to lend a hand. He appears to be in my age range and isn't wearing a ring of any kind. Shelly gives me a knowing nudge, but I just smile and thank him for his help.

Sean is all I can think about right now.

The heatwave drags on.

17

EVERY THREE OR four years, one of the partners' kids gets hired on at FACK. These inexperienced PKs (partners' kids) have no familiarity with or training in accounting; they entertain us until they discover that accounting is not nearly as much fun as they'd envisioned and move on to greener pastures.

So no one is surprised when Dean's daughter, Elizabeth, finds her way to the FACK bullpen. At thirty-five she is having trouble 'finding herself,' and the partners think FACK might be the grounding experience she's looking for.

I have my doubts as to whether Elizabeth will find herself at FACK, but I find her fascinating exactly as she is.

She has a Bachelor's degree in psychology, a college diploma in fine art and is certified to teach ashtanga yoga. As prerequisite to taking the FACK job, she had enrolled in several accounting courses at Georgian College. When not pursuing a higher education, Elizabeth lives in Banff, waitressing and creating arts and crafts. Passionate about animals, she lives with two Burmese cats and a cockatoo. A less likely candidate for accountancy I have never met.

In less than a week she has coated her cubicle walls with photographs, cards, dried flowers, sketches, postcards and motivational words of wisdom clipped from *Oprah* magazine. Rather than embracing the traditional business-casual wardrobe of dark suits and sensible shoes, she's prone to showing up in track pants, a flannel shirt and a pair of work boots. On the odd occasion she brings one of her cats along for company. Only a partner's daughter can get away with such nonconformist behaviour.

Tight for cash, she's also waitressing a couple of shifts at Kelsey's Restaurant; her remaining time is devoted to her animals and her art.

Elizabeth isn't beautiful in a traditional sense. She has the unfortunate luck of having inherited her father's large, square face. But her confidence and outgoing nature make her attractive to everyone she comes in contact with.

I develop a bit of a girl crush on her. She reminds me of a simpler time when creativity meant everything to me. Observing her happy hippy-chick lifestyle generates artistic stirrings I haven't felt in a long time. Despite being only two or three years younger than me and lacking any kind of financial stability, she carries herself with confidence and enjoys life to the fullest.

Spurred on by this new inspiration, I work even harder on my bass lessons and bring in some of my favourite photos to pin to the bulletin board behind my desk. Elizabeth, I think, is not the only right-brain woman struggling to survive in a left-brain world.

To celebrate her first day at FACK, Anne suggests we take Elizabeth out for lunch.

"That's a great idea, guys. Thanks for inviting me," she responds with enthusiasm.

"Where would you like to go?" Anne asks.

"There's a new tea room downtown that looks really cool," Elizabeth throws out.

"East Side Mario's is always good," Anne chips in.

"Or the fish-and-chip place down by the water has delicious food," Elizabeth suggests.

"I was thinking of East Side Mario's," Anne says, fishing in her purse for her keys.

We walk to the parking lot and Elizabeth shoots me a funny look.

"This is how it works," I tell her. "Anne says to everyone, 'Where do you want to go for lunch?' and we give her a bunch of suggestions. Then Anne tells us where we're really going."

"So, where are we going?"

"It depends on whether she's in the mood for a quarter-chicken dinner or cheese cappelletti."

"Oh, I get it."

As it always does when single women go out for lunch, the conversation drifts to the men, or in my case the lack thereof, in our lives.

Anne drones on about new husband Doug.

"Is there anyone special in your life, Elizabeth?" I ask.

Her eyes brighten. "Yes, his name is Brian. He's actually just moved in with me."

I do the math. Elizabeth moved back to Owen Sound less than three weeks ago and has already found someone she likes enough to move in with.

"How did you meet him?" Anne asks.

"He's a bartender at the restaurant where I'm waitressing part-time."

I can't help feeling a twinge of envy. I've been back in town for almost nine years and haven't had a decent relationship yet. But of course now that Sean is in my life, everything will be different.

It's Tuesday already and he hasn't called, leaving me hot and bothered, literally and figuratively, for three days. My raging sunburn from my romp on the beach and my bruised breasts from my time in Sean's bed serve as sore reminders of my Saturday.

Friday night finds me home alone waiting for the phone to ring, feeling neglected and forgotten.

A new couch, chair, end table and loveseat had been delivered to my place that afternoon. After viewing Sean's meticulously decorated home, I felt my ragtag assortment of used furniture donated by various family members could use an upgrade. I'd been meaning to replace the boat-sized orange-and-brown-floral couch and assorted garage-sale and beanbag chairs for months but hadn't quite gotten the funds or the time to do it. Now that I might actually be entertaining a male visitor, I had made an effort to make my home look like it belonged to a grown up.

The phone finally rings.

"I'm sorry I didn't call sooner, but I've been busier than a one-armed paper hanger."

"Oh," I say, trying to sound nonchalant, like I've been so busy with my own extensive social calendar I haven't even noticed.

"My mom had a heart attack on Monday and had to be rushed to the hospital. I've been visiting her every day after work, but she's stabilized now."

"Oh my god. Is she okay?"

I'm such a jerk. Of course he hasn't called—his mom is in the hospital.

"Still shaky, but she's pulling through. Do you want to go out for pizza tomorrow night?"

What a sweetheart, looking after his mom like that. Why am I so paranoid?

18

WHEN I ARRIVE at Sean's place he's standing outside. He's wearing a sateen black polyester button-down shirt with white topstitching and patch pocket, circa the disco era.

We go to Europa's, an old-fashioned Greek pizza place, where Sean flirts outrageously with the waitress then orders for me in that charming old-fashioned way of his. We skip dessert and drive to Dairy Queen.

Everywhere we go we seem to bump into someone Sean knows. He stops and says hello to a plump middle-aged woman standing in line for ice cream, then introduces me to her.

"How do you know her?" I dig into my chocolate-chip cookie-dough blizzard.

"She used to be my sister-in-law."

"How long were you married?"

"Way too long."

"So, marriage just wasn't your thing?"

"It was like being married to my sister. There was no passion between us. She came from a big family and was always
dragging me off to all these family gatherings."

"It sounds like hell."

"Thank God I was still drinking in those days."

"So you're a loner with an alcohol problem who hates
kids."

"I'm not fond of animals, either."

"Let's go back to your place and watch TV."

Sean sits on the couch beside me, notices some dust
on his remote control and sprays it with furniture polish.
It promptly stops working. He is disgruntled, pointing
the malfunctioning unit at the big television and clicking
away in vain.

He finally locates an inane cop show he likes and we cud-
dle on the couch, pretending to watch it for several minutes.
The close proximity quickly becomes too much for me and
I rest my head on his shoulder. His neck smells of the same
Old Spice aftershave I used to buy my dad every Christmas
when I was a kid.

"I want to make love to you all night and then make coffee for you in the morning," he says, standing up to strip off
his clothes.

And there he is. Standing in the big bay window in the
moonlight, all tan muscled shoulders, washboard abs and
that unforgettable penis.

But the vision evaporates en route to the bedroom,
where his proud phallus morphs into an elongated water
balloon. Dangling between his legs, it sways pendulum-
style with every step.

Sean can't look at me, and I fight to keep my eyes above his waist.

"I can't do this; my conscience is bothering me," he says, avoiding the limp pink elephant in the room.

But it will not be forgotten any time soon.

"We can just cuddle and fall asleep in each other's arms," I suggest, padding to the bathroom to take out my contact lenses. Returning to bed, I crawl under the covers and put my arms around him.

He sits up.

"You should go home," he says.

I feel like I've been slapped. I try looking into his eyes, but in the darkened room I can't make out any expression. I have no idea how I'm supposed to act. Situations like this never come up in romantic comedies.

The silence that follows is interminable. Finally, I speak, my voice quavering. "What happened to my coffee in the morning?"

"I'm worried about what the neighbours will think when they see your car still in my driveway tomorrow."

The excuse is limper than his dick.

Ashamed, humiliated and hurting, I crawl from his bed, put on my clothes and slink home. It's three a.m.

Outside it's pitch black and raining. I drive slowly, straining to see in the glow of my muted headlights. I stop at a 24-hour Mac's Milk convenience store and load up on junk food. When I'm feeling this low there's nothing I won't eat. I become the human equivalent of a catfish.

Wanker has spent the night impersonating a dachshund doorstopper, his elongated body pressed flat against the front door, awaiting my return. He springs to life at the sound of my key in the lock, leaping from foot to foot in a dachshund dance of love then racing figure eights through my legs.

I scoop him up and hug his little warm body. "Well, at least one wiener is happy to see me," I murmur. "I should have walked away the moment he told me he didn't like animals."

I carry Wanker and my freshly purchased comfort food up to bed and overindulge in a junk-food orgy of unprecedented proportions.

I call Kristen in the morning and tell her all the humiliating details. Kristen is the only friend I'm comfortable discussing intimate matters with. It's funny; she's a talker and loves a good gossip as much as the next person, but ask her to keep a secret and she will take it to the grave.

"Maybe it's my new super power: the ability to deflate tall penises with a single glance."

"How can you blame yourself for this? It wasn't anything you did. Didn't you say he was almost sixty?"

"Maybe it's the swan song of his long schlong."

"Okay, enough already with the penile humour. It's beneath us."

It's twelve days before I hear from Sean again. He leaves a message on my phone. "Just called to say hello."

I don't return his call and never go to the singles club again.

19

IN DECEMBER OF Grade 13, Kyle talked me into holding a New Year's Eve party in my parents' rec room. Normally he and Angie played social conveners for our gang of nerdy friends and would have arranged such events, but Angie was off skiing at Mont Tremblant with Xav and his offspring, leaving us to fend for ourselves.

The parties we'd held up to this point had been simple affairs. Impromptu euchre tournaments played around a kitchen table, backyard pool parties or air-guitar challenges were among the activities we considered highly entertaining.

But Kyle was determined this party was going to be memorable. Mid-afternoon, he arrived with a raw chicken and all the trimmings tucked under his arm. With continuous coaching from both our moms, we had the bird stuffed and settled in a big black-and-white-speckled roasting pan. That gave us plenty of time to get our walnut-wood-panelled rec room set up for the party.

Kyle struck a match to light the artificial log inside our cast-iron Franklin stove, where it emitted a weird yellowish-blue chemical-glow flame. We kept the little orange curtains of the high basement windows drawn. No need for extra light with the bronze cupids holding up orange globes to keep the basement lit. The gigantic orange, brown and tan floral couch was perfect for snuggling. I thought of Christopher and sighed. We'd broken up over a year ago, and there hadn't been a boy since who could hold a candle to him.

For extra seating we unfolded a slew of webbed lawn chairs from the garage and brought down a few hard-backed chairs from the dining room. Kyle abducted Shelly's beanbag chair from her bedroom. We took the net off the ping-pong table and covered it with a bed sheet, transforming it into a makeshift dining table. After dinner we would fold its table wings up above it like Darth Vader's TIE fighter to make room for dancing.

Ian and Mark arrived early to unload Ian's elaborate stereo system from Mark's Datsun and set up a makeshift DJ station. Ian, who took his DJ duties seriously, wore a Tshirt that said "Disco Sucks." Albums stacked in a red Sealtest milk crate included music by Styx, Loverboy, Genesis, Foreigner, Bob Seger, Pat Benetar, Led Zeppelin, Journey and ZZ Top.

Michelle 'The Murph' Murphy brought a jiggly round cherry Jell-O mold with fruit cocktail on the bottom. On top she had spelled out "1981" in pastel miniature marshmallows. Unfortunately, the circle shape made the outer "1"s curvy, so it looked more like "98" with brackets around it. Everyone else brought chips and drinks. All in all, Kyle and I were quite proud of our domestic accomplishments.

Since we were all under the legal drinking age of nine-teen, Kyle's cool older sister Abby had bought a bottle of cherry brandy from the liquor store for us. In an attempt to make a punch that resembled our cocktail of choice, the cherry hooker, we mixed grenadine and orange juice with our contraband alcohol.

I'd frozen round ice cubes with maraschino cherries in the centres for the occasion. Not realizing there was already alcohol in the mixture, Jamie McKinley added the vodka she'd siphoned from her parent's liquor cabinet into a contact-lens-solution bottle and smuggled to the party inside her leg warmers. She could have just put it in her purse, but carrying contraband alcohol in under your pants felt much more rebellious and clandestine. The final concoc-tion tasted more like violently potent cough syrup than the popular cocktail.

In the beginning our guests refused to mingle. Boys took the chairs on one side of the basement, girls on the oppo-site, just like our dances in public school. But eventually the effects of the alcohol began to loosen everyone up and the male and female lines began to blur.

Since we hadn't thought to get any New Year's hats or kazoos, Murph, who was enamoured with a new show called *Magnum PI*, fashioned some leis out of toilet paper and began draping them around everyone's neck and shouting "Aloha!" On a trip upstairs to the washroom, Mark pilfered a pink poodle from the collection of stuffed animals on my bed, and it became his favourite dance partner. Someone smoking on the front lawn accidentally let one of our barn cats into the house. It jumped onto the kitchen counter and began licking clean the remaining chicken bones.

A fight almost broke when DJ Ian refused Murph's request to play "Keep on Lovin' You" by REO Speedwagon. Before violence erupted I stepped in to mediate, and Ian relented enough to play "Time for Me to Fly" instead.

I didn't think anything of it when Kyle asked me to dance. In those days at parties we danced with everyone in attendance. At midnight on New Year's Eve, normal barriers were abandoned and inappropriate kissing and fondling were the norm; even staid married folk might find a wayward husband frenching the friendly farm wife from two side roads over. So, we all kissed at midnight, and I was having so much fun I wondered just once who Chris was kissing.

Kyle and I had been enjoying more than our share of the cherry-hooker cough-syrup mixture when he took my hand and led me to our makeshift dance floor. Kyle, being so tall, bumped his head on one of the heavy square wood beams that hung from the white stucco ceiling. Right on cue, Steve Perry started singing "Lovin', Touchin', Squeezin'."

Was it just the punch, or was Kyle holding me a little closer than he usually did?

"Na, na, na, na, na," Kyle hummed in my ear, his lips brushing my hair.

He was following Journey's instructions to the letter. His hands pressed gently against my back, pulling me close to him. He was so tall that my head rested against his chest.

I looked up into his eyes. He bent down and slowly, softly kissed my lips.

"Nah, nah, na, nah, nah, nah, na, nah, na, nah."'

I looked up at him in surprise. It was well after midnight and we'd already done the "Happy New Year!" thing. What exactly was happening here?

The moment was shattered when the pulsing opening bars of "The Time Warp" reverberated through the rec room. Kyle and I broke apart, and I looked at him quizzically for a second. Then Ian did the pelvic thrust into my mother's gigantic glass punch bowl, its blood-orange contents spilling out everywhere. In what felt like a slow-motion horror movie scene, we watched as a cherry brandy vodka sunrise slowly spread its rays across the cream-coloured shag carpet.

By the time we got the mess cleaned up, the party buzz had worn off, and everyone began packing up to head home.

The next day I couldn't stop thinking about Kyle. We'd been friends for so long, it had never occurred to me to think of him any other way. Did he have feelings for me, or was it just the alcohol rubbing off on him?

When we returned to the halls of West Hill High in January for our last semester of Grade 13, it was as if the kiss had never happened. Kyle never mentioned it, and the two of us remained friends.

Mid-February was West Hill's annual Valentine's Day dance, and our gang was there. Angie, who was home from university for reading week, brought Xavier as her date. Everyone mistook him for a chaperone, and the female teachers kept asking him to dance. This ended abruptly when he and Angie danced their first slow dance, bodies swaying sensuously under the revolving lights of the disco ball.

I had heard that Chris Graham might be bringing his out-of-town girlfriend and kept a casual eye on the door, but he never materialized.

We were all having fun dancing and drinking. Kyle, Mark and Ian built a gigantic structure out of drinking straws that spanned two tables. Jamie McKinley, who'd been drinking Boone's Farm apple-blossom wine out of a brown paper bag in her Camaro in the parking lot, vomited so much in the girls' washroom that we were forced to share the boys' facilities for the rest of the evening.

I got up for fast dances with the girls and slowed danced with all the guys, including Kyle. Our New Year's kiss seemed a distant memory. Perhaps I'd dreamt it. The last song was announced, and the DJ put on "Stairway to Heaven." Kyle held out a hand, beckoning me to join him.

There was an unearthly silence, followed by the song's haunting opening notes. The disco ball ceased its relent-less spinning, down-shifted and bathed the room in soft reds and whites. At the tables, Mark and Ian began scooping up the miniature Dixie cups filled with pastel candy hearts imprinted with "Be Mine," "True Love" and "xoxo."

As the eight-minute song stretched on, so did the bound-ary between friendship and something more between Kyle and me. Once again his arms pulled me close, and as he bent to kiss me I felt myself give in to the comfort of being wanted and desired. For a moment I saw Angie, dancing with Xav a few feet away, looking on curiously, but then Kyle kissed me again and I forgot about everyone else.

Walking quietly to our car on the way out, I couldn't stop thinking about him. Several boys had asked me out since Chris and I had broken up, but none had even registered. All I'd been able to think about was how badly I wanted to get him back.

But Kyle was different. We'd been friends for so long. He knew my strengths and my weaknesses and appeared to like me anyway. I'd been looking for love in all the wrong places; all this time it had been right under my nose.

Minutes after I got home Angie phoned me, upsetting Shelly, who complained she'd been sound asleep.

"What's going on with you and Kyle? It looked like you were getting pretty hot and heavy on the dance floor."

"I don't know. He kissed me at the New Year's Eve party and I didn't think anything of it. I don't know what's going on."

"He kissed you on New Year's Eve and you didn't tell me."

"Well, you've been a bit busy, and I just thought it was because we were both drunk."

"So, are you his girlfriend now?"

I really wasn't sure.

"Well, I've always been his friend, and I am a girl." Suddenly I remembered the mood ring from all those Christmases ago. The tag had said it was from a secret admirer.

I'd no sooner hung up when the phone rang again, inspiring a rage of screaming epitaphs from Shelly.

This time it was Kyle.

"Um, Jane."

"Yes, Kyle."

It was weird. We'd been calling each other for years. Suddenly there was an awkwardness between us.

"Do you want to see a movie next weekend?"

And just like that he became my boyfriend.

I fell in love with the boy next door.

20

WHEN I ARRIVE at work early Monday morning Anne is waiting in my office. She appears to be in a good mood and is not drinking coffee. I look at her and blink, wondering if my troubling weekend with Sean has upset me so much that it is causing me to hallucinate.

"I'm pregnant!" she announces with uncharacteristic gusto.

I push the On button on my computer and listen to it go through its morning routine, whirring, clicking and blinking until the familiar red, green, blue and yellow squares of our operating system float up on the screen.

"Well, that was fast."

"Yes," she says, smugger than the infamous feline feasting on the finch. She licks her lips and I wait for tiny yellow feathers to emerge from the corners of her mouth.

Unsure whether a hug or high five is called for, I settle on "Congratulations. That's great news."

And I really mean it, because not having Anne around for several months while she is off on maternity leave will be a treat. This babe brings good tidings of great joy to everyone who has to work with Anne. One can only hope she gets bitten by the maternal bug and decides to become a stay-at-home mom.

"How are you feeling?" I ask.

"I am soooooooo tired." She lets out the sigh of a pachyderm in her seventh trimester, as opposed to a mere human hosting a microscopic zygote.

And with that she's off to share her news with the rest of the office.

Everyone is happy and excited for Anne until Wednesday afternoon, when a much-less-animated mother-to-be emerges from a meeting with Sam. She tracks me down in Katie's office. Apparently the partners had met to discuss her news, and since Anne works mainly for Sam, he'd been appointed spokesman. She recounts their conversation, which had gone something like this:

> Sam: I hear you're with child. When is your due date?
> Anne: February 12.
> Sam: On behalf of the partners, we'd like to offer you our consolidated congratulations. We'll have to find someone to cover your audits for March and April, of course. Are you thinking of coming back early or are you planning on taking the full six months?
> Anne: Well, actually, Sam, the maternity-leave laws are changing in 2000. Women now get a full year off.

Sam (*voice extremely loud, agitated*): A year! That's ludicrous! Who on earth would take a whole year off?

Anne: Well, me for one.

Sam (*face turning red, beads of sweat materializing on bald cranium*): Anne, you're a public accountant. That means you're not covered by the Employment Standards Act. I don't have to give you lunch breaks, coffee breaks or any breaks. I don't have to pay you minimum wage or overtime pay or paid vacation. And there's no way in hell I'm giving you an entire year off to sit at home and play with your baby. You have clients here who need you.

Anne: Well, I'm going to have a baby at home who needs me, and even accountants are entitled to a full year.

Sam: Anne, if we have to hire someone to do your job while you're gone, I'm going to give her all your best clients and let her keep them. When you get back, we're going to give you all the crap jobs that no one else wants.

Retelling the story for Katie and I, Anne is close to tears. "Can they really force me to come back early?"

Katie, who'd worked at FACK since her co-op student days in the early eighties and had three children, is well equipped to answer.

"I got married really young, and since I specialized in tax the partners told me right away that I could never take my maternity leave during tax season, so I'd better plan my family accordingly."

"So, did you?"

"I did with the girls. I had a really hard time getting pregnant with them and eventually had to get fertility treatments in order to conceive. It was easy to schedule the treatments so that both girls were born in the summer. I came back a little early in December to help Frank with year-end tax planning, but for the most part it worked out pretty well."

"What about Bobby?" Anne asks, referring to Katie's feisty four-year-old.

"We weren't planning to have any more children, but because I'd had such difficulties getting pregnant with the girls, I didn't bother with birth control. Bobby was our little surprise."

"And he arrived during tax season?"

"The second week of March. Bobby has always refused to follow anyone's schedule but his own."

"What did you do?"

"I worked right up to the day he was born; my water broke in the boardroom. I was working on a complicated estate return at the time, and Frank practically followed me into the delivery room with it. Fiona and Betty boxed up my tax returns and Frank drove them over to my house. For the first nine weeks I worked on them at home with the baby, then I put Bobby in daycare and came back to work."

• • •

It's not like the partners are completely ungrateful. Every summer they host a party for the staff and their spouses as a thank-you for all the extra hours we put in during busy season. Dean has chartered Owen Sound's infamous party boat the *Drake* for our annual shindig in August.

The Drake is a Fairmile motor launch originally built for the Royal Navy in the forties. After a decade spent sweeping for mines and searching for subs off the coast of Nova Scotia, it was sold to a merchant in Montreal, where the ship remained for the better part of two decades. In the late eighties our client, Jake Goodson, purchased the old boat at auction, had her spruced up, overhauled and sailed to Owen Sound. Now it takes tourists on two-hour sightseeing tours of scenic Georgian Bay.

Since Jake has a habit of not paying his bills, he was several years behind on his FACK invoices. As a result, Dean has been able to swing a deal, exchanging a party cruise for some of Jake's outstanding debt.

At one hundred feet long and twenty feet wide, the *Drake* can easily handle our motley crew of accountants. A bar and buffet has been set up on the main deck, while speakers on the upper deck pump out music for anyone who wants to dance. It is a beautiful Saturday afternoon, the sky so clear you can almost see Michigan. Everyone is in a good mood and ready for a party.

Elizabeth has brought a male friend who works with her at Kelsey's, the restaurant she's pulling double shifts at. With the sun shining on her date's balding head from across the boat, he looks vaguely familiar. He reaches up to scratch at a tiny pimple on his chin and, with a jolt, I realize it's Glen, the waiter Shelly gave my phone number to a couple of weeks ago. I wedge myself in behind Cindy and spend the rest of the evening slinking around, hoping he won't recognize the desperate daft woman he hasn't called.

Elizabeth had told us she was seeing a bartender named Brian; now here she is out on a date with Glen. I've been back in Owen Sound since 1994 and have not had a single boyfriend. Elizabeth has been here for a few short weeks and she's dating two men? I'm impressed.

Anne is twenty-five minutes late, keeping the boat and all of us waiting for her at the dock. Though his eyes betray nothing, I can see the set in Dean's jaw as he discusses the situation with the captain. Just as we're about to pull up anchor, Anne's car pulls in to the parking lot. Holding a Tim's coffee, she nonchalantly boards with her husband Doug in tow.

"What happened, Anne?" Dean asks as she walks up the gangplank.

"I laid down for a nap and slept longer than anticipated," she says, patting her non-existent baby bump. "This baby's making me so tired."

It is an excellent meal and a beautiful night. The only blemish on the evening is Larry.

Cindy and I sit at a table with him and his wife, Mary, and Anne and Doug. Mary, I quickly discover, is nice and pretty and passionate about her career as an addictions counsellor. I fail to see what she sees in Larry.

The partners have given everyone two free drinks tickets for the bar, but there appears to be no limits on wine at the tables; port flows more freely than at the last supper.

"I need a man," Cindy moans.

"Don't get married. That's when all the fun ends," says a tipsy Larry.

Mary reddens and stares at her plate. I have an urge to kick Larry, who sits directly across from me, under the table.

"I fixed you up with Bart last time you asked," says Kim. "What did you really think of him?"

"I liked him, but just as a friend," Cindy replies.

"One of our clients took me out for a ride in his cabin cruiser last weekend. We tooled around Wasaga Beach looking to pick up sleazy women," Larry says to no one in particular.

Mary looks hurt. *Is this what happens to men as they approach fifty?*

Images of a Speedo-clad Larry eyeballing Wasaga Beach babes with binoculars, wearing deck shoes, argyle knee socks and his perpetual pocket protector pop unwilled into my mind. I feel a ripple of nausea and take another swig from my wine glass. Seriously, it's time to ban the banana hammock on public beaches.

There had been a storm the night before, and the bay is still rough, the waves rocking and rolling the old boat. A fishy smell emanating from a sea shell filled with red snapper on the buffet assaults my olfactory glands. I watch Lori scoop a big glop of prawn paella onto her plate, change her mind, and scrape it back into the serving dish.

Lori is the FACK office spinster. Now in her mid-fifties, she'd originally planned on being a high school math teacher, but she suffered from chronic irritable bowel syndrome. A year at St. Mary's Secondary School had led to severe anxiety. She'd quit teaching to pursue an accounting designation.

Lori had lived in an apartment until she was almost forty, when she moved back in with her parents as her mother's health began to deteriorate. When her mother died in the early '90s, Lori had stayed on to take care of her father. He recently passed away. Now she lives alone in the family home, a beautiful house on the lake-view side of 3rd Avenue West, where she enjoys birdwatching and going for nature walks. She's never had a boyfriend that anyone knows of and once admitted to me that she is a virgin. Her true passion is music. She plays the organ at St. Andrew's Presbyterian church every Sunday, is a long-time member of the Georgian Bay Concert Choir and holds season tickets to the symphony orchestra.

Despite her eccentricities, Lori has many loyal clients who've been devoted to her for years. She is also in charge of staffing and recruitment for FACK and was very support- ive of me when I was hired. Anne and Collette regularly make Lori the butt of their jokes, but I like her and we get along well. I occasionally attend symphony performances with her, although I find her inability to control her excite- ment during the livelier pieces somewhat distracting.

It's a hot humid night and, even in shorts and a Tshirt, I feel feverish. I'm about to run up to the top deck for some fresh air when I spot Elizabeth standing by the stairs with the waiter Glenn, so I turn back, hoping they haven't noticed me.

I head for the ship's bow, where I'm engulfed in a heavy cloud of nicotine from banished tax partner Frank. Chain- smoking and staring out at the water, he doesn't notice me. My mission a failure, there's no choice but to return to the dining area on the main deck.

I stand at the railing of the boat, gulping the fresh air. The rocking is getting worse. Larry walks over.

"You know I was only twenty-three when I got married."

"No, I didn't know that, Larry."

"Mary and I had been dating for four years and she told me we either had to get married or she would break up with me."

I look at Mary, sitting at the dinner table, talking animatedly with Anne and Doug. She's lovely. It isn't fair she has to put up with Larry. I wonder if she stays with him for the kids.

"We hardly ever have sex anymore, and when we do she just lies there."

Why is he telling me this? I feel sweat forming on the back of my neck.

"Have you ever thought about getting some marriage counselling?" I ask meekly.

"Last Saturday I wanted to have sex, and do you know what she said?"

I shake my head, praying he'll stop talking.

"She said, 'Larry, can you just pull my nightie back down when you're finished?'"

I take a deep breath, lean over the white pipe rail and vomit my supper into Georgian Bay.

21

AT WORK THE next week, Elizabeth asks me how I'd enjoyed the cruise.

"I was moved by it. Did you and your boyfriend have a good time?"

"Oh, that wasn't my boyfriend. That was Glen. I work with him at Kelsey's. He's a nice guy, but we're just friends."

"He seemed very nice," I say, trying not to sound too desperate.

"Are you interested, because I could give him your phone number."

"Well, actually my sister already gave it to him." I tell her the whole embarrassing story.

"I'll ask him if he remembers you, but I won't tell him who you are."

Next morning, she walks into my office, all excited. "I told Glen that I work with this girl who likes him, and that you left your number for him one night but he never called you. He says he doesn't remember anyone doing that, and if you wrote it on the back of a bill he probably just didn't see it."

This goes on for a week and a half. Elizabeth would go to her Kelsey's job and they'd talk about me. It's driving him crazy that she won't tell him who I am.

On Friday, Elizabeth brings me a card with a picture of a dachshund in a tutu on it.

Inside it says "I'd like to paws à deux with you."

"I'm dying to meet the mystery woman," he's written. "Come and have a drink with me on Sunday night."

I'm to meet him at the restaurant on Sunday at seven. I've never been on a blind date before and am extremely nervous.

Glen's sitting at the bar when I walk in.

We find a booth near the back of the restaurant so we can have some privacy.

Glen is not what you'd call a looker. He's balding, and he has pockmarks on his skin the size of moon craters. But he's tall, looks good in jeans and has nice eyes. He tells me he's recently declared personal bankruptcy and has not filed his tax returns for the last three years.

"Do you think that's bad?"

"Yes."

"Is that your professional opinion?"

"Yes. Please pay me $465."

"How about a drink instead?"

"Okay."

"I liked your card," I tell him.

"All Elizabeth would tell me was that you worked with her and you have a wiener dog. I told her if she didn't tell me who you were soon I was going to knock on every door in Owen Sound and ask whoever answered if I could see their wiener."

"You could get arrested for that."

I start to relax and enjoy his company. He's only a year older than me and appears to be in good health, so I suspect there would be no erectile difficulties should such opportunities arise. I find myself attracted to him.

The time flies by and before I know it we've talked for over two hours.

"I have to work the late shift tonight, but do you want to go out again this week?"

I nod.

"I'm not working Wednesday or Saturday. What works best for you?"

I would like it to be Wednesday, but my secret bass lessons means I have to wait for Saturday.

I offer to pay for our drinks.

"No, you can get it next time," he says.

He walks me to my car.

"Look. We both drive cars with Mitsubishi motors," he says. "We must be meant for each other."

It's the most romantic thing a man has said to me in years.

"Can I have a hug? I'm a hugger," he says.

He's so sweet. I can't wait to see him again.

• • •

Friday night all hell breaks loose.

Kim asks Cindy and me to meet her at Summerfolk to watch her favourite band, Tanglefoot. Kim's love of the old-fashioned upright double bass is almost as strong as my feelings for its electric counterpart. Cindy pulls into the parking lot the same time I do and we walk toward the band shell together.

On our way we bump into an inebriated white-haired gentleman who's in a chatty mood.

"I can tell you girls are single," he says, pointing a bony finger at me. I hope he's not the grim reaper, come to track me down in the parking lot.

"You're tough because you've been hurt before," he continues. "We should talk more. My name is Wilkinson. I live in Collingwood; you should call me."

Cindy is impressed. "You've been hit on already and we haven't even left the parking lot."

Summerfolk is an outdoor folk music festival held every year in the third week of August. It brings renowned musicians from all over North America to play in Kelso Beach Park and has thrived on the west shore of Georgian Bay since the seventies. The main stage is a limestone theatre that seats three thousand people.

I have a couple of beers with Cindy; Kim shows up an hour later with Bart and Gord in tow.

Cindy gives me a look. "I think we've been set up."

Bart sits down beside me; Gord sits beside Bart. We don't get much time to talk before the band starts up. The music's great, but we can't talk over it.

Gord's looking good in a black Tshirt and jeans. Bart has taken the time to spiff up as well. He sports a fresh haircut and newly grown goatee.

Gord starts up a conversation with the woman sitting on his left and, despite the fact I'm looking forward to my date with bartender Glen tomorrow night, I feel a twinge of jealousy.

Tanglefoot finishes their set. I can't believe my luck when Chet's rockabilly group takes the stage. He's an incredible musician, and I love watching him play.

When we walk by the stage on our way to the beer tent, Chet looks up, recognizes me, and a look of happy surprise lights up his face.

I should be in heaven, enjoying the superb entertainment in the company of good friends. But I've been binge-eating sporadically since the whole Sean dating debacle, and the eighteen pounds I've gained make me feel heavy and unattractive. I've squeezed into the last pair of jeans that still fit, but they are tight and uncomfortable and getting worn out from carrying the brunt of the load for the rest of my wardrobe.

Gord climbs onto the picnic table beside me. Bart is across from me with Kim and Cindy on either side of him. I'm tempted to slide in close to Gord, but, feeling fat and lacking confidence, I keep a respectable distance between us.

"They gave me this cell phone at work today," he says, pulling a little black gadget from his pocket. With its numeric keypad and side antenna, it looks like the walkie-talkie toys I played with as a kid.

"Go on, call somebody," he urges, handing it to me.

I dial Shelly's number and pass the phone back to him.

The two of them have a lengthy chat.

He makes Shelly laugh, and I can tell she likes him. I wonder if some of the pain and frustration inflicted by previous boyfriends could have been avoided if I had paid more attention to my friend's perceptions of the men I'd gotten entangled with. If love truly is blind, perhaps a second opinion from a sighted friend or family member is called for.

It's loud in the beer tent, so Gord and I take turns shouting into each other's ears.

"I'm shy," he tells me. "You miss out on things when you're shy, because you're afraid to ask for them."

Hmmmm. He hadn't seemed shy an hour earlier conversing with the woman beside him.

"Normally I'm an introvert as well, but I've discovered I can transform into an extrovert any time I want to simply by adding alcohol," I say.

"Can I get you another beer?" Gord asks.

Bart dances with Kim. Cindy tells me he calls her all the time at work. Kim's marriage is horrific. Is trying to fix Cindy and me up a ruse to get out on the town herself? Are we her cover?

It's a beautiful night. I want to ask Gord to dance but I'm not sure if he's interested—plus my confidence had vacated the premises when I donned my fat pants. And it wouldn't be right to leave Cindy sitting alone at our table.

I can lose my inhibitions when I have a few drinks, and I seriously contemplate making some kind of play for Gord.

But I hold back. Such actions are likely to lead to a one-night stand, and that's something I can never do. It's not just the dangers of disease, and I'm not a prude. I'm a romantic, and for me it's got to be the real thing or nothing at all.

And of course there's my date tomorrow night with Glen. I don't want anything to ruin it.

22

GLEN STANDS ME up.

I can't believe it. He was so nice and attentive and interested.

How can I be such a bad judge of character? I spend hours on the phone being consoled by Mom, Shelley, Cindy and Kristen. Thank god for my support team.

But I'm not the only sexually frustrated mammal pacing around my house. Wanker, who at six months of age has just hit puberty, is going through some drama of his own. Nothing in my house is safe. In a frenzy of horniness, the likes of which I have never seen, he humps pillows, bed posts, stuffed animals, my legs and my friends' legs.

He even tries to mount a massive malamute while we are hiking on the Bruce trail. His seduction attempt is wasted on the good-humoured husky, who just sniffs Wanker's tiny butt and looks confused.

"Well, I give you kudos for confidence," I tell him. But the continuous assault on my furniture and guests is becoming intolerable. When he knocks little Billy over after Shelly stops by for a coffee, she gives me a stern look. "Either that wiener or his cojones have got to go."

When Wanker returns from his overnight stay at the vet's office, he's noticeably subdued and has a large purple stain on his underbelly.

"I know how it feels, contemplating a lifetime without children," I sigh, gently massaging his back. "At least we'll always have each other."

After I fret the rest of the weekend over Glen not showing up for our date on Saturday and not calling to explain or reschedule, Shelly talks me into calling him.

Her reasoning is simple.

"There must be something wrong, some reason why he hasn't been able to reach you. How could he not call you after he said all those nice things to you? If you don't call him, you'll always wonder what happened. Both of you probably spent the whole weekend stewing about it."

"Well, I certainly did."

Unable to find a hole in Shelly's logic, on Sunday night I set my pride aside and make the call.

His machine picks up on the fourth ring and I manufacture a cool- and casual-sounding message. "Hi, Glen, it's Jane. Just wondering if you wanted to go out again sometime. Call me if you do."

I'm feeling good about this. If he's not interested, fine. At least now I have closure.

Monday night I work late. When I get home I see the red light on my answering machine flashing.

"I'm really sorry I didn't call, but things got kinda funky with my apartment. I'll be home all night. Give me a call."

I call. He's not home.

I stew all day Tuesday.

Wednesday morning I wake up determined to put the whole mess behind me. I call a singles club in Kitchener and leave a message for them to call me back with information about joining. Shelley and Billy stop by my office for a surprise visit; Billy flings his chubby little arms around me and we go out for lunch. Kim makes plans to send me out to audit a "super hot" client of hers. I'm feeling better and moving on.

In the afternoon Glen calls me at work. He's sweet and super smooth.

"I just wanted to apologize for not calling. I'm off Thursday night. Why don't we go out?"

We decide to see the new Hugh Grant movie.

"I'll call you Thursday night to confirm. What's your home number again?"

I give it to him one more time.

"Great. I'll pick you up at your place."

Thursday night I leave work early to prepare for our date. Glen has left a message: "The movie starts at 7:40. I'll pick you up at 7:15."

Nervous and excited, I shower, pick out an outfit that looks spectacular but not like I'm trying too hard. I tidy up my apartment.

He calls at seven.

"Jane, I'm so sorry I can't make it. I'm having a floorboard emergency with my apartment. I'm really sorry."

"Oh, okay then."

"Are you pissed? I know you really wanted to see *Micky Blue Eyes*.

"For-ged aboud it."

"What?"

"Never mind." I hang up.

What a gigantic moron. I'll never call or speak to him again.

I fantasize about having dinner at Kelsey's with my sexy Dr. Fiancé and our four fabulous children. Glen is our waiter, and we don't tip him.

• • •

According to the calendar, autumn officially starts the third week of September. But in Owen Sound I always sense summer's demise sometime near the end of August. You just wake up one morning and that hot heat has broken and you know it won't be back until next year. The sun keeps on shining, but there's a hint of shady coolness in the air. It's really quite lovely. I wear a sweater when I take Wanker for our evening walk.

We're deep into August when I bump into Sean at a gas station.

He'd been cutting his grass and run out of gas. He's wearing bleached-out cut-off jeans and an old Tshirt. His hair, all gelled and shiny when we were dating, is curly, as though the wind has blown it dry.

He looks incredible.

He saunters over to my car, gas can in hand. I roll down the window and say hello, polite but cool. I don't take my sunglasses off.

"Have you been really busy at work, Jane?"

"No, the summer isn't usually busy for us."

After several awkward silences, we mumble hasty goodbyes.

He calls that evening, and this time I answer.

"I just wanted to make sure you weren't mad at me."

"I'm not." On the phone I sound calm, but my hands are shaking.

"Do you want to go out again sometime?"

"That probably isn't a good idea."

"You're right. We'd probably just start making out again and things would get out of control."

"Yes, we were always out of control."

"We always had a good time together, even though we didn't really do anything exciting." That isn't true. Sean has been the most exciting thing to happen to me in years.

"I had a lot of fun too." I speak quietly, feeling sentimental not just for this loss but for all the loves that have come and gone. Does anyone ever really get the happy ending? Are the romantic comedies I love so much just fairy tales for grown women?

"You're a beautiful woman, Jane, and I hope you'll always remember me."

I hang up the phone and begin to cry.

23

IT'S FITTING, I suppose, that I have to work on Labour Day weekend.

Anne is in charge of the audit for Haven House, an organization whose fiscal year ends August 31. Located in downtown Owen Sound, it serves as a homeless shelter, food bank, drop-in centre and thrift store for Grey County.

As part of our audit procedures, we come in the following weekend to verify their inventory count, which always falls on Labour Day weekend. When I started at FACK eight years ago and got assigned the audit, Anne asked if I'd be willing to work on the long weekend, promising we'd alternate years. She has yet to take her turn.

"Jane doesn't have a family, so she doesn't mind working on statutory holidays" I overhear her telling Paula, who is Haven House's chief financial officer/office manager, on the phone.

I meet up with Paula bright and early Sunday morning at Haven House. In addition to counting the inventory, she's peeling potatoes and chopping vegetables.

"Sometimes I help out in the kitchen when we're short-handed," she explains. "When you rely as heavily on volunteers as we do, it can be difficult to schedule staffing needs, especially over the holidays when everyone's out of town. I don't really mind, though. It gives me a little break from all the paperwork and reminds me why I show up every day."

I've always liked Paula, who is also the longtime best friend of my fellow FACK buddy, Kim. In her mid-fifties, Paula is short and stocky with salt-and-pepper hair and a take-charge attitude. She knows how to get things done.

We finish the count quickly, the food bank inventory being a little on the low side these days. Paula invites me to join her for a coffee in the staff room.

"Do you like auditing, Jane?" she asks.

"Not at all. I've always wanted to be an accountant for a charitable organization. I'd like to feel I was doing something worthwhile with my life."

"So, why don't you?"

"Jobs in Owen Sound are as few and far between as single men over the age of thirty. Believe me, I've looked. I don't have to do that many audits, though. Mostly I do review engagements and compilations."

"What are those?"

"Well, as you know, an audit is the most thorough investigation we do. Every line on your financial statements gets prodded and probed. If an audit were a medical procedure, it would be the equivalent of a colonoscopy."

"A review engagement is less invasive?"

"Yes, it's more like a rectal exam."

"What's a compilation, then?"

"We just take the client's numbers, input them into our financial-statement template and crank out your corporate tax return."

"Bend over, drop your pants and cough."

"You got it."

Back at the office on Tuesday, it's obvious summer slack time is over and it's back to business as usual.

As part of her scheduling duties, Lori goes around the office every Monday morning to discuss current workloads with the staff and report her findings to the partners. She keeps track of the jobs we have in progress on a spread-sheet, which she updates weekly. Officially Lori does this to resolve any scheduling problems, but she also loves the opportunity to socialize and catch up on office gossip. Since Lori has no filter, she tells me exactly what's on her mind, regardless of whether it is relevant, appropriate or any of my business.

"I had to go to my sister's in Mississauga on the week-end because her uterus collapsed," she announces on her weekly trek to my office.

"Oh my god. Is she going to be okay?"

"Yes, I think it's quite common, actually. She had a dif-ficult labour with her second child, and now her pelvic floor muscles are so weak her uterus just slipped right through and it's sticking out of her vagina."

Try as I might, I cannot come up with a suitable response. I have yet to meet Lori's sister, but if I ever do I'll be right up to speed on the comings and goings of her genitalia. I wonder if the fact that Lori never married or had children of her own allows her to take some small comfort in the fact that her own lady parts will never stray from their proper position.

We go through the list of clients I'm working on and update Lori on the status of each file. Then, with a quick "Cheerio," she's off to touch base with the rest of the staff.

• • •

After my crazy, out-of-control summer, I've decided it's time to focus on my Find a Man Before I'm Forty project. To get back on track I'd signed up for a singles bowling league that started the first week of September.

I call Shelly.

"But you hate bowling; you must be feeling pretty desperate," she says.

"I may have hit rock bottom. But I can't go back to the singles supper club; Sean might be there."

"So, did you meet anybody interesting?"

"No, it was mostly women in their fifties and sixties. There was a postman who I think liked me, but I'm sure he was in his fifties too, and there were a couple other male nerds who looked approximately my age."

"Isn't an accountant calling someone a nerd the proverbial pot calling the kettle black?"

"Denial ain't just a river in Egypt."

"You need to get out more, Jane. How about we go to Kelsey's for a drink?" I can feel her smirk right through the phone line.

"Yeah, let's do that—when monkeys fly out of my butt."

I bowl horribly; the warped old lanes at Thunder Balls Bowling Emporium and my supreme lack of coordination make for a deadly combination.

• • •

After a long week working out of the office on the Haven House audit, I slip into FACK on Sunday afternoon thinking I'd tidy up a few things so I can start the week off organized.

I haven't been there since Thursday morning, but I've been checking phone messages regularly. So it comes as a surprise when I find two notes on my chair with a stack of files from Dean saying he wants the Kilsyth arena bingo audit on his desk for tomorrow.

I cancel my plans to catch an afternoon movie with Shelly and work on the file in the big empty office until almost five. I'm so focused on my work I don't notice the battleship-grey storm clouds scuttling across the sky. Tired and hungry, I decide to run out and grab a quick supper then come back to the office to finish the file.

Just as I'm leaving the building, the sky opens and a torrential downpour soaks me to the skin.

Trying to drive through the storm, I can hardly see through the curtain of rain, my windshield wipers slapping against the streaming windshield. I don't notice the crater-sized puddle until I drive right into it. My car starts dying right there in the middle of the street.

I put on the four-way flashers and somehow manage to manoeuvre the car off the road and into the McDonalds parking lot. Running inside in search of a pay phone, I get soaked a second time.

I call Kristen, who is at home with the kids. She packs the three of them into her van, picks me up and takes me back to the office. Wet, hungry and miserable, I stay until ten o'clock, when the file is finally finished. I pick up all the files and leave them on Dean's chair so he has them first thing in the morning. By then my car has dried out and is running reliably once again.

• • •

On Monday evening Scott the postman is waiting for me when I pull into the parking lot for singles bowling. I vaguely remember him telling me the week before that he belongs to a hiking group called the Sydenham Bruce Trail Club. He hands me a brochure with their fall schedule on it as I walk through the door with my bowling ball.

"We're going for a group hike to Spirit Rock on Sunday. Give me a call if you'd like to join us."

Although Scott's team is playing on the far side of the bowling alley, he traverses the lanes on several occasions to seek me out. Everyone goes for a drink afterward and he follows me to the bar.

I'm being stalked by a postal worker.

It's funny how life plods along uneventfully for days, then you have one crazy night and everything changes.

Kim asks Cindy and me to hit the Barking Frog for the meat raffle with her that Friday. It's so sweet the way she looks out for us.

I've lost ten of the nineteen pounds I'd gained at the end of the summer but am still feeling fat and self-conscious, so when my radar picks up Bart and Gord en route to Kim and Cindy's table in the corner of the bar, a wave of shyness hit me. I just say a quick hello on my way by.

Moments later a young guy comes and sits with us. He's a nice kid but quite drunk and rather loud. I can't figure out what he's up to, since we're all old enough to be his mother.

A twenty-year-old bricklayer, he asks all kinds of questions. Where do we work? How old are we?

He gazes at me with a glazed look.

"Jane, do you like younger men?"

"I used to like older men, but the younger ones are getting better looking all the time," I quip. I don't think for a second he might actually be trying to pick me up.

"A friend of mine, Roy, that guy at the bar wearing the pink hat, thinks Cindy is cute," he says, pointing.

After much yelling back and forth he cajoles a rather shy Roy to come to our table. Roy seems nice, if somewhat embarrassed by all the commotion. I go to the bar to buy a round, giving Cindy and Roy some time to get acquainted.

The Frog is packed, and it takes me a while to order the drinks. When I return, Cindy and Roy are alone at the table and the young guy is yelling angrily at Roy from across the room. It's extremely noisy, but I pick out "fuckin' [this] and asshole [that]."

After enduring this for several minutes an embarrassed Roy slinks away and returns to his perch at the bar. But the yelling does not let up, so we retreat to the safety of Bart and Gord's table on the other side of the bar.

Cindy tells me that after Roy arrived at our table he'd immediately asked our bricklayer boy what happened to the girl with "the great ass," and that had started the fight.

A twenty-year-old boy was really trying to pick me up and then got into a brawl over my butt? How cool is that? My battered ego gets the best boost of the year.

I sit between Gord and Bart, with Cindy on Bart's other side.

"There's something I've always wanted to know Jane," says Gord, looking deeply into my eyes.

My heart skips a beat. "What's that?"

"When accountants can't sleep, do they count sheep?"

"Absolutely. We take a complete inventory; sometimes we do FIFO, first-in first-out, sometimes LIFO, last-in first-out, or sometimes we just put the sheep in a blender and take a weighted average."

Buoyed by my youthful hit man, it feels as if Gord and I are finally hitting it off.

Kim leaves, and I hope Cindy will take the hint and follow suit so I can have Gord all to myself. But then Gord leaves too, and I deflate faster than a balloon.

24

BY MID-SEPTEMBER IT'S beautiful: still warm enough for shirtsleeves but without the stifling summer heat. Smatterings of gold, orange and red peek through green leaves. Sunsets are getting earlier; it's dark when I arrive at the Rumpus Room for my weekly music lesson on Wednesday. The darkness and close proximity in Chet's small studio above the garage lend a new coziness to our time together. In early lessons, we'd sit self-consciously on opposite sides of the room. But Chet hovers closer with every week that passes. Parched as I am from years of traipsing through the desert of celibacy, I feel the sexual tension building between us, tauter than any guitar string.

Usually Chet stands beside me to demonstrate new techniques on his bass, which I attempt to imitate. Tonight he parks his instrument for most of the lesson and stands behind me, demonstrating the fingering positions on the guitar's long neck and reaching over me to tighten the tuning keys. At one point his hand rests briefly over mine, and a shock that doesn't come from an amplifier runs through me.

"What's the best way to clean my bass?" I ask him in an attempt to break the awkward silence that follows.

"With guitar polish and a soft cloth. You need to take really good care of your instrument so you can sell it and get a better one."

"But I haven't mastered this one."

"You will. I'm going downstairs to record us. We'll make a tape of some of our exercises tonight so you can practise them at home."

And with that he goes thumping down the stairs.

He's still fiddling with the knobs on his mixing console when I hear a door open and the sound of small feet and excited breathing.

"What's up, Matt?" I hear their voices through the speakers.

"Mommy won't give me a cookie."

"How many have you had so far?"

"Four."

It's the third week in a row Chet's son has come up from the house and interrupted our lesson. Chet chats with him for a few minutes before sending him back to the house.

My playing is improving. I don't have 'an ear,' but I'm trying to memorize as many chords as I can in order to play without a book. Nobody, after all, ever saw John Paul Jones staring down at his music stand while performing *Whole Lotta Love.*

• • •

The other classic-rocker in my life, Frank the tax partner, has a tremendous ruckus going on outside his office when I arrive for work the next morning.

"What's going on?" I ask Cindy.

"Oh, Frank just sent out an email that he's giving away his Platers' season tickets today. He doesn't want to go to any of the games, so he's offering them up on a first-come first-served basis."

Every year the partners get season tickets to our local OHL hockey team, the Owen Sound Platers. Northern Ontario towns tend to take their hockey seriously, and we are no exception.

Officially, the partners buy seasons tickets because they can be written off as a business expense, the idea being that they're to be used to entertain clients, potential clients and other business associates. This bodes well for the FACK partners who, with the exception of Frank, are obsessed with the team. From now until hockey season finishes in the spring, Joe, Dean and Sam will hold impromptu post-game meetings by the photocopier, going over each play with the same degree of detail they'd apply to analyzing a set of financial statements.

A quarter of the tickets are allotted to each partner. Frank, however, couldn't care less about sports, thus the feeding frenzy around his office. It continues in waves for another twenty-five minutes until all his tickets have found new homes.

25

FIVE MONTHS AFTER embarking on my *Meet Your Soulmate* challenge, I'm no closer to finding my one true love. All worthy candidates thus far have flickered briefly before flaming out, and the fall, normally my favourite season, finds me somewhat discouraged. I'd actually believed, or wanted to believe, that Sean could be 'the one,' and I still think a lot about him. But time is marching on. I'm almost at the half-way point.

I must continue to think positively. I read my horoscope and am heartened by the prognostications for Taurus. "Although October and November are challenging, this won't stop you from accomplishing the goals you set in your birth month. These goals should be much easier to attain now, as you are feeling motivated and alive."

This is great news.

Right on cue, a somewhat inebriated Kim calls to report that she'd bumped into Gord at the Barking Frog.

"I tried to steer the conversation around to you, Jane. I asked him if he remembered you."

I remember the way the corners of Gord's eyes crinkle just a little bit when he smiles, and I smile.

"What did he say?"

"He said 'Of course I remember Jane. What's not to like?'"

My mental analyst goes to town on this. What, precisely, does "What's not to like?" mean? Does it mean Gord likes me? Maybe he is indifferent—sure, there's nothing "not to like" about me, but is there anything about me he actually does like?

Men are so complicated.

Women get a bad rap as the irrational, emotional sex. In my experience the opposite is true. When a woman says or does something, there's almost always a reason behind her actions.

Men, however? Not so much. They'll watch grown men bandy a prolated spheroid between two upright posts on artificial turf for three hours on a glorious Sunday afternoon. What is the point of this?

"I wrote down your name and phone number for him, but I was a little bit drunk and it might have been a combination of your home number and my cell phone number," Kim says.

"Ooh, that's not good."

"But I know I told him you're in the phone book under J. Parker.

"That should narrow it down for him."

"He's so much fun, Jane. We should do something with him and Bart again soon."

I heartily agree, but my phone has yet to ring.

It's time to stop focusing on what I don't have in my life. Since it is Thanksgiving weekend, I take a moment to concentrate on what I do have. A supportive family, good friends and a job that keeps me from going hungry.

And, of course, a great dog.

Sunday afternoon I contemplate my blessings sitting at Mom's big old kitchen table, cutting shapes out of construction paper for my niece and nephew. I wrap a wide strip of white Bristol board around Billy's head until it fits snuggly, then staple the band into a circle. We add a black-construction-paper topper and tinfoil silver buckle to complete the pilgrim's hat.

Madison announces that she wants a hat too, but we don't have enough black construction paper left. I attempt to make her a bonnet from a paper doily and string. I think I do a decent job on it, but Maddie is not satisfied with anything less than what Billy has and yanks the stovepipe hat from his head.

He retaliates by pulling the elastic band under Maddie's chin as far as it will stretch and lets go. It snaps her hard in the face.

She wails, and my mother comes to see what the commotion is about. She gives me a withering look, as though I'm somehow responsible for these hooligans.

"I did not give birth to them," I remind her.

"Who did that?" she asks, pointing past our arts and crafts to the end of the table where the desserts are laid out.

Smack dab in the centre of the pumpkin pie she was up all night baking is a child's handprint, perfectly preserved in the whipped-cream topping like an ancient insect exoskeleton fossilized in amber.

Bill and Madison blame each other and Mom looks at me. "You're supposed to be watching them, Jane." I look pointedly at Shelly, relaxing in Dad's recliner with a beverage while watching Nascar, oblivious to the chaos she's become so accustomed to tuning out.

Mom banishes the kids to the rec room where she's recently spent several thousand dollars on a 50-inch full-screen plasma television in hopes of keeping them entertained during just such occasions.

Normally the kids' high-energy hijinks amuse me, but this weekend I'm feeling punchy from overwork, sleep deprivation and sexual tension.

"Did you know condoms come in new packages now?" Shelly asks me.

"How would I know this? I haven't purchased a condom since 1981."

"They come in three-packs for high school students: Friday, Saturday, Sunday. Six-packs for college students, Tuesday through Sunday. And twelve-packs for married couples: January, February, March..."

"I'm married. I only get the twelve-pack," Steven grumbles.

He's not getting any sympathy from me. "Quit complaining. At least you have a sex life. Anything's better than the zero-pack. I haven't had sex since Brian Mulroney was Prime Minister."

"Can I fix you up with someone, Jane?" Aunt Myrt asks. I smile and give her a grateful look.

"Sure, and I'm no longer looking for husband material; I just want to have sex one more time before I die."

"Don't forget your father is in the room."

"Let me rephrase that. I'd just like to have sex once before I die."

Aunt Myrt's stepdaughter Janice, who's been exploring Europe and Australia having all kinds of adventures, stops by for a rare visit.

Always gregarious, she entertains us with stories of her travels. At one point she'd maxed out all her credit cards and had nine dollars to her name. But she managed to stay for the rest of the year and raise enough money for her flight home.

She's been living with Aunt Myrt and Uncle Harry for a couple of weeks but will be moving to Calgary at the end of the month. She doesn't have money or a job lined up. She's just taking off.

I admire her spirit.

"Why'd you choose Calgary?" I ask.

"I want to be in a big city with lots of job opportunities, and it's a good place to meet guys."

"A little different from Owen Sound, then."

"Yeah, the guys here are creepy. When I first got back I met this guy named Glen."

I felt myself tense. She couldn't possibly be talking about Elizabeth's friend.

"You don't mean Glen, the waiter from Kelsey's, do you?"

"Yes, do you know him?"

"Not really. He's friends with a girl I work with who waitresses there."

"I met him at the Hanover Raceway. He asked me out for dinner and when the bill came he made me pay for my order."

"Seriously, what a cheap creep."

"Then he started stalking me. He'd show up at the end of my shift at the restaurant and hang around the bar until I was done."

Janice is twelve years younger than me; Glen is one year older than me. Is that the attraction? Do men prefer women in their twenties to those approaching forty?

Maybe it's in their DNA, a biological imperative to find that fertile female. Maybe Janice has the right idea. Starting fresh in a new city with thousands of single men who don't know your history has its advantages.

But I'd had a stint in a big city and, while I'd made some good memories, for me there's still no place like home. Those four famous women may love their sex in the city, but I just want to keep romancing the Sound.

26

AFTER THE RAUCOUS Thanksgiving Sunday with my family, I wake up in my quiet little house on holiday Monday feeling a bit blue.

With all the stores closed for the holiday, the town is quiet. I spend the morning watching *The Prince of Tides*, one of the movies I'd rented on my weekly visit to Video Town, to distract myself. It's one of the most romantic movies ever, and my heart melts for Nick Nolte, whose hunky blondness reminds me of Sean. A new wave of loneliness and loss for our sad ending washes over me.

I need to get out of the house. I load Wanker into my car and we drive down 8th Avenue A.

Sean is sitting on his front porch talking on his phone. He's wearing a new shirt and his hair glints in the morning sun. Is he getting ready for a breakfast date with someone new, I wonder.

Embarrassed and hoping he doesn't see me, I slink low in my seat and drive on by.

I'm so pathetic.

There are a million things I should be doing around the house, but I keep driving along the lake.

Nobody does autumn quite like Grey County. Bronze and scarlet brushstrokes streak through the trees, making them stand out against the deep-blue backdrop of Georgian Bay. It's easy to see what inspired Tom Thomson to paint so many fall landscapes in the area. Autumn on the Bruce Peninsula is nature's work of art. I'm reminded again of how much I love it here.

I roll down my car window and breathe in the fresh Lake Huron breeze. The nights are getting colder now, and the heat that drives us to pools and beaches is long gone. This is the weekend most folks close up their cottages for the winter. To be Canadian you really have to embrace it all, I think—not just the brilliant autumns and summer sunsets but the icicles on bare trees and shivering as your car warms up on January mornings. I miss most of spring's onset due to tax season, so I soak up every autumn moment I can get.

I turn south until I arrive at the old stone gates of Harrison Park. Wanker has assumed the role of co-pilot, riding shotgun on the passenger seat, front paws on the dashboard, nose atwitch as we pass the mini-putt range and the brightly coloured paddleboats. We disembark by the truss bridge and he bounds ahead of me as we cross it and walk toward the Old Park Inn. The Sydenham River dwindles to a creek here, its bed only two or three feet deep. Bolting toward the water, Wanker suddenly throws on his brakes and stands motionless on the bank, where we're both assaulted by the most putrid smell imaginable.

I peek down at the water and quickly suss out the source of the stench. Several Chinook salmon are fighting for their lives as they swim upstream in search of spawning beds. The smell is coming from the brown-speckled bodies of the fish that have failed to complete their quest.

Normally native to the Pacific Ocean, the salmon were brought to Owen Sound in the sixties. They thrived in the cold water of Georgian Bay, and fishing clubs stocked the lake for many years.

Raised in hatcheries, the young smolts are released every spring into the Sydenham River, where they make a beeline for the bay. There, they go about their fishy business, swimming merrily until maturity, when Mother Nature issues a recall. They swim the six or seven kilometres upstream, returning to the place they were born. Their life's mission complete, they lay their eggs and die.

The small stream Wanker and I are walking beside is called the fish ladder. It was built many years ago to help the salmon bypass the mill dam that blocks their journey upstream. A few extremely energetic fish will attempt to leap over the dam, but most find the steps in the ladder tough enough.

We take a moment to follow one of the fish on its journey, with Wanker attempting to cheer it on with his barking, but it stops to rest for what seems like forever. Just when I start to pull Wanker's collar to motion him on, the fish heaves itself over the cement wall of the ladder and moves up to the next twenty-foot level. There it continues to thrash and splash its way out to the middle, where it must rest again before journeying onward.

27

IN A TIME when teenagers were trying so hard to blend in, Kyle stood out. With Angie away having the time of her life with Xavier, it was suddenly just the two of us. I looked at Kyle through different eyes and liked what I saw.

In the beginning we were shy and awkward with each other, which seemed strange considering how comfortable we'd been as friends for all those years. Finally, on Canada Day, when my parents were away on a weekend trip to Niagara Falls, we lost our virginity together in my childhood ruffled-canopy bed at the farm. Kyle was so nervous he couldn't stop shaking. Afterward he left the used condoms stretched across the top of our garbage bin like shed snake skins. "I think maybe you should camouflage those a little better," I suggested.

We spent the remainder of the summer having sex every place we could think of. We did it in a hidden bend of the Bruce trail, which sounds romantic but actually led to bug bites in hard-to-reach and extremely sensitive spots. We did it at his house or my house, any time our families vacated the premises. At the Springmount drive-in we barely got the speakers attached to the windows before we were steaming them up.

Like all teenagers, we believed we were the first and only humans to make love, as if we had simply sprung from our parents' gardens. In that summer of my sexual awakening I became addicted to the rollercoaster ride of breathtaking anticipation followed by bursts of intense pleasure. We rode it every chance we got.

In the back of my mind I knew I'd be moving to Toronto in September to attend university and launch myself into the world of fashion. And I was in love. My life was perfect exactly as it was, my future filled with unlimited possibilities.

Parting with Kyle when I left for Ryerson and he stayed behind to enrol in the computer-programmer/analyst program at Georgian College was a tearful ordeal. We swore to each other we would never let time or distance come between us.

On the last day of that sizzling summer of 1979, my dad, like a Highland Games caber-toss competitor, heaved my matching three-piece burgundy softsided luggage into the trunk of our Ford LTD II. We settled in for the two-hour trek to Toronto with Shelly and I precariously positioned in the back seat along with my purse, knapsack, hot pot, tea pot, blow-dryer, curling iron, comforter, jewellery box, books, sewing supplies, art supplies, portable typewriter, fashion magazines, pictures, groceries and a stuffed sheep I'd abducted years ago from Shelley's crib in a rare act of defiance as a toddler.

As usual, Shelly complained non-stop about having to hold the aloe vera plant Aunt Myrt had given me. She had already polished off the tin of my favourite home-made hermit cookies Nana had baked for the occasion. She threw a fit when Mom chose an old-fashioned tea room for lunch in Orangeville instead of McDonald's. But, overall, she was thrilled to be taking over my old room and had already started moving her things into it. I wasn't sure why this was so important to her, as her room was bigger and had the nicest view.

I'd grown out my Charlie's Angel's winged hairdo, and my stick-straight blonde hair hung halfway down my back. In an effort to channel Brooke Shields, I'd stopped plucking my eyebrows.

"With that unibrow you look more like Eugene Levy from *Second City TV* than the girl from the *Blue Lagoon*," Shelly pointed out.

"It's the natural look."

"You look naturally stupid."

Shelly felt that *The Preppy Handbook* was the ultimate fashion bible and prided herself on being a purist. She owned a dozen button-down oxford shirts in various pastel shades, with tiny equine figures embroidered on the breast pockets. She paired these with cotton pleated pants and boat shoes or duckies. For over a decade her uniform never varied.

She pooh-poohed my bohemian ways with disdain.

When we turned off Bond Street down the long drive that led to O'Keefe House, Shelly pointed at a banner stretching across the two stone pillars on which someone had written in blue and gold, "Stop. Go Back. Bye, Bye, Virginity."

But it was too late; there was no going back.

My emotions ran the gamut from fear to excitement, sadness to hope. I'd enrolled in the four-year fashion design program. It would be the start of my brilliant, creative career.

But homesickness hit hard as I watched Dad's car pull out of the parking lot to be swallowed up in the long-weekend Toronto traffic. I missed him, Mom, Angie, the horses and my old room at the farm. But mostly I missed Kyle. He'd had to stay at home to attend his orientation at Georgian College. Unpacking, I set his picture on the little table beside my single bed, popped the mixed tape he'd made of our favourite songs into my boom box and pushed play.

Immediately the sultry sound of Champagne singing "How 'Bout Us" filled the air and brought me back to Kyle's arms; we swayed together on the dance floor.

Evidence suggested that my roommate had moved in already, but she was nowhere to be found. There was a picture on her bulletin board of a roan horse, which I later learned was named Strawberry, and a shaggy-haired rookie hockey player named Wayne Gretzky.

Eventually the hall monitor showed up and chastised me for unpacking.

"I lived out of my suitcase for the whole first month, Jane! Come on down to the common room. We're going to have a barbecue."

My roommate was apparently partying somewhere; she did not come home that night. Overwhelmed with homesickness and needing to hear a familiar voice, I called Kyle.

"I miss you," I cried. "I just want to come home."

"I miss you too, Jane. I can't wait to see you again."

"Do you think you could come down for a weekend? There's lots of stuff we could do together here."

"They gave us our outlines today. I'm going to be insanely busy keeping up with school and working for Dad at the shop."

"I won't get to see you until Thanksgiving, then."

"It will be here before you know it, Jane, and I'll call you every day."

I moved the mixed tape to my Walkman and listened to it through my headphones until I fell asleep.

My roommate surfaced Wednesday morning, when frosh initiation days had finished and regular classes officially started. She was from Montreal, and her father was the vice president of Canadian Pacific Railway. Her best friend lived several doors down on the same floor, and the two of them shared my sister's love of preppy clothes and the J. Crew catalogue. Her goal was to be the star of the Faculty of Business; she didn't have much in common with her rural roommate.

Despite our differences, we managed to maintain a cordial relationship. And after the first week, I was able to push through my homesickness and start enjoying my courses and campus life.

The teachers captivated us with stories from the industry. We studied textiles, marketing, colour, design, illustration and the history of fashion. I wasn't exactly sure where this road would take me, but the view from my window was spectacular.

Just as I was starting to relax and enjoy my new world, something happened. Or, rather, something didn't happen. Specifically, my period did not make its regularly scheduled appearance.

I assumed the worst.

Kyle and I had relied entirely on condoms. I couldn't imagine asking old Dr. Brayer to put me on the pill, and they just seemed easier. Enthusiastic newbie non-virgins, we'd hopped into bed, or the bush, or the back of his truck bed with a sleeping bag, at every opportunity. What we lacked in experience we made up for in passion. There'd been several instances where the condom had fallen off or just not felt right, or there'd been substantial contact before we'd gotten around to getting it on.

Could such things make you pregnant?

I called Kyle.

"Don't panic. They must have a student clinic down there. Can you make an appointment?"

"But what if I find out I'm pregnant?"

"I love you, Jane. If you're pregnant, we'll get married. Call the medical centre and make an appointment. Let me know as soon as you find out."

The earliest appointment was two days away. It was the longest forty-eight hours of my life.

Kyle's vow to stand by me was comforting, but my panic continued to mount. I thought of all the dreams I'd been nurturing. I wanted it all: a university degree and a stellar career. I wanted to travel and see the world. If I had a baby now, it would all be over. My parents would be mortified, and it would be so embarrassing to "have to" get married. I knew I loved Kyle, but I wasn't ready to give up my dreams; we were both too young to settle down.

"Please, God," I prayed, hoping to make some sort of pact with the universe. "Don't let me be pregnant."

The night before my appointment, I started going to the farthest stall in our communal dorm bathroom every hour.

I'd insert a tampon, wait a few minutes and then check it for faint traces of blood. When nothing appeared, I'd flush the evidence and attempt to distract myself for another hour. After half a dozen rounds of this I finally fell into a restless sleep.

I awoke in the morning to shouts from my dorm mates. The toilet in our washroom had overflowed, flooding the floor and forcing everyone in our quadrant to use the facilities while standing in two inches of water. Too embarrassed to admit I'd caused this unnatural disaster, I slunk off to the campus clinic.

A nice nurse ushered me to an exam room and asked me to undress and put on a paper gown. It crackled as I pulled it over my head and stepped out of my underwear.

And that's when I saw them. Fresh red spots, dark as watercolour paints splattered sweetly on my new cotton Jockey french-cuts.

The door opened, and I threw my arms around the nurse, enfolding her in a bear hug.

"Well, dear," she said when I'd calmed down enough to explain the situation. "Maybe we should think about getting you on the birth control pill."

28

IN THE MIDDLE of October, Chet and his jazz quartet hold a sold-out concert at the Roxy Theatre.

"I put aside two tickets for you, Jane. Is that enough?" he'd asked at my lesson four weeks earlier.

"Yes, two will do," I told him.

Although Chet finds steady work gigging with a variety of bands in the area, he hasn't actually put on a concert since the Spastics' ill-fated reunion tour in 1992 was cancelled due to poor attendance. It seems the younger generation has trouble connecting with the Colons.

They certainly make my sister irritable.

"But you have to come with me, Shelly," I plead. "Chet is so excited, and I really want to be there for him."

"Why are you wasting your time on this music stuff, anyway? Accountants don't play in bands. And you're supposed to be out there searching for your soulmate, not cooped up in your house practising."

"Maybe my soulmate is a music lover, and I'll bump into him at the concert."

I persuade her to go by agreeing to pay for her ticket, buy her dinner and babysit the following two weekends.

The morning of the concert, Dean gives me eleven tax returns for the McGonagalls, a family of farmers from Hoath Head. Dean had met with them back in August, left their information under a stack of books on his credenza and forgotten all about them. They'd been accruing interest and penalties from Revenue Canada for over two months when Mr. McGonagall happened to call Dean this morning to inquire as to their status.

"They're coming in tomorrow, Jane," Dean says. "Can you please do them ASAP so I can review them right away?"

It isn't really a question.

I work full throttle on the returns all day. Late in the afternoon it becomes evident there's no way I'm going to get all eleven done by end of business day. By the time I'm to meet Shelly for her bribery dinner, there are still two returns left, so I take them home to do after the show.

I just can't miss Chet's big night.

He wears the loudest shirt—a mix of red, orange, yellow, purple and green—I have ever seen. He could literally stop traffic.

The show is well received by the hometown crowd, who embrace its local semi-celebrity. The seats Chet has reserved for me are in the second row on the aisle, so I can see him pluck every string.

At the intermission a woman stands in the aisle beside us while she chats with the elderly couple in front of me. She tells them how much fun her son is having backstage.

It doesn't take me long to figure out she is Chet's wife.

I've never seen her before. In my imagination she was middle aged and haggard, a former groupie from the sixties to whom the years and recreational drugs have not been kind.

In actuality she's quite cute; a petite brunette with a pixie haircut and tortoiseshell glasses. She's closer to my age than to Chet's.

Her only unattractive feature is a sad little frown that plays on her face in a continuous loop. Am I imagining things or does she keep glancing at me and Shelly, lingering beside us until the curtain comes up on the second half?

A frothy wave of guilt splashes up on my shore and then it recedes.

I'm not doing anything wrong. For years I've fantasized about playing the bass. All I'm doing is taking a few innocent lessons.

In the second half Chet goes all out, rocking an improvisational bass solo that lasts over twelve minutes alone on the stage. When he plays the final chord, the audience gives him a standing ovation.

He's sweaty and out of breath as little Matt goes up on stage with a towel for him. Chet puts his arms on his young son's shoulders and introduces him to the crowd. He thanks everybody for coming out and supporting the band but, conspicuously, does not thank his wife, as the other musicians have done.

The audience is invited to a reception at Joe Tomatoes after the show, but Shell is anxious to get home and I don't want to walk in by myself. Besides, I still have two McGonagall tax returns to be prepared before Dean's morning meeting.

Even though it takes me until two a.m. to finish them, I am too keyed up from the concert to sleep. My adrenalin rush abandons me the next morning, however, when Dean drops another four returns from the same family tree on my desk.

"They're coming in at one; you'd better have them done."

I slog through them as best I can, barely keeping my eyes open.

When Friday night finally comes I collapse into bed and sleep like a baby.

• • •

The next morning I'm up early for my niece Maddie's first communion. Not having been raised Catholic, I have no idea what type of present is required for such an occasion. I seek Shelly's advice.

"She's been wanting a hamster for the longest time. You could get her one."

"That sounds way cooler than a crucifix or a Bible."

I pick up a cage and a hamster at Super Pet, where they put the creature into a small orange cardboard box that has a handle and breathing holes.

I set the box on the passenger's seat and head up Highway 26.

I've barely got going when the distinctive sounds of sharp little teeth gnawing away on cardboard come from the makeshift pet carrier. I glance over and see a small head and shoulders emerging from the box. Bright beady eyes survey their new surroundings, my passenger a tiny rodent sailor about to come aboard the poop deck of his orange submarine.

I pull off onto the gravel shoulder of the road, tear open the cage box, assemble it as quickly as possible and dump the hamster in. Breathing a sigh of relief, I move the cage to the back seat and resume my course to Meaford.

Alone with my thoughts, I turn on the radio to relax and replay Chet's concert in my head. It's a beautiful, sunny day. As I approach a bend in the road, I glance over my right shoulder and freeze. Standing on his hind legs on the passenger side, the triumphant hamster has freed himself yet again and is gibbering and waving his paws in the air like Godzilla about to attack the Empire State Building.

Shocked out of my reverie, I jerk the steering wheel and my car veers into the oncoming path of a woman driving a vanload of kids toward Owen Sound. Close enough to see the sheer terror in her eyes, everything appears to move in slow motion as she swerves onto the gravel shoulder just in time to miss me.

Shaky from the mishap, I pull over in front of the Woodford Community Centre to catch my breath and pull myself together.

It takes a few minutes to calm down and locate the errant escape artist, who'd vanished somewhere in the recesses of my car. All dressed up for Madison's big day, I clamber over the seats in my suede mini skirt and heels, performing several unladylike gymnastic moves before finally cornering the hamster, who screams like a banshee when I gingerly drop him back into his cage.

Of course the morning's drama is quickly forgotten when I see the look in Maddie's eyes as I deliver my gift.

"What's his name, Aunt Jane?"

"How about Harry Houdini Hamster?"

"I think you should call him Gaylord Focker," Billy says.

"I think that's a perfect name," I say, ignoring a pained look from the priest who's presided over the ceremony and been invited back to the house for lunch. "I'm doing some work at a client's in Meaford early next week. I'll stop in and see how he's doing."

Plan H successfully executed, my return trip home is uneventful.

29

MONDAY MORNING FINDS me on the road to
Meaford, setting out from the office loaded down with my
laptop, audit bag and calculator, to do the annual review
engagement for the law firm of Tropper Giffen LLP.

Meaford seems somewhat subdued. The last of the summer boating, fishing and beach tourists have packed up and
headed home; it'll be weeks before the snowmobile/ski
tourists breeze in to take their place.

I'm grateful for the warm cup of coffee Tropper Giffen
office manager Sonia offers as she helps me get situated
in one of the client meeting rooms. Sonia is an attractive
lady in her mid-fifties. Deeply tanned all year round, she
drives a Chrysler Lebaron convertible and wears the kind
of bold faux-gold statement jewellery favoured by the
cruise-ship crowd.

I hope to get the job done in a day and work steadily
through the morning. I walk up the main street in search of
a suitable spot to have lunch. The sky is overcast, occasional

rain drops adding to the ghost-town feel of the offseason downtown. The trees are losing their dazzling autumn coats, and the Big Apple, Meaford's landmark fruit-shaped tourist centre, has been boarded up for winter.

Back at the lawyers' office, my work hums along until I hit the payroll test. I notice Sonia's salary is well over ninety thousand dollars. This is almost three times what I make and double what managing partner Reginald Giffen pays his two lawyer associates. Damn, I think. *Maybe when Sonia retires I can apply for her job.* I'd be an excellent bookkeeper.

I turn the situation around and around in my head. In a small business operation where one person performs all of the accounting functions, there is always an increased risk of fraud. Could Sonia be dipping her fingers into the Tropper Giffen pot? She's worked for Jonathon for years and does everything for him: opens the mail, does the banking, invoices clients and pays bills. In some ways she knows more about his business than he does.

It's a classic case of lack of separation of duties.

Contrary to popular belief, public accountants don't find fraud all that often. It's only happened to me twice in my career. In most instances where we do encounter fraud, someone from management has found something suspicious and brought us in to investigate further.

I decide to discuss the situation with my FACK manager, John Jamieson, as soon as I get back to the office. It's a beautiful day, so I take the scenic route around the bay. Heading into town I see the *Chi-Cheemaun*'s upturned nose returning to the harbour and am reminded of the pact I'd made five months ago. Time is ticking.

I drop everything back in my office before heading down to talk to my manager. "Did you know Sonia makes over ninety grand a year?"

John looks up at me quizzically. "I wondered how she could afford that new cottage."

"Do you think she's stealing? I've never heard of a book-keeper making that kind of money."

John starts laughing, and I can't figure out what's going on. Finally, he clears his throat.

"I believe Sonia does more than just Mr. Giffen's books. She may, in fact, provide other personal services."

It takes a minute before I realize what John is getting at. "Ohhhhhh."

"Oh, yeah."

"But I thought Reginald was married." For someone who'd lived in Toronto all those years, I guess I'm not overly sophisticated.

"He is. The only fraud being committed is against that 'forsaking all others' vow."

"Well, he is a decent lawyer. Maybe he had that one stricken from the record." I sigh.

"What's wrong, Jane?"

"I thought I'd be the perfect candidate to replace Sonia when she retires. So much for my budding legal-accountant career."

"You know you could never leave FACK, Jane. We're your family."

30

AUNT MYRT MAKES good on her Thanksgiving promise to set me up on a blind date, calling the first week of November to make arrangements.

"I took a picture of you at Madison's confirmation and Harry showed it to his friend Peter at work," she says. "Peter said he thought you were nice looking."

Ten years ago George Clooney couldn't have coerced me into such a setup, but back then my biological clock hadn't morphed from functional wall décor into a ticking time bomb.

And, since relying on my own judgement doesn't seem to be working out so well, maybe family does know best when it comes to affairs of the heart. Worst-case scenario: I'll have a nice meal and a night out.

So, on the first Thursday of November, Aunt Myrt, Uncle Harry, Peter and I meet up at the Leaky Canoe in Meaford.

Peter and Harry have known each other for years. Right away I notice his nice eyes, a receding hairline, and glasses. He's wearing a crisply ironed plaid cotton shirt and jeans.

"Harry told me you live in Mississauga but your work often brings you to Owen Sound," I say. "Do you like it up here?"

"Yes, my roommate Victor often joins me when I travel. Unfortunately, we can't leave Mississauga because he's a decorator and most of his clients are in the Toronto area."

"That's interesting. How long have the two of you been roommates?"

"Eleven years."

"And it's just the two of you?"

"No, we have four cats as well."

How could Harry and Myrt not realize Peter is gay? I'd told them I was looking for someone who was single, suitably employed and age-appropriate. I'd assumed heterosexuality was a given.

Then it dawns on me. Harry really likes Peter, and they've been friends for years. But for reasons I've never understood, Harry's always been deeply homophobic. Rather than lose a great friendship, he subconsciously chose denial.

I give Peter a knowing smile, and he winks. Too bad, I think. Maybe it's true all the good ones are either married or gay.

Our steaks are tender and delicious and we all laugh and have a great evening. In a tableau performance, presumably to show us how couples are supposed to behave during courtship, Harry and Myrt flirt coquettishly in a way I've never seen before. Peter and I ignore this embarrassing display and dig into dessert.

Unable to contain her curiosity, Myrt calls me at the office the next day to check in. "So, Jane, what did you think of Peter?"

"I really liked him, Aunt Myrt, but he just wasn't my type," I say quite honestly.

"You're getting awfully picky in your old age, Jane."

"I'm sure he felt the same way about me."

"Tick tock, girl."

I'm looking forward to a quiet weekend to relax and recharge when, at precisely ten minutes before five on Friday afternoon, new partner Ken Lawrence comes into my office with some changes he wants done on a compilation I'd prepared for Uptown Motors.

"I'm meeting with them first thing Monday morning."

This, of course, is partner speak for "You need to cancel your plans and work all weekend without pay."

I'd submitted the file to Ken for review nine weeks ago. He'd reviewed it that afternoon.

I arrive at the office early Saturday morning, hoping to get the changes cleared quickly and get out of there, but something's off. I can't get the bloody financial statements to balance. I vaguely remember having some difficulties when I prepared the file two months and fifteen jobs ago. The more frustrated I become, the more out of whack the statements get.

Joe arrives with his son Bradley in tow and immediately buggers off to work on FACK's computer network. Bored with watching his father hook up desktops, Brad makes a beeline for my office, where he launches into a detailed plot summary of *Thomas the Tank Engine* and *The Magic Railroad*. It's virtually impossible for me to focus on the financials. Brad's sister Jilly joins him and they begin dialing my phone, going through my desk, fighting, and blasting the Back Street Boys from their portable Discman. After about an hour of this I give up and drive to the farm to do the chores for Mom and Dad, who are off to Chicago for the weekend. I tell myself I'll come back to the office and try again when it's quieter. I'm behind on my laundry, so I'd taken a large load to do at the farm while the horses enjoy a quick run in the pasture.

On my way back to the office, I barely get past Range Road when the car's battery light starts blinking. Then my power steering cuts out, which makes driving incredibly difficult.

I drive shakily through the hordes of Christmas shoppers at the Heritage Place mall to get to my garage on the other side. They're all out of loaner vehicles, so I'm forced to walk down Highway 26 carrying my laundry basket, purse and briefcase, desperately trying to keep my lacey lingerie from fluttering kite style in the cold wind.

Shaky and upset, I get up early Sunday morning and take a cab to the office, where I finally finish Uptown Motors.

31

ON MONDAY MORNING Kim folds her arms across her chest and looks disgusted when I tell her my sad story.

"Never kiss the ass of people who treat you like shit, Jane. It will leave a bad taste in your mouth every time."

Easy for Kim to say, I think. George might not be up for Husband of the Year award, but if Kim lost her job he could easily pay their bills.

Cindy is excited. "I've got a date with a guy named David," she announces.

"Okay, who is this David of whom you speak, and how did you meet him?" I ask, my curiosity piqued. I do admire Cindy's fortitude. After her last two blind-date fiascos, I'd throw in the towel. But here she is, ready and willing to put herself out there once more.

"I haven't met him yet; he found me on the internet." She states this casually, giving the impression that David had just happened to be searching the internet for a decent strawberry-rhubarb strudel recipe when he stumbled across

Cindy, who, coincidentally, was cyber-searching for fruito-
pian pastry the exact same nanosecond.

"You can find dates on the internet. Who knew?"

"You can find anything you need on the internet."

This is easy enough for Cindy, of course. She is a self-proclaimed techno geek and one of the first people I know to
get the internet in her home. The partners love this about her
and routinely charge exorbitant rates to have her help clients
convert their manual bookkeeping ledgers to accounting
software programs. She also has a cell phone and is currently
comparison shopping the new digital cameras that have just
come out. Whenever I have trouble programming my VCR to
tape *Friends* or *Seinfeld*, Cindy is the first person I call.

"Even in Grey County?" I ask, still incredulous.

"You'd be surprised what can be delivered to Grey
County."

This is all news to me. Even at FACK we've only had the
internet for four years. Emails have been a godsend for the
staff, who previously had to line up outside a partner's office
when they had a question regarding a client. This could be
especially annoying if the partner was prone to chattiness
and allowed phone calls to jump the queue. "Our client's
needs come first" is the longtime FACK motto. Now we can
just type our inquiries into an email, hit Send and move on
to other business.

John Jamieson had inundated us with jokes when the
internet first arrived. This went swimmingly until the partners noticed we were all putting between seven and twelve
minutes of unassigned time on our timesheets every morning while chuckling over our Inboxes. They put the kibosh on
indiscriminately emailing items from questionable sources.

But this Dave fellow is no joke; he's the real thing.

"That's great, Cindy. I really hope it works out for you."

I'm trying hard to be supportive, but I'm worried for Cindy. I mean, what kind of loser has to look for dates on the internet?

I envision this David character as an obese parolee sporting a beard so long it tickles the keyboard as he types, naked, at his desktop. His eyes are bleary from smoking weed while washing down a poutine supreme with a six-pack of Jägermeister as he pecks out "Handsome single entrepreneur seeks svelte single lady for moonlight walks on the beach and pickle ball" on his remaining non-gangrenous digit.

Cindy, on the other hand, is already nurturing some seriously sky-high expectations.

"I'm worried about having to explain to my mother how we met."

"Just tell her you were both surfing and caught the same wave." It's a semi-truthful explanation.

My own social life is suddenly quiet, Chet the Fret now the only man I'm seeing on a regular basis, thanks to my Wednesday-night music lesson. And I'm paying for those.

I decide to do a little internet surfing of my own and dig up more information on Chet. The Spastic Colons broke up in 1978 during a long tour as the opening act for The Guess Who.

The group wasn't getting along, and lead singer Gaston Direah was unhappy with their manager. One night he walked out, and the Spastics collapsed. Chet hung around Toronto doing session work for a while then went on tour with Platoon. I'd actually seen this band in the spring of

1980 when they performed at a Ryerson student pub. I'd gone with a girl from Toronto whose boyfriend had been killed in a car accident the previous summer.

At the pub she'd written a note to the band, requesting that they play one of her late boyfriend's favourite songs.

Platoon had dedicated the song to the boyfriend and invited us backstage to meet the band after the show.

I was terrified. Naive little Jane from County Road 17 had never seen drugs other than in movies. The band members signed a program for my friend and then offered us their communal pipe. I shook my head, too scared to utter a word. The drummer asked, "Would you girls like to hang out?" but I just wanted to get the hell out of there.

Had I met Chet that night all those years ago? I had a vague recollection of a shirtless bassist wearing chains, big eighties hair and red-and-white-striped Lycra culottes. Could that have been him? Has destiny brought us back together after all these years?

A Spastic Colons reunion tour was attempted in 1992 after Direah's last two solo CDs bombed, but it was eventually cancelled due to pour attendance.

My research is interrupted by a phone call from Jake Goodson.

"Jane, I just bought a new hot tub for seventy-six-hundred bucks and was wondering if I can deduct it on my personal tax return as a medical expense."

"Sorry, Jake. The Canada Revenue Agency won't accept hot tubs as a medical expense."

"But I need it for my fibromyalgia."

The last time I'd seen Jake he'd been waterskiing behind his yacht at Balmy Beach.

"What if I get a letter from my doctor saying I need the hot tub for health purposes?"

"I'll double-check with one of our tax specialists and call you right back."

I walk down to the hall to the tax department. Both Frank and Katie are available, but Frank scares me so I default to Katie.

"The CRA historically has frowned on spas and exercise equipment of any kind as medical expenses," she tells me.

"I'm not sure if Jake will take no for an answer."

"Do you want me to talk to him?"

"That would be awesome. Thank you so much."

What would we ever do without Katie, I wonder.

32

IN ADDITION TO being our favourite watering hole, the Barking Frog is also a FACK client. Cindy assists the owner's wife, who makes a mean margarita but struggles with her computerized bookkeeping system.

"Houston, we have a problem," she announces every time she calls Cindy for help.

When Cindy receives a twenty-five-dollar gift card from the Frog with a note that reads "Happy Birthday, Houston," I know exactly where we're going to celebrate. I volunteer to be Cindy's designated driver. She's already imbibed a bit when I pick her up from her family dinner.

"Oh god, there's Bart," she says as I pull open the heavy oak doors of the Frog.

My pulse quickens as I note Gord sitting with Bart and Kim at the bar.

I sit beside Cindy, who deigns to take the bar stool beside Bad News Bart. After two beers I switch to pop; Cindy moves on to greener pastures with brown cows.

I discreetly oggle Gord, who's looking good in a Tshirt and jeans, black leather jacket draped over the back of his barstool. I relax with my girls and Kim's funny neighbour, Donnie, who hovers behind the three of us telling jokes.

On the bar stool to my left, an attractive man in his early thirties is smoking as he sips a rye and Coke. At first I'm too engrossed in our conversation to pay him much attention. Then I feel someone tug a few strands of my hair.

"What's going on with that guy?" Kim says. "He keeps staring at you."

"I don't know, but I think he just tugged my hair."

Right on cue he swivels on his stool and asks me if I have a light.

I've been sitting in a smoky bar for two hours and haven't lit anything; obviously, I don't smoke. To be polite I offer Kim's lighter and he lights himself another cigarette.

Just then Gord, who's been standing with his back to us, turns, smiles at me and waves.

I wave back.

At least I hope he was waving at me. With my luck a twenty-something size-zero supermodel has just stepped into the bar for a Fresca and is standing behind me.

The hair-tugging smoker introduces himself as Jamie and insists on buying me a drink. Since I'm only drinking pop anyway, I figure what the hell.

I introduce Jamie to Cindy and tell him it's her birthday. He buys her a B-52, which she downs handily.

At first I'm delighted with the whole situation. I hope Gord notices this hunky guy flirting with me, feels a twinge of jealousy and joins us. Jamie may be the best-looking man in the bar, but Gord's sharp wit is infinitely more appealing.

"What do you do?" I ask Jamie politely.

"I'm a pipefitter."

"Do you like your job?"

"I like making the big bucks. I'm also a member of the golf club; we just came from there." He makes a point of shuffling through a pile of fifty-dollar bills in his wallet, pulling one out for the bartender when she brings our drinks. He tells her to keep the change.

I'm bored with Jamie. I'm asking all the questions: where does he work, what does he do, yada yada. He has nice eyes, but he's so drunk they're more red than blue.

"You are the prettiest woman in the bar and you have really white teeth," he says.

"My dentist is very proud."

I need an escape plan. Kim and Cindy are having a riot with Fun Donnie. A nice boy with black curly hair and glasses buys Cindy another brown cow. Gord's playing pool with some buddies at the end of the bar.

I give up carrying on a conversation with Jamie, hoping he gets the hint and starts talking with the person on his left or, better yet, just moves elsewhere. Instead he sits there smoking and leering. I wonder if he's normally this dense or if it's just the alcohol.

He leans in closer and closer to me. I lean so far back to avoid him touching me that I eventually fall off my bar stool, landing in Cindy's lap. She laughs hysterically and orders another brown cow.

I try desperately to make eye contact with Gord, hoping he'll sense my peril and come to the rescue. But if he notices, he isn't letting on.

Then Jamie's hand grazes my breast and he gives me a smarmy smile, proud of his accomplishment. Startled, I jump off my stool and grab my coat.

"I have to go," I say abruptly and sprint over to Kim.

"Oh, are you leaving?" she asks.

"He touched my boob."

I drop this bomb with unplanned aplomb. The fifteen conversations that have been buzzing around me cease; a rare moment of silence descends over the bar.

In my peripheral vision I glimpse Gord's grin grow big enough to split his face in half.

We don't stick around long after that. I feel compelled to say goodnight to Jamie as I walk past him on my way out, but he is sulking and refuses to answer. What a mess. At least Cindy has enjoyed her birthday.

I'm right back where I started: waiting for Gordo.

33

"JANE, DO YOU want to go on a date with me Thursday night?" Scott from singles bowling asks me out in front of the entire league.

I don't know what to do. I feel no sparks with Scott, but it'd be rude to say no and embarrass him in front of everyone.

"Sure."

Then I can't find my bowling ball.

I ask the bowling tech to look for it, and he searches backstage while both teams wait.

The captain of the other team looks over at me. "Hey, what's in that bowling bag under your chair?"

Sure enough, it's been there the whole time.

When I arrive at Chet's studio for my lesson that Wednesday, he's sitting in a chair beneath a framed photo of himself with his arm around Randy Bachman, polishing his gold record with intense concentration.

He spends the hour trying to teach me how to play chords without the book, but I'm struggling. I've been devouring all

the beginner bass books I can find, memorizing the different chords and finger patterns. With practise I could master
many simple songs that I have sheet music for, but I don't
have an ear and am lost without the written notes to follow.
Since Chet could play by ear almost from birth, he doesn't
explain things well and gets frustrated when I don't pick
everything up right away.

"I'm going to keep pushing you. You'll either get really
good or you'll quit."

He doesn't seem himself tonight. He wears baggy sweat
pants and looks like he's gained weight.

"I've been feeling bored. I usually don't get this way
until February, but it seems to have come on early this
year," he says.

Chet is bored and I'm lonely. We're a dangerous
combination.

• • •

It's Thursday and I'm regretting my dinner date with Scott.
I had a long day at the office and just wanted to go home,
practise my bass and snuggle on the couch watching movies
with Wanker. Instead, I'm sitting in a booth across from him.
He's brought photos of himself with the Sydenham Bruce
Trail Club, his house, all his renovations, and his cat.

I listen to his explanation of each one appreciatively and
ask the appropriate questions. When he reaches the end of
the stack I ask how old he is.

"Let's just say I'm somewhere around my mid- to late
fifties."

Why do all these men fifteen years older than me think I'd be interested in them? I wouldn't ask a twenty-five-year-old boy out. And even if a May–December relationship were palatable now, how would I feel when I'm sixty and changing hubby's diapers and pushing his wheelchair about?

When we finish eating I insist on paying for my dinner, but he's having none of it. I feel bad ditching him so early in the evening, but there's no way I'm inviting him back to my place. Earlier I'd mentioned that my car is on its last legs and I'm in the market for a new one.

"Do you want me to take a look at some of the car lots with you?"

So, we drive through a few dealerships before he drops me off at my house. I say goodnight and make a beeline for the door.

When I get home from work on Friday evening my answering machine is flashing. The phone rings as I'm shrugging out of my coat.

"Jane, it's Scott. I reviewed the back issues of *Consumer Reports* magazine for the last three years researching compact cars. I called three dealerships in Owen Sound and got prices. Do you want to take a test drive with me tonight?"

"I'm sorry, Scott. I've already got plans." I don't mention that they involve walking a dachshund.

"Oh." There's an awkward pause, then he asks me to get a pen so I can write down all the data he's collected for me.

"Thanks for your help, Scott. I really appreciate it."

"You're welcome. I'll see you at bowling on Monday."

"See you Monday."

"One more thing. You should never buy a dark-coloured car. They're hard to keep clean and they get too hot in the summer."

I quit singles bowling and purchase a nighthawk-black–pearl Honda Civic.

34

FIRST THING MONDAY morning Sam calls me into his office to discuss a query he had when reviewing the Haven House audit file.

"I'm confused about the way you wrote the date on the working papers, Jane. You've written 11/03/1999. How am I supposed to know if that's March 11 or November 3?"

"Well, seeing as I handed in the file last week, I think you're safe to assume it's the November one." I give him my best mollify-the-partner-who-signs-our-paycheques smile. One is never prepared for these types of questions in school.

"This is serious, Jane. How will I know which date the work was completed on if I have to look something up in this file four years from now? I'm calling a staff meeting so we can make an executive decision on a consistent policy."

For some reason this strikes me as incredibly funny. I try to stifle a giggle, but a tiny one leaks out.

"What's so funny?"

"It's just that you can be a tad anal sometimes."

"I prefer to think of myself as detail oriented."

"Hmm."

"Do you think you could get these queries cleared today? Paula needs them for their annual meeting on Thursday."

I look at Sam's big stack of fuck-up sheets and think about all the other deadlines I'm chasing. "I'll do them right now," I promise.

"Good. Let's rock 'n' roll."

Sam leaves for a meeting and I look around his office. Like all four partners at FACK, he has one of the large corner offices, his being the upper north corner, opposite Frank the tax partner in the upper south, with Joe and Dean each taking the corner offices on the main floor.

Sam's orderly office is the calm epicentre in the whirlwind of activity that is FACK. His desk features a perfectly centred blotter with a hole punch, stapler and tape dispenser laid out in neat parallel rows. In his pencil holder, every pencil stands side by side with an up-facing eraser leaning against the wall closest to Sam's chair for expedient use. On the bulletin board behind his desk, each tacked-on piece of information is spaced 1.5 centimetres apart, push pins in each of their four corners.

I pick up a pencil and study the gold engraving on it.

"At FACK, client service is our number-one priority."

I wonder how clients would feel if they knew they were being charged $285 an hour for Sam and $105 an hour for me to change the order dates are written in their working papers.

I flip the pencil upside down and place it back in the holder pointy side up. I remove a handful of tiny paper circles from his hole punch and sprinkle them confetti-style on the desk pad. I move the stapler so it's off centre by approximately three centimetres.

Perfectionism is just another word for perpetually disappointed.

Shelly calls me in the afternoon.

"I think I may have accidentally gotten pregnant."

This takes me by surprise. Shelly quit working eleven years ago when Maddie was born and had been planning on going back part-time next fall when Billy starts junior kindergarten.

"Abraham Lincoln said 'There are no accidents.'"

"Honest Abe never drove a minivan down Highway 6 in a snow storm."

"You didn't use protection?"

"We left the snow tires in the garage."

"Well, congratulations," I say, mustering my best big-sister support voice.

"Thanks," she says nonchalantly. "Mom is going to be soooo mad." Shelly sounds exactly like she did the time she'd borrowed Mom's Lava Luster lip gloss without asking. She left the lid off so that it crystallized into an obsidian-like substance and had to be junked.

I wonder why Mom's feelings on the matter seem to be Shelly's first and foremost concern. It isn't like baby number three will be renting a room in Grandma's womb anytime soon.

I refocus on my work, trying not to think of the unfairness of it all. Why are some women able to get pregnant with a shrug of their shoulders while others who are desperate for a child can't find a suitable sex partner to speak of, let alone someone who loves them and wants to procreate? For lonely women struggling to come to grips with the fact they may never have a family, Christmas is not the joy-filled occasion it's cracked up to be.

• • •

I'm at the dentist having a loose filling replaced. Dr. Orin begins drilling on my lower left molar without freezing it. Then the pain gets worse, courtesy of his long-time dental assistant, Audrey, who grew up on the farm right beside us on County Road 17A.

"So, I heard your sister is pregnant again," she says as she passes Dr. Orin a small mouth mirror.

Good lord! News travels fast in rural communities.

"Yes, baby number three is on the way."

"Wow. Is she trying to make up for your never having kids?"

It's the first time I've heard someone say I'm never having kids. The effect is crippling and immediate. Audrey has hit me hard. Unaware of the raw nerve she's just exposed, she carefully selects a shiny silver dental pick with sharp hooks at both ends of it. I wonder briefly if she's preparing to finish what she started—plunge the thing into my heart—but she simply passes it to Dr. Orin.

"Oh my god, Jane—are you okay?" He looks up from his handiwork and sees my eyes glazing with tears, the tube that sucks saliva from my mouth hissing like a snake. "It was such a small filling; I didn't think you'd want your mouth frozen for the whole day."

"I preber to be pro zen."

Audrey looks miserable.

I know she didn't mean to hurt me. It's the sort of thing non-childless adults say without thinking. On my way home I stop at the nearest convenience store and load up on junk food. I always feel embarrassed bringing my twenty-five-dollars' worth of sweet treats to the checkout clerk. Surely he knows I'm taking this glutinous gorge-fest back to my lair, where I will indulge myself in mass consumption. To make things worse, the woman in front of me produces twenty-seven lotto tickets from her purse and proceeds to have the clerk check each one individually. I glance anxiously at the door, hoping no one I know walks in and catches me holding on tight to my stockpile of comfort food.

I pay with two twenty-dollar bills, drop the change into the bottom of my purse and make a break for the exit. As I push open the heavy glass doors, the cashier calls out, "Candy is dandy, but sex won't rot your teeth."

I get home and flop on the couch. Burying my face in a pillow I let out great, gulping sobs while hugging my knees like a child. A concerned Wanker leaps up beside me, pushes his long snout under the crook of my arm and rests his head on my shoulder. But nothing can stop the soundtrack of Audrey's words playing in an endless loop. "You're never having kids; you're never having kids, you're never having kids..."

I eventually get up, open my recently purchased pint of Häagen-Dazs and sink a big spoon in. But the damage is done. Even cookie-dough ice cream can't fill the cavity or dull the pain.

I prefer to be frozen.

35

I DECIDE IT'S not a good idea to spend Friday evening alone in my current state. I call Cindy.

"Come on over. I just made way too much spaghetti. Why don't you join me for dinner and we'll go out for a drink later?"

Cindy lives in a really cool apartment in an old brick house on Alpha Street with her immense tiger cat, Sally. I tell her about my dentist appointment.

"Has anyone ever said anything like that to you?"

"Yes, people can be so insensitive sometimes."

After dinner we go to the Barking Frog. Gord is sitting in his usual spot at the bar with Bart. To avoid another encounter with Bart, Cindy leads us to a table in the back and we order beer. Gord's clothes look new; even his shoes and belt are shiny. He's dyed his hair an inky Elvis black, which is in sharp contrast to his pale skin and light-brown brows. His natural grey is starting to grow back, so that he appears to be wearing the pelt of an aging Labrador retriever on his head.

When Bart leaves, Gord begins flirting with a girl at the side of the bar. I sip my beer and watch his reflection in the window beside me.

"I let that creepy Jamie buy me a drink on your birthday, hoping it would make Gord jealous. Instead, it backfired, and I ended up getting groped in a public place," I say to Cindy.

"At least you didn't get groped in a private place. I got an email from Dave from Nova Scotia today," Cindy says, referring to her upcoming internet hook-up.

"Are you nervous about going out with someone you've never met before?"

"A little. A year ago I met this man from Chatham online. We emailed each other for over a year and I felt really close to him. He told me he was in love with me."

"How could he love you when he'd never even met you?"

"We emailed each other and talked in chat rooms all the time. He kept telling me that he wanted to come to Owen Sound and meet me, but he was self-employed and couldn't take time out from his business."

"So what happened?"

"One day I was visiting some friends in Windsor, and I thought, What the heck? I'm going to stop in and pay him a surprise visit.

"How did he react?"

"A woman answered the door. When I asked for him, she said he was at work. I never heard from him again."

Gord seems to know every patron in the bar and be determined to touch base with every one of them—except me. He briefly visits the table next to us and moves on.

I look over at Cindy. "Let's go to Jazzmyn's."

The roads are starting to get slippery as we drive across town. The snow, which has been falling all day, continues to accumulate. No doubt my dad will be working overtime tonight.

We're forced to detour around 2nd Avenue East, which is blocked off for the opening of the Festival of Northern Lights. Mom and Dad will freeze, I think. Every year they take Shell's kids to the festival while she and Steve attend his dealership's Christmas party at a posh Collingwood restaurant. The temperature has dropped below zero, and Mom and Dad will have to arrive early in order to find a decent vantage point for checking out Kris Kringle. I wonder how they'll make out next year with two kids and a baby.

● ● ●

Every week at my music lesson Chet tells me what gigs he'll be playing on the weekend. So far I've resisted the temptation to go and watch him.

I know he's playing tonight in Mark Mobley's backup band at Jazzmyn's. Mark is a well-known singer who grew up in Owen Sound and has been performing in the area for years. He does a decent job of covering classic pop and folk tunes from the sixties and on, with a few of his original songs thrown in for posterity. I'd met Mark briefly a couple of years ago when he performed at my cousin's wedding. He's pretty popular around town, and the place is packed. Cindy and I have to take a table near the back. I'm pretty sure Chet hasn't seen me come in.

He's having fun improvising on the bass line from "Ain't No Sunshine," its gloomy melody echoing off the walls of the old hall.

Strumming his twelve-string, Mark sports shaggy brown hair and a day and a half's worth of stubble, baggy jeans held up by a battered leather belt over a hint of a beer gut. Occupational hazard, I suppose.

"He's kind of cute if you're into the tortured-artist kind of thing," I say to Cindy.

"Did you know I dated Mark in high school?"

"No way." Cindy is full of surprises tonight.

"Way."

"Okay, details. How come you never told me this before?"

"I guess I forgot. It only lasted a week and a half. I was going to OSCVI and he went to St. Mary's. We met at a mutual friend's party and he asked me to go to a movie with him."

"How did that go?"

"Our date was fine, but then the next week, I was sitting in chemistry class on the third floor and all of a sudden there was a commotion outside. A bunch of kids stood up and ran to the windows to see what was going on."

Cindy looks nostalgic, and I picture her in her Jordache jeans in Mr. Hamilton's Grade 12 class, pouring brightly coloured liquids into beakers and test tubes.

"I figured it must have been a fight or something, but when I went over to look for myself, there was Mark, standing on the front lawn of OSCVI and playing Peter Frampton's 'I'm in You' on his guitar. When it was over he dedicated it 'To Cindy, with all my heart.' This brought on all kinds of clapping and booing and yelling. One girl got so excited she accidently burned a hole in the sleeve of her Roots sweat-shirt with a Bunsen burner."

I'm entranced; it's like all my favourite romantic come-dies playing out right here in real-life Owen Sound.

"That's the most romantic story I've ever heard. It's even more romantic than Lloyd Dobler holding the boom box over his head under Diane's window in *Say Anything*, which is, like, the most romantic scene in movie history. Did you rush down the stairs and leap into his arms?"

"No. The vice principal showed up and escorted him off the property."

"That's too bad. What happened after that?"

"I broke up with him the next day."

"You heartbreaker. Do you ever regret it?"

"Are you kidding? I had to put up with boys humming 'I'm in Yoooooou' everytime I walked down the hall for the next three years."

I sigh. Am I truly the only remaining romantic on the planet?

"Besides, do you know what they call a musician who's not married?" Cindy asks.

I shake my head.

"Unemployed."

"But he's so cute and talented. Is he married?"

"No, but he lives with a girl. They've got a trailer in Fairview Park."

I'm enjoying the show immensely, but Cindy is slightly asthmatic and the heavy curtain of smoke in the bar is both-ering her. When the band wraps up the set and settles in for a break, we decide to leave.

Chet and the other band members come down off the stage and lean against it, facing the audience. I hope to slip by Chet unnoticed on our way out, but he spots me and follows us out to the porch, wearing only a thin sweater in the freezing winter night.

I turn around to say hello to him.

"Why are you leaving?" he asks.

"Cindy's having a bad reaction to the smoke," I say, gesturing toward my friend.

I'm about to follow her when he takes both my hands in his and holds my gaze.

"Stay."

I want to so badly, but I can't. I follow Cindy to the parking lot, fighting the urge to turn and run back up the stairs. I hope Chet doesn't think I'm playing games with him. Remembering the look in his eyes and the feel of his hands in mine has my heart racing.

I go to the office Sunday morning and work all day on the Pearson Lumber year-end, throwing myself into the file to bury these urges.

He's married and he has a kid. I want a family so badly, but I could never destroy a family that belongs to someone else.

36

ALTHOUGH I EXPERIENCED some culture shock living in Toronto after growing up in Grey County, I soon settled into university life.

I loved my classes. Our professors were some of the best in the country, and they inspired me.

But while my creative self basked in this new universe, my practical, worrywart left brain was scared. After the glory days of the profitable seventies, the Canadian economy had plunged into a deep recession. Interest rates climbed to an unprecedented 21 per cent and unemployment rates got higher every day.

I worried there wouldn't be a job in the industry for me after graduation. My fellow students were mostly dynamic go-getters who'd already made connections in high places. Would a quiet, hardworking girl like me be able to compete for those coveted positions? And was I willing to move wherever the market took me to get the job I wanted?

Mostly I missed Kyle. After being literally joined at the nether regions for an entire summer, being separated from him felt like having my umbilical cord cut prematurely. In order to get cheaper long-distance phone rates, we waited until the wee hours of the morning to call each other. Both of us were busy with schoolwork, and we were often too exhausted to stay up late enough to call. As the first few weeks of autumn passed, our calls became fewer and farther apart.

I waited anxiously for Thanksgiving weekend, when I would go home and we could finally be together again.

I thought wistfully of Christopher Graham, remembering our plans to take Toronto by storm. But he had changed course and gone to McGill to pursue a Master's degree in fine arts.

Meanwhile, in Windsor, Angie and Xav's relationship was beginning to suffer the strain that a sixteen-year age gap, various ex-spouses and stepchildren can impose.

Angie's parents felt the shift away from the honeymoon phase and prepared to make their move.

Her mom, Lynn, was a bank teller. One day a customer who happened to be the matriarch of Serena's, Owen Sound's classiest ladies' wear shop, told Lynn she wanted to retire and was looking to sell the store.

In a bold and daring move, Angie's parents bought the business, which had been a downtown staple for more than seventy-five years, for their daughter. Angie was born a fashionista, and owning her own clothing store had been her dream for as long as I'd known her. This opportunity of a lifetime was simply too much to resist; there was no saying no to such a grandiose gesture. In September of 1981, just three short weeks after I'd left for Ryerson, Angie moved back to Owen Sound and set about modernizing the store.

The top floor had been converted into a private apartment, which she also redecorated before moving in.

Unable to leave his work and family behind, Xav had no choice but to stay in Windsor. But he was a fighter, too. Two months after the sale of the store closed, he made a deft countermove, surprising Angie with an engagement ring.

On the first Thursday in October I took the bus back to Owen Sound for the Thanksgiving long weekend. Kyle met me at the bus station and threw his arms around me. I wanted to spend the whole weekend snuggled right there, making up for lost time.

But Kyle's older sister, Abbey, a sweetheart whom I absolutely adored, was getting married that weekend, and Kyle was in the wedding party. Several out-of-town relatives had been billeted with family, and our services were required to transport and entertain them. Angie also volunteered to help, and although it felt like old times with the three of us hanging out together, I couldn't help longing for more intimate moments with Kyle. It wasn't until Monday afternoon, after the newlyweds' family brunch and gift opening, that Kyle and I finally got some time to ourselves. We snuck off in Kyle's truck and had sex on a side road. This was much more difficult than it sounds. Since it was too cold to do it outdoors, we squeezed into the cab of the small Chevy pick up truck. The gear shift threw a monkey wrench into the equation. Our time together ended much too quickly. That night I caught the bus back to Toronto. We both had midterms coming up and had little time to study.

At Ryerson the pressure was starting to get to me. In Owen Sound I'd been the rising star of the art department and a standout seamstress. In the denim-clad halls of West

Hill High, Angie and I had strutted our stuff in our original creations and stylings.

But the fashion program in Toronto attracted the best and most talented students in the country. I often felt like a hick among the sophisticated fashionistas with their worldly experience and big bank accounts. Somewhere in the two hundred kilometres between Owen Sound and Ryerson I'd slipped from the top of the heap to the bottom of the barrel. And the constant pressures of competition, deadlines, exams and projects took their toll.

Eventually December came around, and, when I handed in my final essay on the history of fashion a day and a half ahead of schedule, I decided to come home early and surprise everyone.

Catching the early-morning bus, I arrived in downtown Owen Sound just before noon. I wanted to catch Angie by surprise at her new store, so I started walking up 2nd Avenue. Kyle was writing a final exam at Georgian College that morning, and I had a different surprise in mind for him later.

It was my turn to be surprised when I turned the corner onto 2nd Avenue. I saw Kyle and Angie heading into DC Taylors Jewellers. Not believing my luck, I picked up my pace and tried to catch up to them but was slowed down by my heavy backpack. When I reached the big storefront window they'd already disappeared inside. My heart skipped a beat as I peered in to see what they were up to. The two of them were standing behind the jewellery counter pointing into the showcase as a jeweller pulled out a ring to show them.

When we were thirteen, Angie and I had made a pact to instruct each other's future-betrothed in the purchase of a proper engagement ring. My instructions to her were clear.

I wanted a simple solitaire set in a plain gold band. Angie, on the other hand, had chosen a one-and-a-half-carat pink emerald-cut diamond set in white gold; anything less would be deemed unacceptable. According to our pact, friends don't let friends' boyfriends purchase engagement rings unassisted. It was ideal in that it would allow our beloved boy to surprise us when proposal time came without him inadvertently purchasing something hideous, the wearing of which would have to be endured for all eternity. Marriages may come and go, but diamonds are forever. Of course, the pact required that said boy would have to be intelligent enough to consult the BFF for advice on the matter. Clearly Kyle had passed this test with flying colours.

Xav, on the other hand, had not asked for my assistance when purchasing Angie's ring. I wondered whether he'd got it right on his own.

Brain swirling, I ducked into a drugstore before Kyle or Angie could spot me. If Kyle was planning to give me the ring at Christmas, the last thing I wanted was to ruin the surprise. I waited a few minutes, slipped out the back door, ducked into the Carney's Lane alleyway and doubled back to the bus station. From there I called my dad, who'd been at home sleeping after a late night ploughing the back roads of Grey County. He drove into town and brought me home to the farm.

After dinner that night, Angie stopped in on her way home from work. It was all I could do to remain calm and pretend I didn't know that she knew Kyle was about to propose. She whipped out her left hand to present Xav's ring.

It was a pear-shaped half-carat white diamond in a gold band.

"It's so beautiful. Congratulations." I gave her a big hug.

"Yes, but I was a little disappointed he didn't get me my fantasy ring."

"But it's so lovely, Angie, and it's from this incredible man who wants to spend the rest of his life with you."

"He said he chose the pear-shaped diamond because it reminded him of my bum."

"So, where did you hide the body? Is that why he's not here to spend Christmas with you?"

"He couldn't come because it's his year to wake up with the kids on Christmas morning. It was Clarissa's turn last year. It's part of the divorce agreement."

"You didn't want to wake up on Christmas morning with them?"

"I'm too busy at my store with all the holiday shoppers. Besides, the only thing I want to wake up with on Christmas morning is a hangover."

"The kids' schedule sounds very complicated."

"I believe it's based on the changing of the tides and the waxing of the moon. I'll head down to Windsor to spend the rest of the holidays with him right after our Boxing Day sale."

The holiday passed in a blur of family, friends, frantic shopping and dreamy anticipation. I'd put off Christmas shopping to focus on my exams; now I was racing around buying the bulk of my gifts in Grey County's limited venues. The one item I had lugged home with me was a beautiful handmade six-string classical guitar for Kyle. I couldn't wait to see his face when he opened the case.

Not since Shelly told me in fourth grade that Santa didn't exist but I'd better keep pretending to believe in order to maintain the status quo had I waited for Christmas day with such anticipation.

When would Kyle give me the ring? Would we get married right away or wait until we finished school? What kind of dress would I wear? Who would be in the wedding party? Angie, of course, would be maid of honour.

My Christmas day schedule was as overstuffed as our turkey. I woke up and enjoyed a few quiet moments at our house, sipping coffee and watching the powdery snow fall, before everyone opened their stockings. At lunch I called Kyle, but he was busy trying out a new snowmobile and bringing in firewood for the family celebrations.

"Do you want me to have him call you back when he gets in?" his mom asked me.

"It's okay. I'll see him tonight."

"That's great, Jane. We should be eating around six. Looking forward to seeing you."

All of us flocked over to Nana and Alph's, where our extended families gathered for the traditional Christmas that I loved. There was simply no smell as good as the home cooking in Nana's big old country kitchen. We feasted on turkey, dressing, baked beans, cherry Jell-O with banana slices, cinnamon rolls, peas, turnips, cranberry sauce, mashed potatoes, gravy, assorted pickles, olives, caesar salad and carrot sticks. For dessert we had English trifle, pumpkin pie, cherry pie, apple pie and Nana's traditional Christmas pudding, along with multitudes of home-baked cookies and squares.

Afterward, almost too full to move, we put on a play of sorts in the living room as Nana cooked homemade taffy on the stove and dropped it in the snow to harden.

"Did you get a ring for Christmas, Jane?" Grandpa Alf inspected my fingers, as he had every Christmas since I was seventeen.

"Not this year, Gramps." It was difficult not to share my news, but I knew I couldn't say anything until Kyle had proposed.

"I hope you get married before I die."

I'd barely had time to digest it all when it was time to go to Kyle's family Christmas dinner. Stuffed from Nana's, my heart rate accelerated as I subtly scanned his parents' house for signs of a wrapped ring box. I could barely eat a thing.

Kyle suggested we wait until after dinner to exchange gifts privately. After family gifts had been exchanged and folks were settled with their Spanish coffees, we snuck off to his bedroom upstairs.

Kyle was thrilled with the guitar, which his mom had safely stowed away for me earlier in the week. He brought me three packages, which I opened with trembling fingers. The largest one held a Faire Isle sweater, black with red and white hearts encircling the neck and waistband, that had come from Angie's shop. The medium box contained my favourite Laura Secord miniatures.

It had to be this one, I thought as I picked up the smallest package and struggled to tear off the ribbon. But when I opened the lid, instead of a diamond ring I found a sour-grape–flavoured Bonnie Bell lip smacker.

"I got Abbey to pick that up for you when she was down south on her honeymoon. I remembered you saw them in one of your magazines and said how much you liked them."

Maybe the ring was inside. I picked up the tube and gently twisted the bottom. But nothing fell out when I pulled the cap off. I picked it up and rubbed some on my lips.

"Let me taste it," Kyle said as he leaned in closer to kiss my lips, running his tongue over them, then moved to unbutton my blouse.

"But, Kyle, your whole family is downstairs," I protested.

"We'll have to make it a 'Silent Night,'" he grinned as we fell back onto his unmade bed.

37

EIGHT MONTHS AFTER the FACK/Montgomery Lawrence merger, our office renovations are still ongoing.

It's early December and Cindy's office is finally completed.
With tearful hugs, our office-sharing days come to an end.

Her new office isn't far from mine. It's just across from
the tax department in a room we'd been using as a library
for accounting texts and manuals, in the northeast turret on
the second floor.

Frank and Katie had been assigned the task of cleaning
out the library before the builders arrived. Frank had com-
posed and sent out the following email to all FACK staffers:

Email from: PartnerFrank@FACK.ca
To: Staff@FACK.ca
Ladies & Gentlemen:
For one week and one week only, the part-
ners of FACK are pleased to announce that the
contents of the entire turret library are on sale
for the bargain-basement price of zero dollars.
You heard me correctly... zero dollars.

We have some timeless classics for you:

The Philosophy of Auditing – Marks & Omar. This is the accountant's version of *Harry Potter and the Philospher's Stone*.

The External Audit – Rob Henderson. Rock and roll never forgets.

Accounting Principles to Remember – Tom Rinnick. A little bit of Elvis in this dude.

And a host of others, including an autographed copy by Sam Austin of Charles Peterman's *Managerial & Cost Accounting* still in its original paper jacket. In his day, Charles Peterman was to management accounting what Tiger Woods is to golf.

If you're interested in opening an accounting and auditing museum as a tax shelter, there's never been a better time to start. The sale ends Friday, December 14. After that everything gets moved to recycling.

Regards,

Frank

Unable to resist, I'd helped myself to the original *Managerial & Cost Accounting*, autographed by Sam. Its use as a sleep aid is unparalleled.

• • •

Cindy's date with Internet Dave is a smashing success. According to Cindy, he is not a crazed lunatic who stalks the internet preying on lonely women, but a lovely man looking for companionship.

"We talked for two hours straight and never had to search for something to say."

I don't point out that Cindy seldom has to search for something to say.

"I thought he lived in Nova Scotia."

"He does, but he's going to be working in Owen Sound for almost a year, and he promised to call me as soon as he moves here."

"How old is he?"

"Two years older than me and divorced. He has two kids, but he says they're gone now."

"Gone as in grown up and moved out, or gone as in their bodies are buried under his house?"

"Hopefully it's the former."

"Well, if he's not coming back to Owen Sound until January, will you still be my date for the FACK Christmas party?"

"Of course. Did you know the firm's going to Vegas Night at the Hanover casino this year?"

"Yes. Larry asked me if I was going and then said, 'Do you think you'll get lucky?'"

"I can't believe he said that to you."

"I told him to ask you, since you're going to be my date."

On Friday afternoon I'm at the bonspiel and dinner that FACK hosts at the Granite Club for all the bankers and lawyers in town. The idea is for us to suck up to them. In return they refer their clients to us.

Larry has volunteered for the position of taping the shoes of curling civilians who don't have the proper shoes or sliders required for the sport. When it's my turn to get my sneakers taped, he focuses on the job with the concentration of Oscar De La Hoya's trainer wrapping the champ's wrists in tensor bandages before an Olympic gold medal round.

My attention shifts to Bob Vandersmyth, a banker I'd met in the summer of 1998 when Sam had forced me to golf in the Big Brothers Charity Golf Tournament. Recently divorced, personable and intelligent, Bob had piqued my interest, and this afternoon he looks as cute as a button.

From the corner of my eye I watch him kneel in the hack. Just as he's about to throw the rock, he pulls off his glove and sticks it in his back pocket. The glow from a shiny new wedding band refracts off the ice, practically blinding me.

How is this fair? When I met Bob just over a year ago, he was freshly divorced. Women over thirty, we've been told, have a better chance of being killed by a terrorist than finding a husband. For men over forty, it's like shooting fish in a barrel.

The good news, I guess, is that it's getting easier to be killed by a terrorist every day.

That night I attend the FACK women's Christmas party. We go out for dinner then back to Lori's house for our annual gift-exchange game.

We each bring a secret gift and put it in a big pile. We draw numbers from one up to however many people are in attendance. If you get number one, you pick a gift from the pile and unwrap it. Then number two has to choose between stealing your gift or picking another from the pile. This goes on ad nauseam until the last present has been unwrapped and everyone is finished stealing.

I'm not sure how long the women of FACK have been playing this game; it predates me. It's incredibly stressful, as no one wants the humiliation of contributing a gift that never gets stolen. Therefore the ten-dollar limit placed on the gifts is ignored by almost everyone except newbies. What starts as a night of lighthearted holiday merriment quickly degenerates into something more sinister as mild-mannered accountant ladies transform into a pack of blood-thirsty savages resembling the kids from *Lord of the Flies*.

Lori, in particular, finds the game excruciatingly stressful and has a reputation for bringing a gift that never gets stolen. Last year I made sure I stole her gift of a nice bottle of white wine in a hand-embroidered wine sock, even though I much prefer red.

This year Lady Luck is not on my side as I draw the dreaded number-one spot. The package I open holds the most ador-able calico bear, which Katie has handsewn. No one has actu-ally made their own gift before, and when I pull it from its gift bag a round of ooohs and awwws rivalling those heard at the Kelso Beach Canada Day fireworks echo around the room. I bond with the bear and manage to fend off all takers, pro-claiming how great it will look in my new home.

Our relationship is terminated, however, when a very pregnant Anne pulls the last straw. Unable to resist an opportunity to flaunt her dominance, she hoists herself from an overstuffed armchair, waddles across the room and snatches the teddy from my arms.

All holiday chatter ceases as the women look on in horror.

I smile serenely and say, "You are one mean mother."

Everyone but Anne howls with laughter.

38

IT FEELS ODD to be working overtime in December, but if I don't get caught up I can't go on vacation. Sam wants Lloyd's Footwear finished, but Dean keeps slipping his jobs in ahead of it, claiming his clients are more urgent and should be a priority. Today Dean springs two law-society reports on me that are due by the end of December, and I'm supposed to be out of here this week.

I take the reports home to work on over the weekend. I finally fall asleep late Sunday night after I finish the last one. Around four in the morning the phone rings. Half asleep, I grab it from the nightstand beside my bed.

"Hello," I answer, my voice groggy with sleep.

"Hello," someone at the other end of the line echoes back. The voice is deep, husky and distinctly masculine.

Silence.

"Is this a wrong number?" I mumble.

"I just got home and I had to call this number," the mystery man says.

"Who is this?" I have no idea.

Silence.

"I just wanted to talk to you." The voice sounds vaguely familiar, but I can't place it and I'm still not fully conscious.

"Do I know you?" I ask.

More silence.

"Al, is that you?" The voice sounds remotely like it could belong to one of our FACK clients. I'm sure it's not him, but nobody's talking and I feel like I should throw something out there.

"Is someone there with you?" The voice sounds anxious now.

"No, I'm alone."

Too late, it occurs to me that this is probably the stupidest thing anyone could possibly say to an unknown caller at 4 a.m.

Another long silence.

"What time is it?"

"4:25."

I let out a groan. "I have to get up in an hour."

"We could talk for an hour," he murmurs. His voice is a soft, seductive tickle in my ear. "You have to get up in an hour anyway."

"I know, but I really need that hour," I say.

And I hang up.

It must have been some random weirdo who picked my number out of the phone book, because when I press the star-69 button to see who'd called, a recording informs me the number cannot be traced. (And, seriously, who's the pervert at the phone company who picked the number sixty-nine for caller identification?)

I can't get back to sleep. At work I'm distracted and have trouble settling in. This creates problems, because it's supposed to be my last day before Christmas vacation and there are files to be finished.

Cindy comes into my office for an update, then Collette spends half an hour giving me the play-by-play on her evening at the Platers game with Bob. Anne comes down and settles in like she's going to be awhile. Then Cindy returns. Larry stops by and invites himself to my house for a holiday drink.

"Any day over the Christmas holidays except December 25 would work for me, Jane. Have cold beer and peanuts ready."

Oh god. He'd better be kidding me.

Finally, John comes to rescue me.

"How's Deli Delight coming along, Jane?"

"I haven't quite got it finished yet."

"Only five hours to go," he says, looking pointedly at his watch.

Everybody leaves except the obtuse Collette, who does not take hints.

"Jane needs to get back to work, Collette," John tells her.

"But I wasn't finished telling her about the game."

"Take it up with Star Command."

I work steadily all day; I don't even break for lunch. I finally solve the investment problem and get the inter-company accounts balanced. Everything's finished except the tax returns. John says that's fine; he'll prepare them himself when he reviews the file. Thank God for John. I really like working for him.

When I arrive for my music lesson that night Chet seems angry and I have no idea why. At first I think he's just in a quiet mood.

He makes me practise extremely difficult doubles exercises over and over again.

I can't figure out what's wrong. Then he says something in a low, gravelly voice, and it comes to me.

Chet was my 4 a.m. phone caller.

Half asleep I hadn't recognized his voice, but alone with him now in the Rumpus Room, it's unmistakable.

"I just got home and I had to call this number."

He'd been in Florida with his wife and son the week before. He must have come home, got ready to make his big move, and I'd hung up on him.

My head is spinning. I'm not sure what to do. Part of me wants to throw caution to the wind. I'm so attracted to Chet, but in my head I can't separate the man from his family.

"I've decided to get serious and buy a new bass and amp," I announce.

Instantly his mood changes. Excited, he launches into a monologue about the various brands, shapes and sizes of bass guitars that would be best for me.

"What should I look for?"

"If it looks shitty, don't buy it."

"Nothing like getting sound advice from a professional," I say to him. "That's why I pay you the big bucks."

He laughs for the first time all night.

• • •

Here I am on my first day of Christmas vacation, and all I can think about is Chet.

He's made the first move; the ball is in my court.

We could have an affair. All I'd have to do is tell him I'm sorry; I was half asleep and didn't recognize his voice.

I'm itching to do it. A fierce desire born from years of forced abstinence is never far from the surface for me. Now it's bubbling over the top.

There's so much at stake, though: his wife, his little boy, his reputation, my reputation. I've never cheated in my life, not even on a boyfriend. Deep down, my woman's intuition is telling me this isn't a good time to start.

39

I DON'T MUCH enjoy the Christmas holidays these days.

Every television commercial, every Christmas song, every Santa in Heritage Mall reminds me that this is family time and my time to have a family is rapidly running out. I'm tempted to work through them, but I've still vacation days left and if I don't use them by the end of the year, I'll lose them.

To kick off my vacation, Shelly, Madison and I are going to the Stars on Ice figure skating show at the Harry Lumley Bayshore Community Centre on Friday night. When I'm ready to head out, Shelly's still shopping, so I drive to Meaford to pick up Maddie; we'll meet Shelly at East Side Marios. Billy refuses to speak to me when he realizes I've forgotten to bring him a treat.

Madison, who has two servings of four-cheese deep-dish macaroni followed by a funnel cake at the restaurant, pouts through the first half of the ice show because Shelly refuses to buy her popcorn. I don't always miss having kids.

I decide to ignore Maddie's histrionics and enjoy the show, which is wonderful. It's being taped to be televised next week on Christmas Eve. All the skaters do their routines for the audience as they would during any regular performance; afterwards they get to go back and redo any missed jumps or other glitches. How would my life be different, I wonder, if I could retake a few of my harder falls?

Some of the skaters have to try the same jump two or three times before they get it perfect. Film editors will put it all together so viewers see a seamless performance.

Kurt Browning is spectacular as always. It is Brian Orser's last year before retirement; he looks great and earns a standing ovation for both of his skates. During the finale I get to shake hands with classy Canadian champion Elizabeth Robinson.

After the show we go to the Boot and Blade for hot chocolate and cherry pie. Shelly gives me a list of what the kids want me to get them for Christmas.

It's well past eleven when I finally head home. I drive past the office and notice Sam's light is on. I know he's up there working. He's so fussy, spending hours and hours on every job, writing the notes to the financial statements, then rewriting them. There is no way our clients could afford to pay for all of Sam's time; he must write a lot of it off. For some people,"I live at the office" is just an expression. For others, like Sam, it's a lifestyle.

I can't afford to go away for my vacation this year and have no one to go with anyway, so I do my best to keep busy. I finish my Christmas shopping, catch up on overdue housework and take my nieces and nephews to the movies. I go shopping with Mom, clean my car and make shortbread cookies and peanut butter squares with teeny pastel-coloured marshmallows in them. These are supposed to be for gifts, but I eat most of them. Now I'm having trouble getting my pants zipped up and will have to look for new ones on sale after Christmas.

I read *A Girl's Guide to Hunting and Fishing* and drive out to visit Nana and Alf. I spend my afternoons doing odd jobs for Paula at Haven House: chopping vegetables, doing dishes, folding laundry, making beds. Paula appreciates my help, as she is short-handed over the holidays, but I do it as much for myself as anyone. Being inside the busy shelter keeps my mind off my own loneliness and feelings of despair. Working with people who are hungry and don't have a place to sleep puts my problems into much-needed perspective.

I practise my bass every day and wonder what will happen on Wednesday. Christmas Eve is on Thursday this year, and I'd hoped Chet would cancel our lesson, but he hasn't.

Thinking about him is driving me crazy. In this season of miracles, logic seems to be deserting me. In a fit of loneliness I reach for the phone to call him. At the last minute I chicken out and call Kristen instead.

Of course she knows who Chet is and listens quietly when I tell her about my secret music lessons, the four a.m. phone call and my feelings for him.

"I was thinking about calling him. Do you think I should?"

"Evan having an affair would be my worst nightmare," she demurs. There's nothing judgemental in her tone.

"We could keep it a secret. That way nobody has to get hurt." *Who am I trying to fool here: Kristen or myself?*

"You can't just dip your toe into the sea of adultery, Jane. You either dive in all the way or stay on dry land."

"But that's just it. I'm so dry I'm practically parched. I've been wandering in the desert of abstinence for so many years, I'm desperate for a drink."

"I thought your drought ended when you visited Sean's tent last summer."

Sean was the closest I'd come to having sex in a long time. But almost having sex isn't anything like actually having it, and the near-miss had only augmented my sexual frustration.

"He couldn't get his pole up, remember. You married girls are so lucky. You can have sex whenever you want."

Kristen's quiet for a moment and I think maybe she's hung up, but then she resumes, explaining she'd set the phone down when Stan upended his juice box.

"Yesterday I had this crazy-hectic day: working, driving the kids to swimming lessons, getting dinner ready and helping with homework. I finally got them to bed around nine-thirty, and I was just snuggling up with this great book I'd been looking forward to reading all day, when Evan came to bed feeling horny."

"So you told him you'd rather read a book than have sex with him."

"No, that's not so great for a marriage."

"So, you took one for the team?"

"Exactly. I faked an orgasm really quickly, then Evan felt free to have his, and within minutes he was snoring. I was able to read my book for like a whole ninety minutes. It was heavenly."

"Did Ev really believe you were able to have an orgasm that quickly?"

"Jane, he's a man."

"Sorry, I forgot." I pause. "Don't you like sex anymore?"

"I do. It's just that the moments I have for myself are so rare. It's difficult when you think you're finally going to have some time for yourself and it gets snatched away at the last minute."

"It's ironic, isn't it? I have 'me' time up the wazoo, but I haven't had sex in years and I'm lonely and horny as hell; you can have as much sex as you want and would kill for a little time to yourself."

I haven't thought about it this way before. Is it just human nature to want what we can't have? Kristen seems to think so.

"It's Economics 101, Jane—the law of supply and demand. The less you have of something, the higher the demand, thus the higher the price we're willing to pay for it."

"Sex-o-nomics."

"What I'm trying to say is, the price of having sex with Chet might be higher than you think. And I thought you were concentrating on finding your soulmate; how are you going to do that if you expend all your energy on a married man?"

"But it's not like I'd be in a real relationship. I could have my little fling with Chet and still search for my soulmate."

"I know you, Jane. Once you connect with a man intimately like that, you won't be able to look at anyone else."

"I really need this; nobody would ever have to know."

"I'm worried about you. More than just your guitar strings could get plucked here."

On Wednesday night I bring Chet some of my home-baked cookies as a Christmas gift and he makes a fuss over them. We try to get down to the lesson and talk for a while about the bass I'm planning to buy. We play together from a book of Christmas carols that has bass lines.

Then he looks over at me.

"I need to sort out your left hand."

He stands behind me and gently reaches around to lay his left hand over mine on the body of the bass. He threads his right hand through the thick leather strap and cups it around my wrist high on the guitar's neck. I can feel the calluses on his strong fingers.

For what seems like forever we stay motionless like that. I finally turn to face him, and his left hand slides down around my waist.

Chet leans in and kisses me. Slowly at first, then more passionately. His mouth tastes like cigarettes and it makes me gag a little. He leads me over to the pillows in the corner of the loft, puts both hands on my bass and begins to lift it ever so gingerly over my head.

We're doing this, I think. We're really going to do this.

Just then the quiet is shattered by the bang of the downstairs door being flung open.

We both jump. Chet drops the bass midflight, and the unexpected weight of it makes me topple over backward. I trip over my amplifier cord on my way down and it lets out an ear-splitting scream.

Chet steps over me and rushes downstairs to find out what is going on.

"Daaaaaddy, Mommy spanked me!" I hear a tiny voice wail.

My heart breaks. It seems like forever, but in actuality it's probably only a few minutes, before Chet settles Matt down and returns him to the house. In the meantime, I manage to pick myself up, pack my bass and calm my harried hormones. Temporarily, at least.

When he climbs back to the loft I already have my coat on and have retrieved Chet's practise bass. It's resting safely on its stand, waiting for the next set of sticky peanut butter fingers. It's my final lesson.

40

BESIDE MYSELF, I come home and eat a dozen of Grandma's home-made Christmas cookies. Then I go to Video Town, where I rent *Knotting Hill, She's All That* and *There's Something About Mary.* I watch them back to back.

When I overcome my inertia enough to get up off the couch and do something productive, I throw a load of laundry in the washing machine. Almost immediately the laundry room floods.

Now, in addition to being horny, lonely and depressed, I'm a bit nervous. When I'd taken the plunge and bought the house last year, my insurance company had told me they wouldn't cover sewer backup. What if it isn't the washing machine but the sewer causing the problem?

It takes some serious mopping to get the room cleaned up, and I have to throw out the rug that covered half the floor. But at least I can see it looks like the water's coming from the washing machine and not the drain.

Kristen calls. "Don't worry; your house is on high ground, so you don't even need a sump pump."

"Well, the home inspector did tell me there was no evidence of previous water damage."

"I'll have Evan come over and take a look at your washing machine tomorrow."

I breathe a sigh of relief. Thank God for good friends like Kristen and Evan. What would I do without them?

Then Kim calls.

"They're having a big Christmas Eve event at the Barking Frog tonight. Did you want to come?"

"I don't have anything to wear." The truth is, I've gained weight from my recent binges and all my clothes are tight. After dealing with Chet and my flooding basement, I just want to pull my comforter around me and watch more romantic comedies.

But Kim's not letting me get away with it. "You need to get out of the house, my dear."

I call Cindy and tell her about the party. "I'll drive, but if I drink too much we can just take a cab home," I say, already sensing I'll need alcohol for support.

The place is packed. The band is an eclectic group of musicians who'd come together for a special Christmas Eve performance. The three of us sit along the bar, close to the stage.

"Hey, Jane. I heard Chet the Fret might be coming over to jam with the band later," Kim says.

Oh, great. Just what I need now is for Chet to show up.

I'm drinking a lot. On my fourth trip back from the lady's room I spot Gord at a table directly across from us.

I whisper in Cindy's ear, "He's here."

She stands up, right hand on her forehead in Eagle Scout fashion, yelling, "Where, Jane? Where?"

So much for subtlety. Shushing her only seems to egg her on. She begins revolving like a lighthouse, trying to flush him out.

Gord finally notices and waves at us.

"I'm so over him, Cindy."

"You're better off without him. If you were dating him, he'd be at the Frog every night and you'd be home alone."

I avoid eye contact with Gord but keep him in my peripheral vision. He attempts to flirt with the young brunette seated beside him. She looks at him like he's out of his mind and snuggles closer to her boyfriend.

Every time I notice Gord chatting someone up, I turn away to watch the band. I'm not going to let him spoil the evening for me.

Then I notice he's sporting the sexy stubble of a growing-in moustache.

I dance with Kim's husband, George, who's made a rare appearance, and with Kim's neighbour, Fun Donnie. Then Kim leaves to take George home.

Gord wanders by on his way back from the men's room.

"How are you girls tonight?" he says, smiling at Cindy and me.

"Fine," we say in union.

He keeps on walking.

"That's all I get," I sigh to Cindy, who pats my shoulder.

"Jane, my old buddy Rob is here. I have to fix you up with him." Kim has snuck back out of the house after George fell asleep. She seems to have a lot of old friends.

"He's the nicest guy, but he's never had much luck with women."

I don't doubt it.

Rob is a big bald guy in his mid-fifties. Kim drags him over and we dance together for a couple of songs. I can't tell if he's drunk or just a terrible dancer. I'm self-conscious and uncoordinated. He doesn't seem interested, and I'm not enthralled with him, either. But I'd seen Gord up dancing and don't want him thinking I'm a wallflower.

In an effort to make conversation, Rob and I begin going through our databanks looking for mutual friends. Rob spits out Sean's name.

"I used to date him," I say, although I'm still not sure if you'd really call our brief fling dating.

Rob peers down at me.

"This lessens my opinion of you."

"It was a big mistake, and it only lasted a few minutes."

Why do I blurt this stuff out? I've never even told Kim about Sean. Why am I telling my sad story to a stranger in a bar?

We sway to the music in a drunken manner and every once in a while he wraps his arms around me in a rather comforting bear hug. Just when I'm starting to feel like he has a rather heartwarming, gentle-giant quality about him, the song ends and he flees across the room like Superman getting away from kryptonite.

Fun Donnie comes over to visit us. He makes a fuss over me, which my battered ego badly needs. He keeps leaning across Cindy to toast me.

He shakes my hand and holds it, flirting outrageously. It's completely innocent; Donnie is happily married.

"You are wonderful. You would be perfect for my son, who is thirty-five and lives in Toronto."

"I would be more than happy to date your son, but I love Owen Sound."

"It must get lonely, being married to a town."

"Sometimes."

I think about my years in Toronto. Would I be happily married with children if I'd stayed? I'd had some good times and I cherish those memories. But nothing compares to waking up in this beautiful place.

The band wraps up at midnight. I've pumped sufficient Diet Coke through my system to drive Cindy home.

"I love you!" Donnie calls out as we walk to the door.

"I love you, too."

I'd originally planned to drive out to Mom and Dad's on Christmas Eve so I won't have to wake up alone on Christmas morning. But, by the time I get back from the bar, it's late. And I don't want to wake up with a hangover at my parent's place. And Shelly, who hates dogs, has banned Wanker from the festivities. I feel bad abandoning my best friend on Christmas; at least this way we can spend some time together in the morning before I leave him alone for the day. I take him for an early morning walk and then drive out to the farm.

Mom, Dad and I open our stockings and a few of our gifts. We attempt to snowshoe, but it's so cold we can't stay out for long. I begin the big job of helping Mom get ready for dinner, peeling potatoes and onions, chopping carrots and celery, carrying chairs to the basement and setting the table.

Around noon Mom and I drive over to Nana and Alph's for a visit. Dad has been ploughing the roads all night and is taking an afternoon nap before the grandkids' Christmas carnage is thrust upon us.

Nana is rolling out dough for cinnamon buns on her big kitchen table; the old farmhouse smells delicious, like a vanilla-and-cinnamon-filled bakery.

Alf is wearing a green sweatshirt with a patchwork wreath embroidered on it. The wreath has teeny embedded Christmas lights that light up. Alf, who suffers from Alzheimer's, doesn't talk much these days, but he smiles warmly when he sees me.

Aunt Myrt and Uncle Harry and a few other family members are joining my grandparents for dinner. We'd had to split off from the older generation a few years ago when Shelley's brood grew too loud for the older folks to tolerate.

When we get home there's been a call from Shelly. Steven's sick. We need to bring dinner to their place so he can stay in bed without missing Christmas.

We lug the turkey, potatoes, salads, squash, dressing, corn, cranberries and desserts out to Mom's minivan, which she'd purchased for transporting the grandkids. We buckle the turkey into one of the car seats. Sitting upright, it looks like a bald naked toddler covered in goosebumps.

With Steve sick in bed, chaos reigns at their house.

I've given Madison a Happenin' Hair Barbie, not realizing she'd also told two other aunts, one cousin and her grandmother that she wanted one. She's snagged five of them. Now she's busy hacking off their hair—with real scissors rather than the little orange fake pair that comes with the kit—converting the dolls into a harem of Hari Krishna Barbies.

Dad and I concentrate on building a complicated Lego Star Wars droid fighter. Madison has just unwrapped her most coveted present, an Easy Bake oven, and keeps howling "I want to use it nowwww" at the top of her lungs.

Dad and I are enlisted to work on all the toys that require assembly, a job that requires the patience of a saint and an advanced degree in mechanical engineering. Meanwhile Mom's in the kitchen getting supper ready.

I've given Billy a fire engine loaded with all the bells, whistles and sirens I could find. It's competing with Maddie's chattering Furby for the Noisiest Gift of the Day award. Luckily, the Discman from Mom and Dad can be played through headphones.

We get Maddie's toy oven hooked up, and there's a brief moment of peace and harmony when she takes our cake orders. Then Billy's fire truck collides with the droid fighter and it breaks into several pieces. Billy's so upset he pushes over the Christmas tree and breaks several ornaments that had been passed down for generations. I give up on the toy Pokémon camera I'm trying to put batteries in and head to the kitchen in search of some Baileys Irish Cream for my coffee.

After supper we put a video of the old *How The Grinch Stole Christmas* cartoon in the VCR. I roll up my sleeves and fill up the dishwasher with Christmas plates, scrubbing at the rest by hand.

At eight I think I'd better get home for Wanker, who hates peeing in a litter box and is most likely hopping about the kitchen with his stubby legs crossed.

For years I've gone through this routine with the kids where I pretend not to like hugs or kisses. It's a cheesy bit of reverse psychology, but it works every time. While my fellow family members are forced to beg and plead for a smidge of the kids' affection, I have to beat them off with a stick.

"Well," I say, as I'm getting ready to lug my exhausted carcass back home to crash on the couch. "I've given this a lot of thought and, being it's a very special day, I will let each of you give me one hug. But just one." I hold up one finger for emphasis. "And don't be trying to sneak in any extras."

They swarm me then, and I am covered in sweet baby hugs and kisses.

"But Aunt Jane," says Billy, stepping out of the melee. "The reason we like to hug you and kiss you is because we love you so much."

"I love you, too," I say. I hug him back and wonder briefly if this trick might work on adult men.

41

AFTER THE CRAZINESS of Christmas, I just want to hole up, watch movies and indulge in a little quiet time. This works well until I need to slip out for groceries in my dog-hair-encrusted sweatpants and ratty baby-spit-up-stained Mickey Mouse sweatshirt Shelly had gifted to me after Billy was born. I'm feeling fat, wearing no makeup, and my hair is styled by wind power.

It's inevitable, then, that I bump into Gord.

Making my way up the cereal aisle, I'm just dropping a pack of pink-frosted strawberry Pop-Tarts into my cart when he rounds a tower of Quaker Instant Oatmeal boxes. The "Don't let him see you like this" alarm in my head goes off so loud I wonder if the other shoppers hear it.

I look for a place to hide but Gord's cart is already on a collision course with mine. There's no time to conceal the frozen diet dinners, diet pop, dill-pickle chips, ice cream, donuts, yule-log cake and Santa gumdrops that were marked down after Christmas.

My only hope is that he won't recognize me in my hideous fat-frau garb.

Recognition registers all over his face.

"Hi," I squeak in a high, rusty pitch, like the much-aligned mouse stamped on my sweatshirt.

Gord barely nods and does not stop or even slow down. We are simply two shopping carts passing in the night.

This isn't how it's supposed to happen.

Rather than succumb to another feeding frenzy, I decide to indulge in a hot, fat-free bubble bath. I break out my Christmas Body Shop gifts and my favourite fuzzy bathrobe, turn my television to CMT and leave the bathroom door open so I can watch while I soak.

"Breathe," Faith Hill advises me.

I take her advice and feel a little better. It's not a crisis situation. I will get myself back on track and get this weight off. I still have 127 days to achieve my goal and find my soulmate before I turn forty. As luck would have it, I get an extra day because 2000 is a leap year.

I hop out of the tub and am drying off when I realize the drain is plugged again. In addition to my laundry flooding woes, the bathtub drain keeps clogging. I've been pouring clog remover down it, which clears it for a few days. Now the potent product has stopped working.

I call a plumber, who arrives 209 minutes later.

He bends over to inspect the clog. I notice his pants fit perfectly, not a crack in sight. I wonder if I should ask to see some identification. Perhaps he's an imposter.

"Where do you keep your plunger?" he asks. I hand him the one I keep under the sink.

He places it in the tub over the drain and gives it three good pushes. There's a whooshing sound and the water begins to drain.

"Who knew plungers weren't just for toilets?" I say.

He writes out a bill for $183, tears it from his pad and hands it to me.

"Do I get a discount for providing my own equipment?" I ask hopefully.

He shakes his head and is on his way. I must learn to be patient and not have a panic attack every time a mechanical failure occurs.

Feeling foolish for having wasted time and money on a small problem I should have been able to solve myself, I'm determined to fix the washing-machine issue on my own.

I throw a small load of laundry in and start the machine. Just as it reaches the last spin cycle, a geyser of brown water shoots out of the sewer hole in the centre of the cement basement floor. Either my sewer has backed up, or Old Faithful's gone underground and resurfaced in my cellar.

A small pond starts to form in the middle of the room. It spreads out to soak the carpet at the bottom of the stairs.

Panic sets in.

When I bought the house a year ago my insurance agent said I would not be covered for damage from sewer backup until I upgraded the electrical system. I have visions of my beautiful finished rec room buried under a foot of sludge.

It will cost thousands of dollars to fix. I'd barely been able to scrape up enough cash for the down payment on the house. How am I going to afford this?

Hold yourself together, Jane. Try to stay positive.

*Well, FACK does have an insolvency department. All I'll
have to do is walk downstairs to file for bankruptcy,* my pan-
icky self catastrophizes. *I'll be ruined for life and I'll never be
able to get credit or financing ever again.*

I'm freaking out. I call Dad, but there's no answer.

I call Shell, who says Steve's still sick with his Christmas
bug. I try reaching Kristen's husband, Evan, but they're not
home either. I call one of our clients who does plumbing and
electrical work. They advise me to call the city and give me
the number for the water department.

It's around ten on Saturday night when Gary the city
sewer guy shows up on my doorstep.

I want to throw my arms around him and weep into his
chest but manage (just barely) to restrain myself.

"I checked the city records for your house, and it has had
sewer problems in the past. Instead of fixing them, the prior
owners just moved on without telling you."

"Oh my god." I am about to completely unravel. "I'm single, this is my first house, I can't afford this."

"You should sue."

That's not what I want to hear.

Then Gary takes charge.

"We've got to locate the clog. If it's on your property, it's
your responsibility. If it's on the city's property, it's ours. I'm
going in there." He pulls on rubber gloves with the serious-
ness of a proctologist preparing for a rectal exam.

"Good luck," I say solemnly. And even though I'm not
Catholic, I cross myself. It seems like the right thing to do.

He works in my basement until midnight and can't find
the elusive clog. He is back with a crew at eight the next
morning.

It turns out the clog is on my property, but the city workers clear it for me anyway. They tell me I can have this one on the house, but if there is a recurrence I'll be financially responsible. They leave a gigantic hole on my front lawn, but my bank account is intact and for this I am forever grateful. Gary the city sewer worker is my new superhero.

"We only fixed the clog, Jane. We weren't able to find what caused it. You need to find a permanent solution or next time you'll have to pay the plumber piper."

"Do you know anyone who does that sort of thing?"

"I do some work with a buddy of mine on the side. We could fix it for you." He leaves me his business card.

I'm finally feeling better. What does not kill you makes you stronger. I decide not to tell my parents. Mom has always been nervous about me buying my own place. Why worry her unnecessarily?

42

THE SHOCK OF Kyle's non-proposal on Christmas threw me for a loop.

Why hadn't he given me the ring? Had Angie shown it to him for future reference? Maybe the store didn't have the right ring in stock, so it couldn't be delivered on time. Maybe he'd just put a down-payment on it.

Then I had an epiphany.

Kyle and I got together last year on New Year's Eve with that first kiss on the dance floor. He must be waiting to give me the ring on New Year's Eve to celebrate our one-year anniversary. It was brilliant and so romantic, just like Kyle. Mystery solved. I breathed a sigh of relief and settled in to savour yet another week of sweet anticipation.

Angie spent Boxing Day at her store, dealing with Christmas returns and blowout sales, then drove to Windsor to be with Xav, promising me they'd both be home for New Year's Eve.

The week passed quickly. I put my university stresses on hold and focused on reconnecting with Kyle. He seemed somewhat distracted with college projects of his own, and we weren't able to spend as much time together as I'd hoped. I chalked it up to pre-proposal jitters. We'd never talked about marriage before. Even his normally voracious sexual appetite had diminished; we had sex only once after our Christmas-night connection, when I coerced him into sloshing about in my parent's four-poster waterbed while they were off at a neighbour's card party.

Kyle decided to host our annual New Year's Eve bash at his parents' house. I spent December 31 helping to clean up, decorate and cook. Angie called in the afternoon to say she was running late and wouldn't be there until din-nertime. When she finally arrived, just as the cheesecake was being cut, she looked teary and Xav was conspicu-ously absent. I pulled her aside and asked if everything was okay.

"Xav's oldest son made it to the final round of his Silverstick Hockey tournament this year, and Xav felt he should be there for it."

"You know if you need to talk, I'm here for you," I said, giving her a hug. Although Angie and I had been friends since first grade, ours had always been a friendship based on actions rather than words. Fearless and outgoing, being surrounded by a crowd was the energy she thrived on.

The music, noise and typical New Year's Eve shenanigans took over the evening. All the while I couldn't stop obsess-ing about Kyle. *Would he propose at midnight?* It seemed like the obvious choice, but all I got from him was a big kiss and a "Happy New Year."

It was all so strange; I couldn't figure out what was going on. Had I imagined seeing him in the jewellery store that day? Every hunch I'd had so far had been wrong, but I couldn't ask Kyle and risk ruining whatever surprise he had in store for me.

On New Year's Day he came to my house to say goodbye.

I was zipping up the last of my bags for my second semester at Ryerson when I looked up and noticed him looking at me oddly.

I smiled. "We don't have time, Kyle. My bus leaves in forty-five minutes."

"Jane, I can't let you leave like this. There's something you have to know."

Surely he wasn't going to propose now. We wouldn't have time to celebrate with our families or make any plans before I went back to school.

"What is it, Kyle?" I looked into the eyes of the boy I'd known since the sixth grade and thought, "We've been through so much together. I'm ready to spend the rest of my life with him."

His words came out in a jumbled rush.

"I don't think it's working out with you so far away at school and everything. And I just think we should maybe go our separate ways for a while. But you know how much I've always cared about you, Jane, and I just really, really want us to stay good friends."

Just like that, I was transported back in time to Kelso Beach, watching helplessly as the one person I cared about more than anyone in the world told me that what we'd meant to each other was over. I knew this was another of those moments I'd never be able to forget, no matter how hard I tried.

"But I miss you so much, Kyle. I'll quit school and come home." I wouldn't let myself cry, because I knew that if I did, this would somehow become real.

"I could never ask you to do that, Jane. If you give up your dreams for me, you'll always have regrets and you'll blame me."

"But maybe my dreams are here with you."

He left before my father took me to the bus station.

• • •

That evening, while I stared out the window of the Greyhound bus on Highway 26, Kyle joined Angie and her family for their annual New Year's Day dinner at Channing's Chinese restaurant. They celebrated the Year of the Dragon. After several helpings of fried rice, egg roll, moo goo guy pan and sweet and sour chicken balls, the waiter delivered a plate of fortune cookies to the table. With a slight of hand that would have made David Copperfield proud, he presented Angie with a fortune cookie.

"Open it," Kyle urged.

She cracked open its podlike shell and unfurled the tiny message inside. A hush fell over the table as she cleared her throat and read, "Help! I'm being held prisoner in a Chinese bakery."

A perplexed Kyle walked quickly to the kitchen and returned with another fortune cookie.

Opening it, Angie promptly spat out her beef vegetable ding and threw her arms around Kyle, who reached into his pocket and pulled out the ring box.

Normally, a student at Georgian College wouldn't have been able to afford a pink emerald-cut diamond weighing in at a carat and a half, but Angie's parents had provided Kyle with more than enough financial assistance to complete the transaction.

And now they could not keep the smiles from their faces.

43

ON THE MORNING of New Year's Eve, John calls me at home.

"Jane, Elizabeth was supposed to do the inventory count for Owen Sound Motors tonight, but she got called in to her waitressing job. The New Year's Eve tips were too lucrative to pass up."

"John, I'm on vacation."

"I know you are, Jane, and I'd do it myself, but I'm at my mother-in-law's with the kids."

"John, it's New Year's Eve... of the Millennium."

"I thought you didn't have plans."

"I'm going to a house party." I didn't disclose the sad fact that it was a party for two, the two being me and Wanker, at my home.

"It will only take an hour or so, then you can go straight to your party."

"But Owen Sound Motors isn't even my client."

"I can't make Elizabeth do it; she's a partner's kid. I told the manager you'd be there when they close at five. He'll give you the inventory listing with the serial numbers for all the vehicles they have in stock at year end. You just need to select a random sample of approximately eighteen cars, go to each car and verify from the serial number that it's physically present on the lot. We're counting on you, Jane."

So, I'll be counting cars alone in an empty parking lot on the final New Year's Eve of the century.

I barely set the phone back in its cradle when it rings again. This time it's Shell.

"Billy and Madison have just come down with the flu that Steven had over Christmas. He's super busy with end-of-year car deals all day and I haven't got anything to wear for the big party tonight. Can you babysit for a few hours while I go shopping?"

Shelly and Steve will be attending a special Millennium New Year's Eve gala at the Roxy Theatre. It's going to be formal, with a big band, champagne, dinner and dancing. Originally I was supposed to go with them, but, the week before Christmas, Shell said her best friend, Mary Anne, thought it would be too weird having three couples and a single at their table, so I'd been nixed at the last minute. It was too late to find another party and I'd already told everyone I had plans.

When I get to their house in Meaford, Maddie looks green. "Why don't you go back to bed sweetie," I say, putting my hand on her forehead. She feels warm.

I fetch grape juice for Maddie and Billy, tuck them under a blanket on the rec room couch, pop a Disney movie into the VCR and settle in beside them on the recliner. Billy, who isn't sick yet, is soon bored and trots off to the toy room.

Minutes later he runs back, bearing important news.

"Aunt Jane, Kibbles just threw up." Great. Now even the cat is sick.

I hurry to the playroom with Billy just ahead of me. Halfway down the hall, he slips in a puddle of puke, falls face first onto the hardwood floor and bursts into tears.

I hug him gingerly until he stops crying, strip him down and put him in the tub. I've just cleaned up the mess and settled back in the rec room with Billy in fresh clothes when Madison says, "I don't feel good, Aunt Jane."

Before I can ask where it hurts, she spews regurgitated purple grape juice all over my new khaki linen cargo pants.

Now it's my turn to strip. I pull on a pair of Steve's old grey track pants and throw my pants in the garbage. They are beyond resuscitation.

"I guess it's just you and me, then, kiddo," I tell Billy once I've gotten Madison cleaned up and tucked in her bed. The two of us play Hungry, Hungry Hippos until Shell returns with a beautiful new cocktail dress.

On my way home I make a quick stop at Walmart. There's a sale on portable generators and bottled water. In the checkout line, the woman in front me has two flashlights, multiple candles and twenty-one cans of pork and beans. I hope that, in the event of an emergency, I do not get trapped in a bunker with someone who's recently consumed massive quantities of canned beans. I'm buying a deep-dish meat lovers' pizza, cheese-flavoured nachos, tropical-mix jelly bellies and a vanilla-bean mascarpone cheesecake with chocolate sauce on the side. If the world is really going to end tonight, this is how I want to go out. And if the world continues to spin at its current rate, I'll start my lifestyle change, no more dieting—that's so nineties—at midnight. New millennium, new me.

When I get to Owen Sound Motors at five it's already dark outside. I do the necessary calculations to come up with the list of vehicles I'll need to physically verify as part of the inventory audit test. Now I just have to locate them on the lot. Al, the parts department guy, helps me find each one, and I shine a flashlight on the windshield to check that the serial number matches our listing. I pencil in a checkmark to indicate the work I've done, a process in auditing referred to as ticking and bopping. With wind chill the temperature has dropped to below minus ten, and I can feel my fingers starting to freeze in the thin leather gloves I'd worn to facilitate note-taking. Frost and ice cover the serial numbers on several windshields. Al helps me chisel it off with an ice scraper.

I want to wrap things up, but there are two vehicles we can't find: a 1999 Ford Taurus and an ancient Volkswagen Rabbit. We track down the Taurus on a hoist in the service department. We search high and low for the sneaky Rabbit but can't find it anywhere. I feel sorry for Al, who's been extremely patient even though I'm sure he's anxious to get home to his family. I photocopy the invoicing and related paper work for the Rabbit; we'll have to look into it later.

I return home to my feast. I'd rented a movie about a lonely ticketbooth operator who meets her future fiancé when she rescues him from a speeding streetcar. Then I tune in to Dick Clark's countdown to the arrival of the new millennium from Times Square in New York City.

Celebrations from countries around the globe are being broadcast, and it appears that the world will go on. No airplanes fall from the sky, elevators do not plummet and my hydro does not go out.

I gain two and a half pounds and kiss my dog at midnight.

44

KIM CALLS ME just before noon on New Year's day. "Paula and I are at the Legion enjoying a couple of cocktails. Come on over."

I squeeze into my biggest pair of Northern Traditions relaxed-fit size-12 jeans.

At the Legion Kim and Paula are waiting for me at a corner table. They're discussing Paula's retirement plans.

"But you're too young to retire," I tell her.

"Well, I'm eligible to start my pension next year."

Apparently, people who work at companies that provide pension plans are able to do this.

It's obvious they have a few drinks under their belts and have been talking about me. I wonder if I should be worried.

"Jane," Paula says, clearing her throat. "The reason I never got married is because I'm too bossy and men don't like that."

"You're not bossy."

At least I've never known Paula to be bossy. She's a powerhouse when it comes to getting things done, and I've always admired that about her.

"Sit your ass down so Kim and I can sort out your man problem."

"Yes, ma'am."

Okay, maybe she is a little on the forceful side.

"We've decided you're going to play darts with me this year," Paula says. "They're starting a league Wednesday night at the Frog. Everyone throws in two bucks, then you draw names for a partner."

"That's a massive cost savings. I almost paid two hundred dollars for a partner at the bachelor auction."

"Have you ever played darts before?"

"No, and based on my lack of athleticism and coordination, it sounds somewhat dangerous."

"Don't worry. We're going to teach you right now, and I live three blocks from your house, so we can take turns driving."

"We're taking on the job of finding amen for you." Kim's starting to slur her words.

"Can I get a hallelujah as well," I say and clink my beer bottle against hers.

Sensei Paula and Sensei Kim proceed to instruct me in the ways of the dart.

"Be the dart, Jane, be the dart," hoots Kim as I nick a bulletin board, wall clock and bottle of rye sitting on the bar. My darts pierce every available surface with the exception of the actual dartboard.

"It's all fun and games until somebody loses an eye," I say.

Kim and Paula are an industrious pair; they get things done and I like them a lot. I tell them about my birthday pact to find my soulmate before I turn forty, which is on the first of May.

"We can help you out with that, but you've got to promise not to put your life on hold for tax season again this year," Kim says. "The partners think that since you're not married they own you."

"I'll do my best to keep caught up and not get too stressed."

"But that's the problem. You have to stop searching for the Land of All-caught-up. It's a mythical place where accountants can never dwell. If you're always thinking, 'I'll have more time for myself when I'm caught up,' it will never happen and life will pass you by. As soon as you finish all of the jobs you're currently working on, the partners will give you more. And they don't pay you overtime, so the more you work, the more money they get. It's as simple as that."

It's the first time I've really thought about it like that. I've been so busy working for Chaos Incorporated, I'd lost track of time. And where has it gotten me? Stuck in the black hole of the dating universe hurtling toward Planet 40.

We all sit quietly, contemplating our beers for a moment.

"Well, it's no good sitting in a corner. Nobody's going to see you back here," Paula announces. With our meeting officially adjourned, we wander over to the bar.

Kim's friend Rob from last Saturday arrives. Sober, he seems very nice, although I don't detect any sparks igniting between us.

Kim tells everybody that I'm going to play darts because "we have to find a sport for Jane."

"Are darts a sport?" I ask.

Rob says, "I can think of a sport for her."

In a brief moment of insanity, I drive by Sean's house on my way home. His car is parked, facing the street, at the foot of the driveway, as though it's about to go somewhere.

When I get home I see he's left a message on my answering machine. "Hi, Jane, it's Sean. I just called to wish you a Happy New Year. Sorry I haven't heard from you lately."

I want desperately to call him, but I've gained so much weight I can't bear to have him see me looking like this.

I'm exhausted. I take a long, hot shower, which causes my laundry room to flood again.

• • •

In January the partners do their annual performance reviews. Enormously pregnant Anne emerges from her evaluation fuming after being berated for not having enough chargeable hours in 1999. I'd managed to sneak a peek at Lori's chargeable hours' spreadsheet, so I know I have the third highest chargeable hours in the office behind John and Katie, who both work insane hours and never use up their vacation time because they want to be partners one day. I've logged over two hundred chargeable hours more than Anne. I figure my job evaluation will be stellar and guarantee a decent raise.

It starts off well enough. Joe and Sam tell me how wonderful I am and how they're happy with my hours. Then they ask if there's anything else they can do for me.

"Do you think I can have one of the 486 computers we're not using anymore?"

FACK is constantly getting new computers in an effort to make us more productive. As a result they have thirty desktops from 1997 in the attic collecting dust. I hope to snag one, partly for personal use but also so I can occasionally work from home.

"I was hoping to be able to work at home sometimes instead of having to come to the office every night and weekend during tax season."

"Everybody wants those computers," Joe says. "We're selling them for $187 each. We'll put your name at the top of the list."

There are days when I believe I work for the cheapest people on the face of the earth.

• • •

"I'm depressed about my birthday," Lori says as, clipboard in hand, she plunks herself beside my desk on her Monday-morning rounds. "Both my parents are gone now, and my sister is busy this year. It looks like it's going to be an alone birthday for me."

"Maybe Cindy and I could take you out for lunch," I suggest.

But Lori isn't done. She has some wisdom to impart.

"Birthdays are bad for me now, Jane. I'm speaking from experience when I tell you, you've got some rough years ahead."

"But I've always enjoyed my birthday."

"They're not much fun when you're going through the change of life and dear Aunt Flo from Red River stops dropping by. That's when you're forced to accept that you're never going to get married or have children."

First the dentist episode, now this. Beyond words, I just stare at her.

Obtuse Lori has no idea how much hurt she's just dispensed. It's the second time in less than a month I've heard "You're never going to have children." Depression, like a fine grey mist, steams up from under my door and filters in through my windows. It will cling to me like a heavy cloud for the rest of the day.

"Well, cheerio then," chirps Lori. All smiles, having unburdened herself, she buzzes off to the next office, oblivious to the devastation left in her wake.

Barely breathing, I make a beeline for Kim's cubicle for some motherly reassurance.

"That's ridiculous. Don't listen to Lori. You've got lots of time to get married and have a family." Kim administers a comforting hug.

But people who do math for a living cannot ignore hard deadlines. There's no denying that time is running out for me.

My thoughts return to Lori and her remarks on the "change of life."

Menopause, I realize, will mark the end of my period's period.

Period.

45

THE BUS RIDE from Owen Sound back to Toronto on New Year's Day 1982 was one of the longest of my life. Devastated by Kyle's rejection, I had no idea I'd lost my two best friends simultaneously.

But nothing in Grey County stays a secret for long.

On Wednesday afternoon, my dad ploughed the driveway of our neighbour, old Mrs. Michelson. This prompted her son to drop by to say thank you. During his visit he mentioned his wife had heard from Lynn down at the bank that Angie and Kyle got engaged over the holidays, and didn't that seem strange because he'd thought Kyle and I were going steady?

My parents didn't know what to do. I'd been so upset when I left for school, they didn't want to heap more hurt and humiliation onto my already-overburdened shoulders. Eventually the problem was solved when Angie herself called to tell me the news.

"I know you guys liked each other, Jane, but Kyle has always been my soulmate." She was clarifying. "We were just meant to be together. You know I've loved him since the sixth grade." They were getting married in June, and she hoped I would be a bridesmaid.

I played that phone conversation over and over in my head. I thought of all the things I should have said. I should have told her that Kyle and I were still having sex right up until he proposed and that he'd told me I was the first woman he'd ever loved. But I couldn't get the words out, and they festered in my head for the longest time.

I hosted a bridal shower for Angie that May.

At school things got worse. My marks became average: mostly Cs with an occasional B. I was confident that if I worked hard I would graduate. But would I be able to support myself with a degree in fashion? In a world where who you knew meant everything, I knew no one. My personality, introverted as it was, seemed to disappear in the presence of my sociable classmates, who fearlessly fought for the attention they'd need to carve out a career in this uber-competitive industry.

Then the economy plunged into its darkest recession since the great depression, making it extremely difficult for new graduates to find jobs in any field. I wrote my exams at the end of April and passed every course but remained uncertain as to my future.

For the first time in years, I had no answer to the question "What are you going to be when you grow up?" My parents were anxious, and my mother made no bones about letting me know they did not intend to support me forever. For once in my life, I did not have a plan.

In June, Angie walked down the aisle of St. John's United Church in a taffeta ivory dress. It resembled Lady Dianna's wedding gown, with its puffy sleeves and long train. I had helped her sew several hundred tiny sequined beads into the bodice. Although her train was nowhere near as long as Lady Di's twenty-five-footer, it did have a tent-like quality. Angie had embroidered a "K" for Kyle in sequins at the bottom.

As one of four bridesmaids, I wore a dusty-rose satin gown that mirrored Angie's with its puffy balloon shoulders and plunging neckline showing ample cleavage. Instead of a train, the bridesmaids had large satin bows strategically placed over their derrieres. The dresses were hemmed in Bo Peep-style lace, and we wore a poufy crinoline under them. Pulling it all together was a pink pearl-beaded headband that culminated in a "v" just above our noses. We couldn't stop trying to find it in our line of vision, and, as a result, our eyes seemed slightly crossed in all the photos. We resembled a quartet of dyslexic shepherdess prostitutes.

Using her shop discount, Angie was able to get each ensemble for less than $150. "You can have it shortened after the wedding and wear it as a cocktail dress," she enthused.

The groomsmen wore matching dusty-pink cummerbunds and bow ties. Tall Kyle looked dapper in his white top hat, tails and a pink-and-grey-striped cravat.

Other than a brief faux pas when Angie vowed "to take thee, Xav" during the ceremony, the wedding went along wonderfully.

At the speeches afterward she burst into tears. "I'm so happy to be marrying my best friend," she blubbered in front of 250 of her closest friends and relatives.

Funny; I'd always thought the role of the best friend had belonged to me.

46

CINDY HAS RALLIED the women from FACK to take Lori out for her birthday. We're having such a good time that we decide we should have lunch together once a month. Cindy and I try to come up with a name for our new club.

"How about the FACK Bitches, because we'll have lots of bitch sessions where we get things off our chests?" Cindy suggests.

This didn't go over, so I float The Accounting Goddesses. It's not a big hit, either.

We finally agree on "The Bitchin' FACK Goddesses," which Kim abbreviates to the BFGs.

I continue to stress over my malfunctioning sewer pipe. I haven't heard from Gary the city sewer guy since the weekend he rescued me, although there's an unknown number on my call display that could be his cell phone's.

It actually feels good to be back at work. All the December year-ends are starting to pour in. I throw myself into working as hard as I can to keep from getting too far behind.

But no matter how hard I try, I can't stop thinking about Gord. He was so adorably goofy last time I saw him at the Frog. I've resolved to lose the rest of my excess weight, get my confidence back, then have a couple of drinks to screw up the courage to make a pass at him. He'll probably reject me, but I can't go on waiting and wondering.

On Friday morning I get up, work out, then drive to the Days Inn Conference Centre for a day of professional development seminars. We're scheduled to have our tax update in the morning followed by Auditing and Assurance in the afternoon. It starts out as usual, with Frank and Katie droning on about changes to the child tax benefit, new science and technology benefits for small businesses and increases in the marginal tax rates for Canadian-controlled corporations. I look out the window and imagine what the offspring of Gord and me might look like.

Then it's Larry's turn to talk about the government's new farm-relief programs. I wonder what's on the menu for lunch and whether Gord has shaved off his new moustache yet.

Larry slaps a set of financial statements on the overhead screen behind him and I come back to reality with a thud. I'm horrified as I realize they're the financial statements I'd prepared for Le Cara Dell Farms last fall. Larry hasn't bothered to erase my initials, which are in bold caps across the top righthand corner of the screen; everyone in the room knows exactly whose work is on display here. I sink a little deeper into my chair and wait.

Larry spends eighteen minutes ripping my work apart, complaining about the extra effort he'd had to make to extract the information required for the farm forms. He even points out that $233 of bad debt expense had been incorrectly lumped in with the office expenses.

It's a not an audit, for Christ's sake. We're not supposed to analyze the expenses when preparing compilation engagements. And the client's records had been a nightmare; the banks had never been reconciled and Dean had needed the job done at the last minute.

I feel tears forming, but I'm determined not to cry in front of the entire office. What is Larry's problem? Why is he behaving like such a world-class prick?

I feel humiliated. My ears burn through the rest of the morning presentations.

Of course, at lunch I get stuck at a table with Larry. Anne sits on my right, so I turn my back on Larry and talk to her.

I manage to get through John's auditing presentation in the afternoon. I think everyone knows how upset I am. Who would do such a shitty thing?

As we're getting ready to leave I hold everybody up as I fumble to put my coat on; I mutter my apologies. Sensing my discomfort, John jokily body-slams me. Lori tells him that's in direct violation of the new "Respect" program we've talked about during the Human Resources update.

"Next time I'll hit her with a chair instead," he grins.

"That may not be considered respectful, either," I say. "But you're too late. I've already been savaged."

I appreciate their attempts to cheer me up, but what a horrible start to the new year. Sewage is spewing into my basement, darts are a drag, my coworkers are using my work as an example of ineptitude, and I'm single and fat and have less than three months to find the father of my children. It all seems too hopeless.

Kim doesn't suggest the meat raffles for tonight; perhaps she's given up on me already, as I am such a loser.

I need a quiet weekend to regroup, lick my wounds and come up with a new plan. At least I haven't binged on junk food yet.

I'm still reeling from the day when, without thinking, I throw in a load of laundry. The laundry room floods immediately.

It's the last straw. I'm probably going to lose my job, because what employee has a whole half-hour presentation devoted to how bad their work is, and my life savings has been blown on this money pit.

I find the number for Gary the sewer guy and keep my voice reasonably calm on the phone.

"My friend and I haven't got our sewer camera back from the shop yet, but we could come over next weekend and look into your pipes," he suggests.

"Unfortunately, I can't wait that long. They're clogged again."

He recommends another plumber, who comes over immediately.

With her special sewer camera, she's able to look way out into the farthest reaches of the pipe and discovers that the root of my problem is, in fact, roots. Apparently, many years ago a big oak tree had graced my front lawn. A previous owner had chopped it down, but beneath the surface the roots kept on growing. Continuously searching for water, they'd forced their way through the seams of the ancient copper pipe.

Looking into the camera, I see a single tampon that, on its journey out to sea, had become entangled in the invasive tree roots. I give a silent prayer of thanks I've hired a female plumber.

"Your pipes are in reasonably good condition," she says. "You could pay a few thousand dollars to have the copper pipe replaced with the new polyvinyl stuff, but a good root killer, purchased once a year for a few dollars at your local hardware store, will likely keep your flow going."

"That's the best news I've heard all week."

"And, of course, no more flushing feminine-hygiene products."

47

WHEN ANGIE AND Kyle returned to their wedding reception in matching cream-coloured going-away ensembles, I knew it was time for me to disappear as well. There was simply no way I could spend the summer in the shadow of their newly wedded bliss.

To add insult to injury, I soon discovered that when couples break up, their former friends declare allegiance to one party or the other. One poor soul always loses custody. While I'd been off at Ryerson, my old high school chums had grown accustomed to socializing without me. When I came home for the wedding it didn't occur to me that I might not be welcomed back with open arms. Instead I began hearing after the fact of movie nights and dinners and other events where my name had apparently been left off the guest list. It was just too weird for Angie, Kyle and I to be together as a trio. Something had to give, and I'd always been the generous one.

As luck would have it, I'd rented an apartment in Toronto with five other roommates for the fall. In order to keep my spot, I'd had to pay for it over the summer anyway. To put some physical distance between me and everything that had happened, I slunk back to Toronto before the new Mr. and Mrs. Jackson had left the heart-shaped honeymoon hot tubs of the Poconos behind.

Oddly enough, the person I missed the most during this time was Christopher Graham. Going home for the wedding, I'd asked various friends and family members if they'd heard how he was doing. Rumour had it he was enjoying life in Montreal and had chosen to spend the summer there.

On impulse I stopped by his family house, where his mom gave me a welcoming hug and his phone number in Montreal. But, try as I might, I couldn't summon the courage to call him.

One of my favourite ways to destress during university was prowling about Toronto's multitude of vintage shops. From Queen Street West to Kensington Market, I'd spent many a happy hour sifting through racks of vintage clothing, jewellery and accessories. Give me twenty-five dollars and I could put together a fabulous ensemble and still have money for a 45 at Sam the Record Man and a rocky-road ice-cream cone from Scoops.

When one of my favourite shops, the Unique Boutique, offered me a job that summer, I jumped at it. The chore I liked best at the store was sorting the merchandise that came in. One woman's junk is another's treasure, and some designer duds arrived with the tags still on them.

While I loved the clothes and the work and the pay-cheques, the customers often frightened me. Some were wonderful, and I got to know the regulars, but I hated the complainers and the barterers who fought tooth and nail over every price point. My introverted self felt drained by the arrogant know-it-alls, hagglers and shoplifters.

While department stores saw profits plummet during the recession of the early eighties, vintage clothing stores benefited from the new frugality forced on some consumers. As Unique Boutique expanded to meet its growing niche market, the store's elderly bookkeeper was growing frazzled trying to keep its manual ledgers up to date. Grateful for a chance to get off the store floor, I was happy to offer my assistance. Much to my surprise, working with numbers came naturally to me and I enjoyed the challenge of balancing the books.

When September rolled around and the shop's manager offered me a full-time job with benefits, dropping out of university seemed like the obvious choice. Giving up on my dream of a career in fashion, I felt like a small child letting go of a balloon. Watching it float away, I told myself it was only temporary, something fun to try until I'd worked out a new way to make a living doing something creative. Living in a dynamic city like Toronto, with an endless stream of roommates coming and going, would be my new adventure.

But after a year eking out a living on just over six dollars an hour, I figured out I'd never be able to afford a car, or a place of my own, or much of anything without furthering my education. I began taking courses part-time in the business administration program at York University. Like so many eighties yuppies, I majored in accounting and finance. It was a far cry from the creative, artistic path I'd always dreamed of. Scared and alone, I found myself craving stability in a way I never had before. I didn't have a boyfriend, and moving back home had never been an option. Starving artists often found it difficult to pay the rent, but no one had heard of a starving accountant.

I threw myself into studying with renewed determination.

48

ON WEDNESDAY MORNING I wake to find there's been a huge dump of snow during the night. The roads are a mess. At seven-thirty, I hear the loud grind of a blade scraping my driveway. My dad, who's been out all night ploughing in the county, has enlisted one of his buddies to put my driveway on his morning route.

I put Wanker in his down-filled red puffer vest and try to take him for a walk before work, but for a small dog the tall drifts are as insurmountable as the Himalayas. With considerable difficulty he climbs up the first drift only to sink like a stone when he reaches its peak. I see the situation is hopeless and scoop him up to carry him back to the safety of the warm house.

I drive to work following the path left by the snow plough until 6th Street. I manage to navigate the treacherous hill and finally pull into the office parking lot.

The Montgomery Lawrence merger renovations are finally complete, so I spend the morning moving into my new office on the second floor. It isn't huge, but it's close to

Kim and Cindy, with a nice view of the open back parking lot. I take a minute to get myself a cup of black decaf and enjoy the sight of falling snow outside my window.

Anne, who's been given a similar office, is furious that both John's and Katie's new offices are bigger than hers. She spends the morning searching for a measuring tape, which confirms that her office is indeed seven square inches smaller than John's and 5.5 square inches smaller than Katie's.

She's livid. "I'm not happy. I'm so looking for another job."

Anne uttered these exact words to me on my first day at FACK and I've heard them many times since. I wish she'd do us all a favour and follow through.

Shelly calls to complain that the schools are closed due to the snow storm, so the kids are home with her. It's only 10 a.m. and already they're driving her crazy.

Why, I wonder, do parents feel the need to continuously complain about their offspring to people who would give everything to have just one child? Is this not the equivalent of saying to a fasting Gandhi, "Gee, I shouldn't have pigged out on all that cheesecake; I feel so bloated"?

And why is having to spend time with your children such a colossal inconvenience? Surely when you're giving birth to the second child, or optimally at some time prior to its conception, it might occur to you that there will be times when you might, in fact, be required to spend time with them? And as to there being so much work involved, wouldn't you get some inkling, after the first one, as to time and effort needed and simply double that, now that you're expecting again? Surely even non-accountants can do this simple math?

"If all the schools are closed and everything else is closed, why is your office still open?" Shelly wants to know.

"I work for an accounting firm," I explain patiently. "The partners make their profits based on how many of our hours they can bill out; thus public accounting firms rarely close."

"But everything else in Meaford and Owen Sound is closed."

"Joe still brags about how last January, when most of Ontario was shut down by that heavy snow storm, he made it in to the office. The schools were closed, the hospital was closed, the roads were closed, and Toronto's mayor had to call in the army to dig the city out, but Joe was at the office assuring clients that their year-ends were still getting done; because, at FACK, client service comes first.

"We could be in the seventh stage of the apocalypse, with fires and floods ravaging the city, and FACK accountants would be in the office, summing ledgers by candlelight. I believe Joe still keeps a box of abacuses and tea lights in the attic just in case such a situation should arise."

I've barely hung up when Kim breezes into my office.

"Rusty's on the phone. He wants to know if you and Paula can sell meat raffle tickets in two weeks."

Rusty is actually Wayne Russell, a fifty-something jock/millwright who works at Bruce Nuclear Generating Station. Rusty is in charge of running the meat raffles for the Grey Bruce Children's Foundation. Everyone calls him Rusty because:

a) He has thick reddish-brown hair, and
b) The name "Wayne" does not suit his spark-plug personality.

"Sure, I have no life. I can sell tickets anytime," I tell her.

She jogs back to her office and returns five minutes later.

"I gave him your message verbatim. He laughed and said he's in the same boat."

Funny; I always thought Rusty had a girlfriend.

I'm not in the mood to play darts that night and hope they'll be cancelled due to the weather, but it's business as usual. It's odd how many people can't manage to get to work in a snowstorm but are fine fighting through the flakes to get to the bar. The snow's falling heavily again, and the roads are a mess. I draw the short straw and get Bart for my partner.

We lose every game. I've been playing in the league for three weeks now and have yet to win a game. Perhaps Paula and Kim are wrong about darts being my sport.

As Cindy discovered on their infamous blind date, conversation with Bart is a workout. Questions yield monosyllabic answers. I'm dying to ask how Gord is doing, but my shyness holds me back.

"I'm lonely. My son is away playing hockey and I'm living alone for the first time in my life." He finally opens up a little.

"Living alone has its advantages." Was I trying to convince him or me?

"My house is too big for me."

"You live in a two-bedroom semi-detached."

I sit with Bart for all three games. When they're mercifully over he picks up his beer and shuffles back to the bar. There may be a soft guy underneath that crusty layer, but I really have to learn to just say no. I hope this whole darts deal isn't some scheme Kim has cooked up to get me and Bart together. So far he's the only single male I've met here.

I wait around for a while in case Gord puts in an appearance, but he doesn't. Has he given up the Barking Frog as part of his New Year's resolutions? Does he have a new girlfriend?

• • •

Shelly decides she needs to get away for the weekend and recruits me to babysit Billy while Maddie stays with her grandmother. He comes to my place for a sleepover and we go for a swim at the Y, visit the playland at McDonalds, get a toy at Walmart and watch a movie we rented.

When he wakes up the next morning I'm on the phone with Kristen. He goes to the fridge and helps himself to what he thinks is a tub of chocolate pudding.

Inserting a gargantuan spoonful into his mouth, he discovers it is in fact my favourite kefir plain probiotic yogurt. He signals urgently that he needs to spit it out.

I point to the bathroom and he runs to it, yogurt spilling from the container in great globs.

I hang up. There is no sign of Billy in the bathroom, other than yogurt goop on the suit jacket and skirt I've just picked up from the dry cleaner. He must have wiped his mouth on them.

I find him in the kitchen, smiling triumphantly. He's located the real chocolate pudding and has managed to eat an entire cup without a spoon. There's more on his face than in his belly.

He looks up at me and buries his little chocolate-covered face in my jeans.

"I love you, Aunt Jane."

"I love you too, charming Billy." I kiss the top of his head and wipe a brown smudge I really hope is pudding off my pants.

The drive back to Meaford that Sunday afternoon is dazzling. The sun, shining down on the white snow, stands out starkly against the blue sky; icicles drip from the barren tree branches. I reach into the back seat and tousle Billy's hair. Even in the dead of winter, there are moments so beautiful they slice right through you.

49

"**HAVE YOU HEARD** the latest?" Lori's doing her Monday-morning rounds and sharing her news.

Evidently, I have not.

"Frank was supposed to give a tax talk as one of the speakers at the Chamber of Commerce business forum on Friday. He didn't show up for his one o'clock time slot and nobody knew where he was."

"That's awful. Were they able to find him?"

"John called his wife to see if he was at home. She said he's been spending a lot of time in the back-corner booth of the Coach Inn."

"That's where he was?"

"Yes."

"Oh my god. So, what happened?"

"Katie got his PowerPoint presentation going, and was doing a pretty good job of winging it, when he came bursting into the conference room completely wellied. He was so away with the fairies he could barely stand up."

"Oh, poor Katie."

"He got to the stage before anyone realized what was going on. Then he tripped over his shoelaces and fell face first into the podium. The partners pretended he was having a seizure and called 911. The paramedics came and rolled him off the stage in a stretcher."

"Is he still in the hospital?"

"No, he slept it off. He's been back in his office, reviewing a group of corporate tax returns, since 3 a.m. last night."

• • •

I'm stressed out over my rapidly approaching doomsday birthday and have put myself on a strict diet. In two weeks I'm going to be selling meat-raffle tickets to hungry-man carnivores, which will require getting back into my skinny jeans.

I keep waiting for the sewer pipe to back up in my basement again. It's been two weeks. I finally tell Dad about it when he stops by for coffee on Wednesday and wonders why it looks like someone has dug a grave on my front lawn. This afternoon he pulls into my driveway with a brand-new vacuum cleaner in the bed of his truck.

"Gee, thanks, Dad. I really needed one of those, but it's not my birthday yet."

"Think of it as a belated housewarming gift. And you know, Jane, you don't have to handle everything yourself. We're always here when you need us. That's what families are for."

"Thanks, Dad. You're the best." I give him a hug. Maybe I'm not married because, when it comes right down to it, no man could ever hold a candle to my dad. I was adamant when I bought my house that I wouldn't be a burden to my parents. Dad works so hard in the winter, and I notice his eyes look a little more tired than usual. I'm not the only one guilty of working too much overtime this time of year.

• • •

This morning I am preparing a T4 for Dr. Brayer.

Karl Brayer has been a general practitioner in Lion's Head for close to fifty years. He sold his family practice five years ago but still sees patients a couple of days a week. He needs a T4 for his one and only employee, his ancient, long-suffering nurse, Norma.

Dr. Karl isn't known for his bedside manner. It's rumoured he never had to spank the bottoms of the babies he delivered—one look at his scowling mug glaring at them through his hideous seventies-style tinted aviator glasses and they howled their tiny newborn lungs out. Some babies, it was said, were so scared they attempted to beat a retreat back up the birth canal.

The fact Dr. Brayer has been able to practice for so many years is a testament to how bad the shortage of family doctors in northern Ontario really is. And I'm lucky enough to have him as a client.

My mother had been his patient many years ago. Shortly after she got married in 1959, she mustered up all her courage and asked him to prescribe her an IUD. Her female coworkers were raving about this great new birth-control device, and she was hoping to delay having kids until she and Dad could at least afford a house.

"Why on earth would you want one of those?" he'd bellowed. Nine months later, I became one of the good doctor's aforementioned howlers. I should be grateful to the cranky old bastard. I owe him my life, after all.

In the package of payroll records he's sent over are two different sheets of paper summarizing Norma's payroll for 1999. Both calculations lead to a different number, and I have no way of knowing which set is correct. Normally I'd call the client and get clarification, but instead I choose the summary that agrees with Revenue Canada's payroll remittances and prepare the T4 based on that. Why poke a snake with a stick if you don't have to?

I fax the T4 over to Dr. Brayer's office for his inspection.

Five minutes later my phone rings.

"You've used the wrong goddamn payroll sheet. What the hell do I pay you people all this money for?"

Obviously, Karl is not mellowing with age.

I adjust the T4 to the other number, fax it back to him and wait anxiously for another call. But my phone doesn't ring for the rest of the day.

Midweek, Lori pays an unexpected visit to my office.

"Larry is looking for someone to help him with all those farm-relief forms he's doing, and we were thinking this might be an area you could get into."

Having dropped this bombshell, Lori waits expectantly for my response.

I'm still furious with Larry for performing a public vivisection on my financial statements. Now he has the nerve to think I might like to work with him?

I know that, for once, no matter how much I hate to do it, I simply have to say no.

"I'm not interested."

Kim leaves work early without saying goodbye, which is odd, because she's mentioned she might play darts with me tonight. I'm just leaving when Anne, who now has a month and a half to go before her baby arrives, stops me in the hallway.

"Is Kim okay? She and Sam had a long talk this afternoon."

"She left a while ago. Why?"

"Well, she did such a horrible job on the golf club audit this year I had to report her to Sam."

"Maybe something's wrong. Did you discuss it with her first?" Kim is an extremely conscientious worker who's been with the firm for years. I can't imagine her doing sloppy work.

"I thought it would have more impact coming from Sam."

I get home and call Cindy. "Did you hear anything about the golf club audit?"

"I guess they ran into some problems with the new computer system the club converted to this year and went way over budget on the audit. As the manager in charge, it was Anne's responsibility. Rather than take the heat for it, she's been blabbing all over the office about what a bad job Kim did. Then when Sam called Anne in to discuss what went wrong, she blamed everything on Kim."

"And Kim's been so loyal to Anne all these years."

I sigh. People like Anne make me nervous. I really hope she won't come back after the baby's born.

• • •

Having now officially lost twenty-one consecutive games, I show up for darts league without Kim for moral support. I'm paired with a guy named Ed, who owns a pub in Southsea England and is in town visiting his brother, Fun Donnie.

It's finally come to this. I'm so bad at darts they had to fly a professional in from across the pond to help out.

And it works. We actually win two games.

Ed is a riot. We laugh, we hug, and he tells me his life story. Then he gives me his business card. "Look me up if you're ever in England."

"I'll always remember you, Ed. You're the first person I ever won a game of darts with."

"Too bad I have to go back home at the end of the week."

Walking to the bar to fetch us another beer, I glance up and spot Gord. Flushed and in a glorious mood from losing twelve pounds, making a new friend and being buoyed by my first victory, my confidence has come storming back. I wave at Gord.

Gord waves back. We're on a roll.

I return for the final set, determined to sit down with Gord and chat him up the second we're finished. I have three beers, get lots of attention from my new English friend, and we win yet another match. I'm psyched.

I turn around to scan the bar. Gord's sitting at a table in the corner. A woman with long blonde hair is sitting in his lap, looking into his eyes, hanging on every word he says.

Deflating faster than a popped balloon, I pay my tab and leave.

50

FIRST THING THURSDAY morning an email comes in from the partners calling an emergency staff meeting in the boardroom. I look to my sources, Cindy, Lori and Anne, to see if they know what's going on. They have no idea.

For once, everyone arrives on time. (Anne, perpetually punctually challenged, is only a minute late.) Fiona has put the phone system on Hold-all-calls mode and sits by the door in case a client comes by.

Our beloved tax manager Katie sits at the head of the long table with tax partner Frank to her right. The rest of the partners look on from their high-backed black executive chairs. The vast white projector screen behind them is blank and no information sheets are being circulated.

No one is smiling.

When everyone has quieted, Katie stands up to speak, seems to think better of it, and sits down.

Instead, Joe leads off. "We've brought you all here today because an unfortunate situation has come up and Katie wanted to tell you about it."

Tiny Katie looks even thinner than usual, her collar-bone protruding through her thin peach cardigan and dark smudges under her eyes. Frank also has a deathly pallor. His fingers are shaking so bad he spills his coffee on the mahogany table. Katie dabs at it absentmindedly with a Kleenex, clears her throat and waits again until the room is silent.

"I was diagnosed with colorectal cancer last week."

A collective gasp ripples around the table, like Jays fans doing the wave at the Skydome.

"It's fairly serious, but I've always been feisty and I believe I can beat it. My doctors have prescribed an aggres-sive treatment plan. I will be undergoing endoscopic surgery to remove the tumour. After that I will have several rounds of chemotherapy. I may have to have a colostomy as well, but the surgeon won't know that until he operates.

"As you all know, tax season is just a few short weeks away, and I feel bad about leaving you all in the lurch like this. My doctor has forbidden me from coming to the office and taking work home with me; basically, I am not allowed to do work of any kind. If I'm going to beat this thing, I've got to give it 100 per cent."

A stunned silence falls over the room. I know without looking that I'm not the only one tearing up. Kim throws her arms around Katie and hugs her tightly.

Joe clears his throat and turns to address us.

"Katie is just clearing a few things off her desk and call-ing some clients, but she will be leaving by the end of the day tomorrow. Frank is going to be pulling double duty this tax season, and everyone will have to pitch in and help him get through it. We're all rooting for you, Katie, and I'm sure

I speak for everybody here when I say if there's anything we can do to help, just let us know."

I think about Katie taking tax returns home on her maternity leave and filling in for Frank when he was too drunk to meet with clients. She's been covering for him for over a decade. How is he ever going to cope without her? *Oh, Katie.*

I hug her goodbye. "Stay strong. I just know you're going to be okay."

I'm still stunned by Katie's news on Friday evening as I help Paula set up for a Haven House fundraiser at the Legion. My job is to help Paula put together an indoor miniputt course with equipment that's seen better days. We unroll dozens of strips of faded-green AstroTurf and battered obstacles. I'm grateful to be out of the office.

I sit with Paula, the janitor lady, and a nice elderly gentleman and relax with a diet pop when they take a break at a table, drinking and smoking.

Alex Ignatowski, a long-time Owen Sound city councillor, drops in. I know of Alex. I've seen him at various events around town, and his picture appears in the *Sun Times* fairly regularly, but I've never met him. Immediately I summarize his vital statistics: mid-forties, barely five feet tall, extremely friendly, heavy Romanian accent. His unruly brown hair looks as though he cuts it himself.

I'm not sure why he's there, but he knows Paula, and she invites him to join us.

"What've you got there, Alex?" she asks, indicating a large cardboard folder tucked under his arm. It's crammed with papers that are sticking out every which way. In his other hand he holds a battered leather briefcase the same chestnut colour as Wanker's coat; the case has a tarnished, broken lock.

"These are my signup sheets and team information for the Big Walk for Cancer in June. Last year the team I put together won first prize for raising the most money. I want to win again this year."

The word "cancer" immediately brings my thoughts back to Katie saying her tearful goodbyes that afternoon.

Alex talks and talks. He keeps glancing in my direction, and eventually Paula introduces us.

At first I'm quiet. When I finally join the conversation Alex is attentive, chain-smoking and hanging on my every word. He keeps getting up to leave and saying, "No, I'm just going to stay for one more cigarette."

"It's time we got back to work," bossy-pants Paula announces after his third failed attempt at departure.

"It was lovely to meet you Jane," he says, holding out his hand.

"Likewise," I say, shaking it.

"That Alex. Once you get him started talking, he never stops," Paula says after the door shuts behind him.

"A true politician."

I hope I get a chance to see Alex again when I drive out to the annual Groundhog Day Festivities in Wiarton tomorrow.

Much as I love our seasonal celebration, Willie's predictions regarding the coming of spring mean nothing to me. On February 2 all Canadian accountants have twelve weeks and five days until they're allowed to welcome spring. Revenue Canada has the power to override all prognosticating rodents. Work is crazy hectic already. It's only the first week of February and John has hinted three times I should start working overtime.

I reach Willie's base camp before 7 a.m. — plenty of time to see the festival officials decked out in formal Victorian clothes. I glance casually around for Councillor Alex, but I don't see him. Maybe he only participates in City of Owen Sound activities.

Anticipation is building, but when the mayor of Wiarton taps on Willie's cage he doesn't stir. The crowd waits with bated breath and the mayor taps again.

Still nothing.

The crowd begins to grow restless and my coffee is getting cold. I glance anxiously at my watch. I really should be getting back to the office soon. At this rate even Anne will get to work before me.

The mayor takes the stage and announces that the poor creature has passed away. Perhaps the job stress was too much for wee Willie, everyone's hopes riding on his tiny albino shoulders. All is not lost, however. Organizers inform us he's left his prediction for an early spring in his will. The search is now on to find the son of Wiarton Willie in hopes he will be able to carry on the legacy.

I wonder why, since everyone is dressed up anyway, they don't hold a funeral for him. The top-hat and tails guys would make perfect pallbearers.

Despite Willie's deathbed pronouncement, we get another dump of snow. The winter drags on.

51

WITH EDWARD THE pub pro dispatched back to jolly old England, Bart is my darts partner again. My luck seems to have turned, and I actually win a game for us by throwing a double.

Back home before bed I'm flipping channels and eating popcorn when I come across a taped recording of Owen Sound's weekly city council meeting.

I watch intently, looking for Alex.

His performance impresses me. He's not the most eloquent speaker, and several times the mayor appears frustrated with his grandstanding, but he's done his homework and really seems to care about his constituents.

Now I'm having trouble sleeping.

It's been seven years since I had sex with a partner. And although my last experiences may have been more of the meat-and-potatoes variety than the seismographic sex

everyone raves about, when you're starving, meat and potatoes can be quite satisfying.

I yearn to be touched.

• • •

It's Friday afternoon and I have no plans or prospects for
the weekend. I'm in my office staring at my computer screen
when I spot Alex's business card; he'd handed it to me at the
Legion.

I could tell that Alex liked me. Would he have asked me
out if Paula hadn't chased him off? Now I'm never going
to see him again, and he's probably already forgotten the
plain-Jane accountant he briefly chatted with.

Then a light switches on.

Alex'd mentioned he was putting a team together for
the Big Walk for Cancer. I could volunteer to be on it.

I quickly type and delete an email four times. I review
the latest version.

> To: AlexCouncillor@cityowensound.ca
> From: Jane@FACK.ca
> Hi Alex:
> This is Jane Parker from Fielding Austin
> Cooper Keyes LLP. We met at the Legion last
> Friday, when I was helping Paula with a fundrais-
> er for Haven House.
> You mentioned you were organizing a team
> for the Big Walk for Cancer in June. If you're in
> need of any more volunteers, I'd be more than
> happy to help.

Let me know if you might be interested.
Best regards,
Jane

My fingers hover hesitantly over the keyboard until, seemingly of their own volition, they click Send.

Panic descends.

Oh my god, what have I done? This is a city councillor. The partners will flip out if I embarrass them in front of City Hall. They've been sucking up to council for months, trying to win the bid for the city audit.

I do some bookkeeping to keep my mind off my email to Alex, but it won't settle down.

Twenty minutes later a message pops up in my Inbox. Heart racing, I open it, and, then... relief.

To: Jane@FACK.ca
From: AlexCouncillor@cityowensound.ca
Hello Jane,
    Of course I remember you. How could I forget your lovely smile?
    Yes, I still have some spots left on my team, and I would be very happy to add you. When would you like me to bring a sponsor sheet over to you?
Yours very truly,
Alex

I breathe again. Heart singing, I don't respond right away; I don't want to appear too eager. When I email Alex back I say he can drop the sponsor sheet off at FACK any time. I'm hoping he'll ask to see me when he comes in and not just leave it with reception. I'll have to make an effort to look hot when he comes.

I can barely concentrate for the rest of the day.

And then it's meat-raffle time.

Selling meat-raffle tickets didn't sound terribly difficult back when I'd agreed to do it. But now that it's time to hit the ground running, nervousness is kicking in.

The process is fairly simple. Paula and I tie burlap money aprons around our waists and walk through the bar selling tickets for a buck apiece. We each have to sell thirty numbered tickets per round for ten rounds. On a busy night, like tonight, we can sell out in under ten minutes. Then we head back to the meat-raffle station with our money.

The whole thing is orchestrated by two men, Rusty, who I'd talked to on the phone the previous week, and Richard Ferguson, known to everyone as Big Dickie.

Big Dickie resembles Humpty Dumpty before his great fall. Big, round and bald, he has a jovial Santa laugh, but his sense of humour is not suitable for children. Though he comes off as a bit of a bumpkin, Dickie is a shrewd businessman who's built a successful company operating cranes for the construction industry. Five years ago he sold the business to a Toronto-based firm for a ludicrously large sum of cash, which had enabled his early retirement.

"Dickie has a robot lawn mower," Rusty informs me. "On weekends we all go over to his place to drink by the pool and watch the robot cut his grass."

"Does it make house calls?" I ask him.

Short and stocky, Rusty reminds me of a football coach. The little lines that play around the corners of his bloodshot blue eyes and neatly trimmed moustache only add to his teddy-bear appeal. He gives the crown and anchor board a hefty yank down and it spins, chuntering away for several seconds before its needle lands on the winning number. He pulls it again so that he has two numbers between one and thirty for each batch of tickets we've sold, then he struts around the bar hollering them out. The lucky winner gets to come up and pick his prize from the meat cooler. The steaks, roasts and prime rib get scooped up first, leaving wieners, hamburger and back bacon for the final rounds.

When I come back to the station after my second round of ticket sales, Dickie and Rusty are deep in conversation with a thin, pasty-complexioned woman whose centre-parted straight hair is so long she's sitting on it.

"You're saying you're a heathen?" Dickie asks her.

"No, I'm a vegan," the woman says loudly. "We're like vegetarians, except we don't eat any animal products at all. We don't eat eggs, milk or cheese."

"What's a vegetarian?" Dickie's winding her up.

"It's the opposite of me," Rusty informs us. "I don't eat anything that's grown in the ground or swims in the sea."

"That's not true, Rusty. French fries and vodka both come from things that are grown in the ground," Dick counters.

I would have guessed Rusty to be a beer drinker; he certainly has the belly of one. But vodka and soda is his drink of choice, and he's rarely without one.

"Well, I've heard of vegans before, but I didn't know we had any north of the 401." Dick's redneck act isn't fooling me one iota, and Rusty is only too happy to play along.

"Oh, there's a few of them on the peninsula. You know, those artist types who smoke a lot of weed and don't pay taxes or shave their legs," Rusty says.

The woman wraps her arms tightly around the meat cooler. "Haven't you ever seen little calves when they're born? They have such big, cute eyes."

I wonder if she might chain herself to the bar.

"They are cute and delicious," says Dick.

"Lady, the money we raise from these raffles goes to the Bruce Grey Children's Foundation and, if you ask me, those kids are pretty damn cute, too," Rusty says.

I'm nervous but keeping it together. On a slow night we let patrons buy two tickets, but not once the joint gets jumping. Paula has warned me there'll be some meat lovers who don't like taking no for an answer.

On my first round, an intoxicated gentleman had insisted on tipping me two dollars, despite my heroic efforts to convince him I was not a waitress. Otherwise, everything had gone smoothly.

Then Gord shows up at a table I'm waiting on and extreme flusterment ensues. I'm still upset after the blondie-on-his-lap incident at darts and had hoped to avoid him. No such luck. Gord informs me I'm holding the tickets upside down; then I give him the wrong change. The bar fills up and suddenly everyone is sticking money in my face.

Paula has divided the bar into two sections. I just have to do Gord's section for the first five rounds, then we'll switch off and I'll be done with him.

On my fifth round our hands touch briefly as I pass him his tickets.

"Your hands are cold, Jane. Maybe I could warm them up later."

I ignore him.

The next time I pass his table he calls out, "Jane, over here."

I glare at him. "You're on Paula's route."

The tenth and final round brings relief—it's finally over—and fear—what if my cash doesn't balance?

Sure enough, we're eight dollars short and I just know it has to be my fault. After counting everything twice, Dickie looks at me. "Jane, there's nothing in your pockets, is there?"

I stick my hands in my jean pockets and feel the cool ridges of loonies and toonies. The missing money is all there.

"Whew!" At least I won't get fired on my first night. That's one thing I like about accounting: no people in your face, distracting you, when you're concentrating on crunching the numbers.

It's time to relax and enjoy a cold beverage. Rusty orders beers for Paula and me. He talks about his work and his glory days playing shortstop for the King Farms fastball team in the seventies. People drift to our table. Stories of legendary misadventures are embellished with each retelling. I'm enjoying myself. These BG Kids group people are a fun bunch.

Rusty flirts a little. Paula and I make motions toward the door but he orders another round. I'm tipsy; Rusty is completely in the bag.

"How come you've never been married?" he asks.

"I have congenital herpes and a lot of men have trouble dealing with that."

Humour, I've found, helps people feel better about the awkwardness of having a thirty-something singleton in a room filled with doubles. I'm not sure if I'll have to up the ante in my forties. Perhaps some type of vaudeville act or musical number will be required.

"How old are you?" he asks.

My fingers caress the stem of my bottle of Blue Light and I pause as though contemplating the secret of the universe. "I'm turning forty in eleven weeks; it's completely freaking me out."

"It's not that bad, you'll survive. I'm fifty-two myself."

Two prominent BG Kids members, Bonnie and Terry, stop to chat with Paula. I can't hear everything they say, but Paula's voice floats above the din.

"She's a big girl. She can handle herself; I don't need to stay and watch over her."

She hovers a few more minutes, taking swigs of my fourth and final beer.

"Thanks, buddy." She hugs me and leaves.

I linger for a moment, say goodnight and pay my tab.

As I'm walking to the door someone calls my name. It's Rusty, standing at the bar with his coat on. I walk over to him and he puts his arm around my shoulders. "Would you like to go for dinner or a movie sometime?"

I smile right back at him.

"Sure."

"When?"

"Anytime. Call me. You have my number."

It gives me tremendous satisfaction that Gord, who's sitting directly across from us at the bar, has witnessed the entire exchange.

52

THE NEXT NIGHT my phone rings at ten after eight. I guess Rusty took me seriously when I told him I didn't have a life.

Not wanting to appear a complete loser, at home waiting by the phone on a Saturday night, I let the answering machine pick up.

"I know it's late, and you're probably out and about, but I was wondering if you wanted to catch a movie or something."

Around eleven the next morning I leave a "Sorry I missed you" message on his machine.

It's funny; I wasn't even thinking about Rusty on Friday and now I can't get him out of my head.

• • •

It's business as usual back at FACK Monday morning. Lori, bursting with news, comes to my office on her weekly rounds.

"My sister's twenty-two-year-old son, Jonathon, just moved into her basement with his sixteen-year-old girlfriend because he lost his job as an apprentice pipefitter," she announces.

"How is that working out for your sister?" I ask politely.

"Not well. They come upstairs when she's sleeping and eat all her filet mignon and cheese puffs, then they just leave their dishes on the counter when they're done. They sleep during the day and have relations all night, so my sister doesn't get any sleep and then she has to go to work to pay the bills."

I am still not sure why Lori tells me these things. It's like her sister shares her troubles with Lori, then Lori must expunge them by passing them on to someone else. Or maybe she just has no one else to tell.

"It sounds like your sister needs to set some boundaries."

"She's worried that the girlfriend will get pregnant so she can go on welfare. She keeps telling Jonathon 'There will be no babies in the basement.'"

But the timing of babies, I am beginning to realize, is not always predictable, never mind practical. I do hope I get to meet Lori's sister one day.

By Wednesday Rusty hasn't called, and my Friday-night beer-induced bravado has completely evaporated. I can't stop kicking myself. What was I thinking? Cute, smart, funny Gord, who I've had a crush on for almost a year, finally makes a pass at me and I brush him off. Then Rusty calls to ask me out and I don't answer the phone.

Perhaps I am the world's stupidest woman.

My spirits have tanked. Despite Wiarton Willie's post-humous predictions, winter goes on. Dead rodents see no shadows.

Cindy's feeling blue, too.

"Internet Dave didn't call me all weekend. He hardly ever calls when he's back east, and he won't give me his phone number."

"That's not good. Do you think there's another woman?"

"I'm wondering. Worst of all, I fell hard for this guy and told everybody about him. Now I have to deal with all the pity stares."

"I've been playing phone jockey all week, too. Don't tell anyone, but Rusty asked me out last Friday and he still hasn't called. I don't want to have to explain to everyone if he drops the ball."

"I wish I'd taken the same tack."

I keep listening to Rusty's message and wishing he'd call. Has he forgotten about me? Has he changed his mind?

I will never understand men.

That afternoon I look out my office window and see Alex cross 10th Street, heading for our front door. He's wearing an Al Capone three-piece pinstripe suit circa the dirty thir-ties, with a khaki cotton bucket hat similar to the one worn by Henry Fonda in *On Golden Pond*. His battered overstuffed briefcase is tucked under his arm.

I hold my breath. Will he just drop the cancer-walk regis-tration form off at reception or will he pop up and say hello?

Fiona calls me from the front desk.

"Alex's here to see you."

I go downstairs to greet him. The two of us stand staring at each other at the bottom of the stairs, blocking everyone's way.

"I was so happy to hear from you, Jane. What do you do here at FACK? Can I call you for tax advice?"

"I'm not really a tax accountant. Mostly I do corporate work for small businesses."

"You must give me your business card so I can refer people to you."

I want to tell him it's not about business or politics. Perhaps I should have a Tshirt made up that says "I desperately need a husband and am checking out all the single men in Grey County." But men, I have learned, are scared off by desperate women.

"I think Jane is a beautiful name. Can I get your phone number? You can call me anytime. My number is 555-373 ALEX."

After he leaves Fiona comes to my office, laughing.

"He really wants you to call him, Jane."

"Do you think I should? I've always had a thing for men with accents."

"He's awfully short."

I don't care about his small stature; he's packed with personality.

By Thursday I still haven't heard from Rusty, and Kim wants me to go with her to the meat raffle on Friday. Not wanting to look like a desperate loser showing up at the bar after Rusty hasn't called, I go out with Cindy instead, and we steer clear of the Frog.

We have dinner at Shorty's Bar and Grill and then see *Wonder Boys*, a quiet gem of a movie about a blocked writer who can't get his second book finished. The writer finally gets himself back on track when his third wife leaves him and he declares his undying love for the woman who is carrying his baby.

I sink deeper into depression. There is no great love in my life; I can't even find a man who will return my calls.

After so much promise, a rather unexciting week has come to an end. It's probably just as well I'm not going out the rest of this weekend, anyway. My back aches from too many hours in my non-ergonomic office chair, and a big zit has just erupted under my eyelid. It goes nicely with my new crow's feet. Who knew you could get wrinkles and pimples concurrently?

53

ON SATURDAY MORNING I wake up feeling doomed. Anticipating another date night alone at home, I set off for Zehrs to stock up on snacks.

When I return, the red light on my answering machine is flashing. I press Play, and Rusty's booming voice fills the airwaves.

"I'm very sorry I haven't called. It's been a terrible week; I came down with the flu on Sunday and a very close friend passed away on Tuesday. The funeral was yesterday."

Of course. Kim had told me that Terry, one of the BG Kids long-time members had died of a heart attack during the week. Why hadn't I put two and two together?

I immediately call Rusty back but hang up when I get his answering machine.

Then he calls me. "Did you just call? Let's hit the Frog for a drink."

I go into hyper drive, searching for something to wear that is suitably sexy but not slutty while simultaneously cleaning the house so he won't see what a slob I am.

He arrives on time and looking good in jeans and a baby-blue golf shirt. Rusty's wardrobe seems to consist entirely of jeans paired with shirts he'd won in golf, baseball and hockey tournaments. He makes a fuss over Wanker, bellowing greetings at him in German.

"Guten tag, Herr Vanker. Guten tag."

Wanker is ecstatic to welcome such a charismatic visitor and instantly falls in love with him, which is surprising, as he tends to be possessive of me and doesn't normally like men. But he preens when Rusty scratches him between the ears and prances about trying to match his drill-sergeant barking with his own.

I'm not sure why Rusty always speaks so loudly. Perhaps he spends so much time in bars that having to shout in order to be heard has become second nature, or maybe all men lose their hearing in their fifties. Regardless, I find it a bit of a turn-on. For a second I wonder if he hollers out orders in bed.

"Auf wiedersehen, meine wiener," he barks back at Wanker as we head out the door.

Rusty drives a black Ford Mustang with red pinstripes and a sunroof. It suits him perfectly.

Walking into the Frog with a date for a change is thrilling. Even more so when I discover Gord is sitting at the bar. He looks good, too, in a navy shirt and jeans. But too many tears have been wasted over Gord.

Rusty guides me to a table full of BG Kids people at the back of the bar. He pulls an empty stool out for me and sits down beside me. Nervous, I chug three beers, but everyone is friendly, and I find myself relaxing in the company of my newfound pals. The mood is sentimental, as they've just returned from the wake of their departed friend, and stories and memories of happier times are on tap.

After about an hour Rusty begins to rub his leg ever so gently against mine under the bar table. At first his movements are so subtle that I wonder if the beer is making me hallucinate. Then the pressure gets more persistent.

It feels very, very good. I'm a woman who's endured a prolonged sexual drought, and Rusty is flicking gasoline at a flame.

Slowing down with the beer seems like a good plan of action, but then some guy named Marty buys us another round plus something called a strawberry tequila shooter. It would be rude to refuse.

Rusty goes to the men's room and Marty asks me if I'm Rusty's daughter. I find this hilarious and share his inquiry with Rusty when he returns.

He's ready to leave, and I'm so plastered I can barely navigate my way to the door. We get into his car and he hugs me. I rest my head on his shoulder.

"I'm very drunk," I say.

Oh god; he smells so good.

We stop at a red light. Rusty leans over and gives me a slow, passionate kiss. The kind of kiss that legends are made of.

"I've never kissed a grandfather like that before," I tell him.

We kiss at every red light. We miss my street and have to make a U turn.

Rusty walks me to my door and we kiss on the porch with the light on, so all my neighbours can see. I don't care. I just want him to keep kissing me forever.

But somewhere in the back of my brain a synapse sparks. I probably shouldn't get polluted on our first date and hop drunkenly into bed with him.

"We have to stop," I whisper in his ear.

With that, he kisses me goodnight like a gentleman, pats Wanker's haunches and rides off into the sunset in his trusty Mustang.

Five minutes later my phone rings.

"I just called to make sure you're all right, and to tell you I had a really good time tonight. I'm sorry we didn't get to talk more. We will next time."

I'm in love.

54

I MET KRISTEN for the first time when she began working at Unique Boutique in August of 1982, exactly seven weeks after I did. On her third day on the job she was sent to sort through incoming merchandise in the basement and did not return for her one-thirty rotation at the cash register. "Can you go and see what's become of her, Jane?" our shift supervisor asked me.

I found her sitting on the floor in the middle of a pile of old books. She was pouring avidly over a vintage copy of *Anne of Green Gables* and looked startled when I entered the room.

"Oh, sorry I'm late. It's just this was my favourite book when I was a kid. I picked it up and lost track of time."

Just like that, we were friends for life.

Not only did Kristen and I share a great love of books and Lucy Maud Montgomery, she was a fellow Georgian Bay girl, having grown up just north of me in Collingwood. Engaged to her affable high school sweetheart, an auto mechanic named Evan, she'd recently moved with him to Toronto in search of employment. The recession was still going full throttle and prospects back home were few and far between.

Kristen and I were opposites in almost every other way. While I was quiet and shy, she was outgoing and rarely stopped talking. But opposites do attract, and a friendship that would last longer than any relationship with a man I've ever had grew from that first meeting.

That first summer on my own in Toronto had been a lonely one. I'd been homesick and was still licking my wounds from the one-two punch Kyle and Angie had delivered. Talking about it over coffee with Kristen and meeting some new friends, along with time and distance, helped heal the hurt. Slowly the process of moving on, rebuilding and trying to figure out what on earth I was going to do with my life, had begun.

It was Kristen who helped hook me into my next relationship.

Carl Webster came to Unique Boutique at least once a week to browse among the Star Wars and Star Trek memorabilia and kill time on his lunch hour. Ten years my senior, he was short and a little on the chubby side, with side-parted mouse-brown hair and a nasally voice. He did not come to the store for the fashion; he wore heavy plastic-rimmed glasses, shoulder-tabbed windbreakers in assorted colours, and cotton pants and sneakers. A self-proclaimed dilly-dallyer, he was fond of the saying "I belong to the procrastinators' club; we were going to have a meeting this week but have decided to put it off."

I'm not sure what it was that first attracted me to Carl. There was a calmness about him, as though he was never in a hurry to go anywhere or do anything. He was nice and respectful, had a decent job as a computer programmer and never gave the cashiers at Unique Boutique a hard time, although they were forced to endure his droll attempts at humour.

Whenever Carl came through my cashier station at the store I did my best to engage him in conversation, but I was too shy for flirtatiousness and he remained clueless about my interest in him.

I told Kristen I liked him.

"Just go up and talk to him. Ask him if he wants to go on the Tour of the Universe under the CN Tower with you. He loves all that sci-fi stuff."

But there was no way. I was just too shy.

Then Kristen had a brilliant idea. "Send him flowers."

"I couldn't. What if he found out they were from me and he wasn't interested? I'd be so embarrassed every time I saw him."

"Don't sign the card. Say they're from a secret admirer."

I selected two bold orange Gerber daisies and printed "From the chick who checks you out at Unique Boutique every week" on the card, writing my phone number just beneath. They were delivered that Saturday morning.

I'd baited the hook and dropped my line. Now all I could do was sit and wait.

And wait some more.

By Sunday night, he had not called. I was mortified. What if he thought I was a stalker? What if my boss found out I'd been harassing the customers? What if I got fired?

A week passed and still there was nothing. Maybe he had a girlfriend, maybe he was gay, maybe he just didn't like me. I decided to chalk it up to experience and move on.

The following Sunday at around seven in the evening, my phone rang.

"Is this the girl who sent me the dead daisies?" Carl asked.

It turned out he'd been on vacation the entire week and came home to some extremely smelly flowers. We arranged to go to a movie that Tuesday, because in Toronto movies were cheaper on Tuesdays, and before long we were seeing each other on a regular basis.

Carl was my safe harbour. The shock of Kyle and Angie's deception combined with my dashed dreams of a career in fashion had left me with the sense that life's rug had been pulled out from under me. I'd stepped off a cliff and was falling blindly into the abyss. Carl was the comfy cushion I landed on.

Carl liked computers, thrift stores, Star Trek conventions, movies and Andrew Lloyd Webber musicals. He did not partake in sports or exercise of any kind. We shared a great fondness for meals and entertainment.

In a city that never stopped moving, we managed to carve out a comfortable niche. He took me to the Spaghetti Factory, Mr. Green Jeans, the Organ Grinder and Ed's Warehouse, where we ordered the prime rib with peas and potatoes. Carl loved to mimic the restaurant's iconic owner: "If you want home cooking, eat at home."

He took me to *The Phantom of the Opera*, *Cats*, *A Chorus Line*, and *Les Miserables*. Since I had a slew of roommates, we generally went back to his apartment on our nights out. I began staying at his place on weekends and hooking up with him once or twice during the week, when we'd buy big tubs of ice cream from Laura Secord and snuggle on the couch watching movies. He'd been in the same apartment for nine years. He was constantly researching the real estate market for a house or condo, but he never got to the point of making an offer on anything.

As I attended night classes at York and struggled to pay for them by working at the store, our relationship flourished. Like all couples, we occasionally fought over inconsequential things. I belittled his beloved Star Trek conventions; he felt neglected because I had to study all the time. But our tiffs were infrequent. We're so compatible, I thought. It must be love at last.

After we'd been together for about eighteen months, Carl asked me to move in with him. "You're working so hard, Jane; think of all the money you'll save on rent." It wasn't the romantic proposal I'd always dreamed of, but living in Toronto was expensive. His offer was tempting.

I kissed his cheek. "We'd just fool around all the time, I'd never get any homework done, and I'd flunk out of school."

"Maybe when you're finished school we could buy a house together."

"A place of our own. That would be awesome." I paused. "I love you, Carl." I was proud of myself for being the first to put it out there.

"I love you too, Jane."

55

WHEN I GET home from work on Sunday afternoon there's yet another phone message from Rusty. "I had a good time. I'd like to go out again. Say hi to Wanker for me."

When I call him back that evening he tells me he'd been at the Frog for a mid-afternoon drink and had said to his friend Marty, "Well, I gotta run. I have to go home and call my daughter."

I can't wait to see him again.

First thing back at FACK Monday morning, I tell Kim about my big date. For the most part I want to keep it under the radar, but I just have to share the news with her. Besides, she's known Rusty for years and I want to get her take on him.

"Rusty has always been a very nice guy and a hard worker."

"That sounds like what you'd put on a job application."

"The only problem I've noticed is that he has a tendency to be jealous and possessive."

"That doesn't sound so bad. It might be nice to have a possessive boyfriend after my year of waiting for Gord to notice me."

Concentrating on work is impossible; my mind drifts back to those stoplight kisses.

Darts on Wednesday night is a sober affair. It's Bonnie's first night back after the sudden death of her husband.

Bart doesn't show up. Rumour is he's trying to quit smoking, cut back on drinking and lose weight, and a bar isn't the best place to achieve such goals. Sweet Jimmy, the bar's owner, is my partner, and we manage to win three of our four games.

Rusty saunters in around eight. He really is good-looking. Feeling awkward, I cross the floor to perch on the barstool beside him. He kisses me hello on the cheek and starts instructing me on how to throw better. He's had a long day at work and his eyes are squinty and red rimmed.

When the last game is over I put down my darts and he buys me another beer.

We move to the corner and watch Paula shoot pool. Rusty leans into me and gently strokes my arm under the table. No one can see what we're up to.

"I really want to kiss you again." His voice is low and husky.

My temperature rises.

"Where did you park your car?" he asks.

"Right there in front of the window," I say, pointing.

"Well, that was bad planning. How am I going to kiss you?"

He follows me home in his car. We stand in my driveway and kiss again. Sweet, gentle kisses, not like the long, hot ones of Saturday night.

Then he's gone.

The next day is Valentine's Day and I'm mildly disappointed Rusty doesn't send flowers or a card or anything. He does call, though.

"I'm so sorry, Jane. I forgot it was Valentine's Day."

"That's okay. I don't get too excited about it, anyway." What's important is how the man in your life treats you every day, not just on a day when the florist industry guilts him into buying hearts and flowers.

We talk for almost an hour. It feels good.

"I had a dream that you were riding a horse naked from the waist up. I kept watching your breasts bounce up and down as you were riding. It was an incredible turn-on." No bones about it, Rusty is not a shy guy.

"I'm not sure how to respond to that." I blush, glad he can't see me.

"Come to the meat-raffle tomorrow night. On Saturday we'll go out for dinner and a movie."

I hang up the phone and Mom calls.

"Alex's picture's in the *Sun Times* tonight," she says excitedly. "I totally get what you see in him." I don't have the paper but assume he wasn't wearing his purple ensemble. I imagine Mom boasting to the Sarawak United Church ladies that I'm dating a city councillor.

I'm still thinking about Mom's call the next morning at work. Out of curiosity I log onto the network, snoop in Fiona's directory and learn that all the city councillors are invited to the big FACK open house next week. Not that it matters to me anymore. Now that thoughts of Rusty take up most of my waking hours, I've lost interest in all other prospects.

Karl Brayer's T4 is ready for pick-up and Fiona, who would normally call him, asks me to do it. Nobody likes talking to the crotchety doctor.

I'm relieved when I call and get his receptionist. I leave a message that his T4 has been prepared and is ready for pick-up any time.

Four minutes later my phone rings.

"Was it you that just left a message for me to pick up my T4?"

He's yelling so loud it hurts my ears.

"Yes it was. Would you prefer that we mail it out to you?"

"I live in Tobermory. Why on earth would I drive for an hour to pick up a piece of paper I won't even need for two months. Are you an imbecile or something?"

I seriously contemplate hanging up. Really, I do not get paid enough to take this abuse. But FACK is on this big "client service comes first" campaign, so I just apologize, saying I didn't know he lives in Tobermory and we'll mail it to him.

I run downstairs to put Karl's envelope through the postage machine and am shocked to see Ryan Larkin sitting in the waiting room of our bankruptcy department.

Even though Ryan was three years ahead of me at West Hill Secondary School, I'd always known who he was; every girl in the school did. Ryan was that guy that every boy wanted to be and every girl wanted to date. He starred in every drama club production, played the acoustic guitar, sang a heartfelt rendition of Rex Smith's *You Take My Breath Away* and was the captain of the Greys' hockey team. He'd left Owen Sound in a blaze of glory, winning a hockey scholarship to an American university. I don't recognize him at first; his trademark Peter Frampton locks have been cropped and are spliced with strands of grey.

Life, I guess, never quite turns out the way we think it's going to.

That night the insurance inspector comes by. As a first-time home owner I've been nervous about this. I love my little house and am proud that I bought it on my own. But sometimes taking on all the responsibility that comes with home ownership is scary. The inspector turns out to be a fun guy who takes pictures of me and Wanker. Unfortunately, he says I must upgrade my electrical system if I want to get insurance. And everybody has to have insurance.

It may be years before I can afford a vacation.

After he leaves I get dressed to go to the Frog, then change my mind. Rusty's working the meat raffle and has told me to come and see him, but I don't want to appear too eager. It would be nice to see what he's like somewhere other than the bar, and we're scheduled for dinner and a movie the next night.

Just then Shelly calls. She's in a rage. Their supplier has awarded the dealership a free Caribbean cruise and Steve's dad has given it to Steve's brother, who works in the parts department. She goes on and on about how Steve works the hardest and is the best at his job and if there are any cruises to be passed out Steve should be entitled to them. It takes me half an hour to calm her down. Then I make the mistake of mentioning that Steve had been sent on several junkets and maybe his dad just wanted to be fair to the whole family. It takes me another eighteen minutes to reverse the damage.

As soon as she hangs up Rusty rings through. "Well, I really wanted to see you tonight." He sounds despondent.

Oh, what the hell. "Come on over, Rusty."

56

I POUR HIM a drink and we kiss on the couch. I remember his naked-horseback-riding fantasy and assume an old baseball legend like Rusty would want to get galloping 'round the bases pronto. After several moments of intense lip-on-lip action, I ask if he wants to go upstairs.

Faster than a superhero, Rusty finds my bedroom and strips down to his underpants. He stands before me, patting his big beer belly and beaming, proud as an expectant mom in her third trimester.

I think about how I've worked out and dieted every day since the first of January to get back into my skinny jeans, something I'm extremely grateful for as I lift my shirt over my head. Men are so lucky.

I walk to him and he slides out of his briefs, which are quickly confiscated by Wanker. Wanker, the pilfered briefs between his front paws, stares up at Rusty's naked body and tilts his head quizzically from side to side. I follow his gaze and see what's disturbing him.

Poking out just below Rusty's distended abdomen is the tiniest penis I have ever seen. Fully erect, it looks like the small head of an ancient sea turtle straining to see over the back of its own massive shell.

Quickly summing up the logistics of the situation it occurs to me that if we are going to get this job done, it will have to be missionary-style. Straddling that belly would feel like surfing; our corresponding parts simply wouldn't be within reaching distance of each other. If I want this man I can never be on top.

But this is just the beginning. More problems arise or, to put it succinctly, deflate, as his hard-on heads south.

In desperation I blurt out those five little words a woman should never, ever say to a potential lover.

"Do you have any Viagra?"

"Viagra!" he bellows, like I've suggested we polka naked down 2nd Avenue in the snow. "What the hell would we need that for?"

Not the most confident of speakers at the best of times, I struggle to find the right words while trying my damndest to avoid eye contact with that teeny peeny. Surely it's a rhetorical question. Everyone knows Viagra is for erection correction.

Memories of that last, horrible night with Sean come flooding back. At least Rusty isn't casting me out into the street, though.

Then I remember it's my house.

Matters are not helped by Wanker, who has never witnessed human amorousness before and keeps leaping into the fray to join the fun.

After several failed attempts, we're forced to suspend our sexual session due to technical difficulties. Rusty sleeps over, but Wanker becomes territorial and engages in a friendly competition to see who can sleep closest to me. None of us sleep much and Rusty leaves abruptly at four in the morning.

He doesn't call later, and I feel uneasy the remainder of the day.

Rusty doesn't show up for our seven o'clock dinner date. My anxiety has built to a fever pitch when he phones, from the Frog, at seven-thirty to say he'll be late. I wonder what he's doing there without me, considering we're scheduled for our first real, non-bar date. He sounds like he's been there for several hours. I've never seen his home, and it occurs to me he might actually live at the bar.

We can't find a movie that appeals to both of us, so we go to Kelsey's for dinner. I'd thought it would be good for us to get out from under the microscopic scrutiny of the bar crowd, but with just the two of us our conversation is incredibly strained. For once I don't have much of an appetite, but Rusty keeps the drinks coming.

"You're too quiet, Jane. I like girls like Jimmy's wife and Kim, who are outgoing, always laughing and having fun."

The sting sends me reeling back to my high school years. In Grade 9 I'd wanted so badly to be one of the popular girls. I was blonde and blue-eyed like the cheerleaders, but when I tried to be pep-squad vivacious, I sounded disturbingly fake. I remember a well-meaning guidance counsellor writing "Jane does very well academically but needs to improve her social skills in order to come out of her shell."

Over the years I've come to accept that I am who I am. I stopped struggling to change my zebra stripes and became my own cheerleader. Was Rusty on to something here? Was I still single at thirty-nine because men just don't care about the quiet girls? Or maybe we don't get noticed because we don't call attention to ourselves. I remember something Gord said to me last year at the Summerfolk Festival. "I'm shy and sometimes I miss out on things."

Oddly enough, my shyness didn't seem to bother Rusty the other night when he was imagining my breasts bouncing naked, equestrian style. I'm mortified. I feel myself wanting to cry and I struggle to hold back tears. Why has so much changed in twenty-four hours?

"I can be funny, too," I say, feeling defensive. "Sometimes I'm freaking hilarious."

"And you're always staring at everybody. It's creepy."

He demonstrates, pursing his lips and glaring in the manner of a psychopathic moron.

I brush a tear away before he can see it. In *Meeting Your Soulmate*, making eye contact and smiling at people is highly recommended. Maybe I've been overdoing it.

I excuse myself to go to the ladies' room, splash cold water on my face and compose myself. The joy I'd felt being with him is gone.

Rusty wants to go to back to the Frog after dinner. I agree, hoping the bar's joviality will bring us back to the fun couple we were less than twenty-four hours ago. But the bar is quiet for a change, although Gord is seated in his usual spot at the bar when we arrive.

We're looking around for a table when Gord says, "There's no maître d' here."

We take a seat by the window. The waitress brings Rusty a vodka and tonic and asks what I might like. I have another beer. I've never drunk this much in my entire life.

"Jane, I don't want a commitment, and I feel terrible about what we did last night, but I think you need to slow down. You're just going too fast."

"Okay."

Hadn't he been the one who called me? Out of the corner of my eye I notice Gord sauntering over to the jukebox, where he pauses before he makes his selection and drops a loonie in.

Immediately Christina Aguilera's sultry voice fills the bar.

"It's just that I'm really bad at relationships." Rusty is on a roll, and I have a feeling this speech has been carefully scripted and rehearsed. "I just got out of a relationship with a woman who burned me really bad. She took everything when we split; I was so broke I had to declare bankruptcy."

"That's horrible. What about your marriage? Was it better?"

He laughs.

"No, but I did get my two sons from it, and they are the best things that ever happened to me."

"Would you ever consider having more children?" I knew I shouldn't float this question so soon, but when you are weeks away from your fortieth birthday you have to put all your cards on the table.

"Nope, and I've been to the vet, so you don't have to worry about that."

Not the answer I'm looking for. This date just gets better and better.

"Rusty, have you been talking to anyone about us?"

"I might have asked a couple of close friends for advice."

"Hmmm..."

The song on the jukebox ends. I hadn't pegged Gord for a music fan. I look around the bar, but he must have slipped out already.

Rusty drives me home and spends the night again. This time the technical portion of the performance comes off without a hitch; we're able to achieve liftoff and sustain atmospheric re-entry, so to speak.

A dejected Wanker is sequestered downstairs, so we're both able to get some sleep.

Rusty leaves early in the morning for the golf course and it's a quiet day at home for me. I can't stop thinking about him. He smokes too much, drinks too much, and his diet consists entirely of red meat and fried food. He comes with financial problems and more baggage than a major airline. I want to get married and have children; he's had a vasectomy and doesn't want a commitment.

But he's sweet and cute and he makes me laugh. He's an amazing kisser, he smells good and my dog is in love with him. I'm absolutely crazy about him, too, and he's all I can think about right now.

Why does life do this to people?

57

SAM TAKES ME out for lunch on Monday for a pre-tax-season pep talk.

"Is there anything you want to talk about, Jane?"

There are lots of things I'd like to get off my chest, but I'm not sure how many of them Sam really wants or would be willing to hear.

The fact that FACK does not have a pension plan for its employees has always bothered me. For years I've wanted to discuss it with management, but I've always been too timid. Today I'm feeling uncharacteristically uninhibited and decide, for once, to throw caution to the wind.

"Traditionally, employees are forced to retire from FACK by age 65, and I'm concerned about my welfare. I don't have a spouse, and living on the Canadian Pension Plan is going to be tough for me. Would FACK consider enrolling in a pension plan for its employees?"

In my imagination the partners' response is "Pensions for employees. What a great idea! How wonderful that would be for all of us."

"Pension!" Sam repeats incredulously, as if I've suggested we abscond to a small South American country with millions of dollars from our clients' accounts and take up milking yaks.

An awkward moment of silence follows as I try to regain my composure. Such outbursts make me uncomfortable; I pray this one passes quickly.

When Sam has calmed himself enough to address the issue, he says, "I don't know of any accounting firms that have pensions, Jane. The partners believe that since our staff is made up of professionals who know a thing or two about money, they should be astute enough about budgeting to save for retirement on their own. You're welcome to have some of your pay deducted directly into an RRSP if you like, but FACK won't be contributing to any part of it."

"But what about the administrative staff? They're not accountants. And the partners all have pensions."

"That's because we're partners."

He eventually agrees to bring it up at the next partners' meeting, but it's obvious he's not taking the suggestion seriously.

After lunch, I feel guilty and anxious. What was I thinking? Sam's right: I've never heard of an accounting firm with pensions for its staff. I'm very lucky to have this job—what would I ever do if I lost it? There'd be no one to take over my mortgage payments; I'd lose my house; I'd lose everything. I just couldn't let it be. I had to keep gnawing at the hand that feeds me.

I resolve to settle down, work hard and get through tax season.

• • •

Three things happen every March that signify the start of tax season for me; the Toronto Blue Jays play their home opener, Tim Hortons starts its annual Roll Up the Rim to Win contest, and Fiona brings the tax envelopes out of hibernation.

In the file room we keep two big bins of jumbo-sized 14-by-18-inch Kraft envelopes, which are used to hold the tax paraphernalia our clients bring in every year. This includes but is not limited to government-issued T-slips, invoices, donation slips, medical receipts, bank statements, etc. When the client drops off his information, it gets deposited into a tax envelope, which is then bound by elastic to the client's personal tax file. Envelope and file travel together on their annual voyage through the inner workings of the FACK office.

In order for this system to be cost effective, staff has been instructed to preserve the envelopes for as long as humanly possible. Envelopes that get ripped or torn during their tour of duty are bandaged with masking tape and sent back to the battlefield to die another day.

Occasionally a distressed envelope that's been stretched beyond its capacity gives up the ghost midflight, causing its bottom to drop out and lose its load at a most unfortunate moment. Some of our veteran tax envelopes have been with us since the seventies. Being caught with a shiny new envelope is considered a cardinal sin. If a partner spots you with one, explanations will be required.

Tax preparation and spring cleaning go hand in hand. Some clients stash every official-looking envelope they receive in a junk drawer throughout the year. In March or April, they upend the aforementioned drawer into a shoebox or other suitable container and bring it to their accountant, who charges them upwards of $100 an hour to open all the envelopes with a silver letter opener. In addition to shoe boxes, I've seen tax receipts stapled to the pages of magazines and in shopping bags, hat boxes, cookie tins, suitcases, briefcases, attaché cases, leather saddlebags, bankers' boxes, picnic baskets, Tupperware containers and a fishing-tackle box.

Other clients are efficiency experts who organize, summarize and alphabetize their data, which makes my job a whole lot easier and their invoices somewhat smaller.

Once the client's data has been dropped off, it begins its journey around the office, moving first to the preparer, then the tax reviewer, then back to the preparer with queries, then back to the tax reviewer, who hopefully is satisfied and passes it on to the partner for a second review, and finally to the secretaries, who print out the tax returns and package them into glossy FACK folders.

Tax has never been my specialty. My attempts over the years to read and understand the Canadian Tax Act have left me with blinding headaches. But because we are short-staffed for tax accountants at this time of year, I've been recruited to put my year-end work aside and pitch in. Right off the bat, I discover that my clients fall into two categories:

a) They are in a refund position and angry because they want their money yesterday, despite the fact they have neglected to bring in half of the items we need to complete their return, or
b) They owe money and hold me personally responsible.

(FACK's commitment to quality client service deems "Do I look like the freaking Minister of Finance?" to be an unacceptable response to item b.)

Frank calls me immediately after reviewing my first tax return.

"Jane, where are the tapes with this?"

"Tapes?"

I give him a blank look. I have no idea what he's talking about.

"When you prepare a return you're supposed to bundle your T3s, T4s, T5s, etc., in the order they appear on the return and staple them together with an adding-machine tape that agrees with each line total on the return. This way I can tick each one off as I review it."

But it's me who's ticked off.

"I'm sorry. Katie and I stopped doing tapes in 1996 when the computerized tax program we use began automatically generating a summary report so you can vouch for and reconcile your T slips. It's a big time saver."

"Well, Katie's not here and I need tapes."

I say a silent prayer that she'll be well soon and that we will all survive tax season.

I'm at work early the next morning to sneak a peek at the RSVP list for FACK's open house tomorrow. Alex's name is on the second page with a checkmark beside it.

I haven't heard a peep from Rusty. Now that he's slept with me he obviously thinks he can jerk me around.

I bet Alex wouldn't treat a woman like this.

58

From: ManagerJohn@FACK.ca
To: JaneP@FACK.ca
Re: Hanover Audit
Jane:

I've been chatting with a few friends who are vacationing in Florida for the March break. I told them, "Bully for you; Jane and I get to go to Hanover!"

Man, are they jealous.

Our journey begins bright and early Monday morning. We don't have a 20-hour drive to get where we're going. We should meet at the office at 8:00 am EST.

Don't forget to bring the client files, paper, pencil crayons, laptop, portable printer, columnar paper and adding machine.

I can't wait.

Cheers,
John

IT'S WEDNESDAY-NIGHT DARTS league at the Frog. Rusty still hasn't called, but he's sitting at the bar when I walk in.

My heart leaps.

Fun Donnie is my partner and we win four of five games. I get high scores and Donnie keeps doubling us out. We are jubilant, but—I can't tell if it's my imagination—is everyone else a little quieter than usual? Rusty partners with Paula and joins in the game. Between throws I sit beside him.

Across the bar, Maurice, a really obnoxious man who is one of the Frog's more unfortunate fixtures, keeps looking at me and saying, "Are you Rusty's date?"

I ignore him, but I start feeling a prickly sensation in my stomach. I don't hear anything or see anything unusual, but my sixth sense is honing in on something strange and uncomfortable. People have been talking about me.

A lot.

Rusty's such a jock; it appears he's indulged in a bit of locker-room gossip.

The situation makes me extremely uncomfortable. After forty discreet years maintaining an impeccable reputation, am I suddenly Jane Parker: Bar-slut Queen of Owen Sound?

Gord comes in and we exchange our customary waves.

Kim joins us. We're all having a good time when Rusty starts whispering in my ear and touching my arm. I feel myself go limp and Kim hurries off. Then he lowers the boom.

"I feel bad about what we did on the weekend, Jane. I can't stop thinking about it."

I don't get it.

"What's to feel bad about? I thought last weekend was wonderful."

"Everything got out of hand."

"What are you trying to say?"

Really, I have no idea. He's not making any sense at all.

"I came here tonight because I didn't want to tell you this over the phone. I can't stop thinking about last weekend. I really enjoyed it, but it just happened way too fast."

"Okay."

"So, nothing is going to happen tonight."

"That's fine. You look really tired and I've got a big day tomorrow. I'll see you around, I guess."

He pays my bar tab and leaves without kissing me goodbye.

Just like that, the thrilling roller-coaster ride I've been on the last two weeks screeches to a halt. I've officially been dumped.

And I can't figure out what I did wrong.

Back home, I can't get to sleep. My body, roused after years of sexual hibernation, refuses to return to its dormant state. I toss and turn all night long.

I get up after a sleepless night, stressed out by FACK's open house renovation celebration. The free-flowing beer provided by the partners does nothing to calm my jangled nerves. Luckily, with all the fuss going on, no one expects much work from me.

I tell Cindy what happened with Rusty, then Kim comes to my office.

"Have you been asked on any more dates?"

"Rusty dumped me."

She gives me a motherly hug.

"He's always been an odd duck. A friend of mine saw the two of you together last week and said she wasn't impressed by him. Don't worry, Jane. There's still plenty of fish in the sea."

"But that's just it. They're all out to sea; none of them swim upstream to Georgian Bay."

"Maybe we need to rethink our strategy. Change the bait and cast our nets out farther."

"Well, I have to do something, because right now all I'm reeling in are dirty old commitment-phobic fish with erectile problems. I can't waste time waiting by the water-hole much longer."

With this in mind, I wait anxiously for Alex's arrival. Best to get right back up on the fish, as it were. Right on cue, Alex makes a dramatic entrance.

The big glass doors of FACK slide open and he tumbles in with a fellow city councillor. Resembling a hedgehog who's just tussled with a wind turbine, Alex's wild hair is sticking up in all directions. He wears a black-and-white hound's tooth suit jacket, red-striped shirt and violet tie.

The FACK staff are supposed to give our guests tours of the newly revamped office building, so I take Alex around. Even in my traumatized state, I'm aware we make quite a spectacle. Since Alex already knows everyone, he ends up introducing me. Some people treat him like an embarrassing annoyance; others are warm and respectful. We end up back in the reception area, and I get him a drink.

"I came over from Romania when I was nineteen and lived with my uncle until he passed away. My mother and two sisters still live there. I go home as often as I can. Have you been to Europe?"

"Yes, but I've never been to Romania."

"I must take you there right away."

"I can't leave during tax season."

"We'll go in May, then."

I'm sure he's going to ask me out for dinner.

"What kind of food do you eat? When is your birth-day?" He fires off random questions non-stop. It's like an inquisition.

"May 1."

"I don't normally believe in astrology, but I'm a Leo, and most of my good friends are earth signs, so I think we would be good together."

All too soon, the councillor Alex arrived with is ready to leave and comes over to collect him.

It occurs to me that I've never seen Alex drive anywhere.

"Well, that's my ride, Jane. It was wonderful spending some time with you."

"Oh, you're leaving already. I'm sorry; I've monopolized you."

"You can monopolize me any time."

Heading back downstairs I bump into John, who's also had a few beers. "What's going on between you and the councillor, Jane?" He looks at me with one eyebrow cocked.

"We're just friends."

"You must be special friends; he doesn't put on his purple tie for just anybody."

"This is the reason I'm still single," I sigh. "These are the types of men I attract."

"He certainly had the windblown look."

"Do you think if we got him a decent haircut and some better clothes?"

"There's no hope."

I decide to lay low and try not to embarrass myself further. I start drinking coffee and chat dutifully while being introduced to clients, lawyers, bankers, the mayor, other city councillors, potential clients, past clients, former employees, friends and families of the partners, etc. When I feel I've put in my required time I slink quietly out the back door and head for home.

I really need to talk to someone, but Shelly's away for the weekend and Kristen's busy with the kids. Mom has her hands full babysitting both grandkids. I call Cindy and dump on her some more. Thank god for good friends.

Friday morning Sam comes into my office.

"Who were you squiring around yesterday?"

"Councillor Alex." Why is he asking me this? Everyone knows who Alex is; he's been on council for over ten years.

"How do you two know each other?"

"We're doing the Big Walk for Cancer together. Did you want to sponsor me?"

"I'm already sponsoring my wife, but you keep tight with him. When we make our proposal for the city audit next year we'll need his vote."

59

I'VE BEEN WORKING seven days a week since March 1 and am already exhausted. Which isn't good, as we have six more weeks to go.

I'm buried in work. Dean wants Grey County Communications by tomorrow. I have a farm-equipment dealership due next week. Ben's Beachwear, which Sam says will be 'the dog's breakfast,' is coming in tomorrow. I have three other major year-ends due the end of March. But I have to put everything on hold for a week because I'll be out on the horrid Hanover audit with John.

Every time I leave my office for a moment, even just to use the bathroom, a new pile of tax returns materializes on my chair. Joe must have a hidden camera in my office so he can sneak in and dump them when I'm not looking. My office looks like a paper bomb has detonated in it.

To make matters worse, Elizabeth is incredulous when she realizes she's going to lose money giving up her weekend shifts at Kelsey's to come in and prepare tax returns for FACK. She abruptly quits both FACK and her accounting courses at Georgian College and uses her newly freed-up time to make beautiful handpainted tablecloths, which she sells at the Owen Sound and District Farmers' Market on Saturday mornings.

Her departure leaves FACK short-staffed at its most critical time of the year. Her work load gets distributed among FACK's already overburdened staff accountants.

Stopping by to say hello, Cindy gingerly steps over a plastic tub filled with bank statements and several files piled on the floor. She surveys the scene and declares, "We need to get you out of the office for a break."

"We should go to the Barking Frog tonight," I suggest. "Rusty has tickets for the Platers game, so he won't be there."

It would be good to have witnesses see me out having fun, I think. After Rusty's behaviour on Wednesday I don't want everyone thinking I'm sitting at home feeling sorry for myself. And I can relax, knowing he's away at the game.

We arrive just as the meat raffle is wrapping up. I feel somewhat awkward at first, then Big Dickie comes over a couple of times to chat us up, and Fun Donnie stops by to relive our champion-style dart playing of Wednesday night.

"Where's Rusty tonight?" he asks.

"He's at the hockey game."

Cindy gives me a nudge. "You should have said 'Who cares?'"

We get a little toasted.

"I'm devising a new strategy to help us meet men. We'll have to get in shape, because I'm rolling it out as soon as tax season's over," I say. "I think we need to let go of the notion that Prince Charming is going to bump into us at the grocery store or rescue us when we accidently fall into Georgian Bay, like we're starring in a romantic comedy. We're going to have to start pursuing our soulmate like the accountants we are. We'll analyze the stats, find out where all the good guys are, then go there and get them."

"They're probably at Smugglers." She's referring to the Sound's one and only strip club.

With alcohol fueling my fire, I warm to my subject like a Baptist minister at a revival. "The mistake we make over and over again is putting all our eggs in one basket."

"And we don't have that many eggs left."

"Eggs-actly."

"We find a guy, fall for him, and before you know it our whole world revolves around him. When the relationship doesn't work out, we're devastated and depressed and it takes us forever to get over it."

Cindy peers at me over her glass. "Rusty must have really done a number on you, Jane. Do you really think accounting techniques are going to help?"

"It can't be any worse than what we're currently doing."

"Count me in. We'll abandon the random and embrace strength in numbers."

"You got it. It's like we're trying to win the lottery: the more tickets we buy, the better our odds of winning."

"Have you ever won the lottery, Jane?"

"Yes, the Stress for Life lotto. I play the numbers every day."

By the end of the night I'm feeling better. I've finally got back into my favourite jeans with the sexy pockets and grease stain on the ass. I have a plan and an accomplice.

Big Dickie comes over and gives me a hug as we're leaving. I sleep soundly for the first time in three days.

The next morning finds me hustling around getting dressed when I notice my answering-machine light flashing.

There's a slurred message from Rusty. "I feel bad; can we talk? I'll call you tomorrow afternoon." He must have called after he got home from the game last night.

Determined not to talk to him, I go to work for another Saturday of tax preparation.

When I get home I see he's left another sulky message. "They're having a live band at the Frog tonight. Do you want to come?"

I debate for an hour. I'd thought he'd broken up with me. I shouldn't let him jerk me around like this, but I want to see him so bad.

I give in and call him.

"I thought you broke up with me."

"Jane, you completely misunderstood me. I don't want to break up; I just want to slow down. Weren't you listening?"

"Pick me up at eight."

He gets to my place early, but something is off. He doesn't kiss me hello. We're not clicking.

The bar is packed for Big Dickie's birthday. Rusty starts bopping on the dance floor with him, and Dickie gives him a big, wet kiss. Everyone laughs and cheers.

"You're blushing."

"Well, Dickie hasn't kissed me like that in a long time."

Rusty's so adorable. I couldn't want him more than I do at that moment.

We sit together at the bar and I drink too much, too fast. We talk to his friends, but it's difficult with the loud music. He doesn't touch me. After an hour I say, "Let's get out of here."

"I was serious about slowing down, Jane."

"That's okay. We could cuddle, talk, get to know each other."

"Do you want to come in?" I ask when we pull into my driveway.

"No." He's adamant. "What happened last week can't happen again."

"I promise I won't try anything." I'm pleading now.

"No."

In that moment my normally endless supply of patience passes its expiration date. Why am I throwing myself at this man? It's so beneath me.

"Goodnight then." I slam the car door.

This is exactly what happened with Sean. He came on really strong, acted like he was crazy about me, and after a couple of less-than-stellar sexual episodes started acting weird and pulling away. It's like these fifty-something guys are excited when they land a younger woman, but when we get too close they're scared and run away like small boys.

Memories of how bad things got with Sean come rushing back. Just when I'd think I was over him, he'd call and we'd repeat the cycle. I lost precious time and gained a bunch of weight mooning over Sean; I simply can't afford to go down that road again. I steel myself and dial Rusty's number.

"I want to break up with you." I'm determined to do this quickly.

"All right," he says, a little too agreeably. This will hurt me a lot more than it will him.

"Don't call me anymore."

"Okay."

"And don't come to darts. I don't want to have to see you."

"'kay." This time I think I hear his voice crack, and my heart breaks.

"Goodbye," I whisper and gently put the phone in its stand.

Now we're finished. He's off the hook and doesn't have to feel guilty about me anymore.

Already I miss him. Am I too needy? How could I get so attached in such a short time? It's the right thing to do, though. It would have dragged on forever and we both knew what the outcome would be.

But it hurts so much, and I can't stop crying.

60

THE OFFICE IS very quiet on Sunday morning. Several of the partners are regular churchgoers, while others prefer not to offend their more religious clients. Frank the tax partner has no such qualms, and the smell of cigarette smoke wafting down the upstairs hallway alerts me to his presence.

Chain-smoking Frank is not supposed to smoke in his office. A year ago he started a fire in his own house when he passed out at his computer with a cigarette burning. With all the paper we keep in the office, FACK would burn to the ground faster than the Great North American Bent Chair Company in 1899 if a fire were to start here.

Before opening the battered tax envelope holding the tax slips of Dr. Brayer and his wife, Camilla, I offer up a silent prayer to the tax gods that he's included all the necessary information. I'd prefer performing an unanesthetized root canal on myself to calling the good doctor at home on a Sunday morning. To my great relief, everything appears to be in order, and I begin entering the data into our tax program.

Flipping through Camilla's medical receipts, I come across an invoice for $2,048 from a registered sex therapist. Aside from the troubling images this generates, the invoice presents a problem. I'm not sure if sex-therapy sessions are deductible as a medical expense. I check our tax manual, but it does not mention sex. It's the kind of question I'd normally get Katie's assistance on.

But Katie's away and there are no other options. I'm dead-woman-walking down the hall to Frank's office.

Frank has a cigarette in his mouth and a second one lit and waiting in his on deck ashtray. He's drinking coffee from a large mug as he thumbs through a stack of working papers, leaving smudgy orange fingerprints from a recently consumed bag of Cheetos. I hope it's one of Sam's files.

Breakfast, I think, truly is the most important meal of the day.

In the background the Travelling Wilburys are singing "Handle Me with Care," and I wonder if Frank's grow-and-go hairstyle is his personal tribute to Bob Dylan.

Engrossed in the music, he doesn't see me come in. He jumps and spills his coffee when he finally notices me a few feet from his desk, clutching the receipt.

"Fuck!" he barks. I run to the bathroom for some paper towels to wipe up the coffee.

"What did you want?" he asks once I have the spill contained.

I hold up the receipt. "I've got kind of a stupid question."

He takes a break between cigarettes and looks up at me. "There are no stupid questions, Jane, just stupid people." I'm surprised to hear him say my name. I hadn't been entirely sure he knew who I am.

"Karl Bayer brought this in," I say, showing him the sex-therapy invoice. "I don't know whether it qualifies as a medical expense or not."

Frank takes his glasses off and holds the invoice just below his bulbous red-veined nose. "Who knew the crotchety old bugger still had it in him?" He takes a drag from his cigarette. "The rules on therapies vary from province to province. Family and marriage therapists are deductible in BC, Manitoba, New Brunswick and Ontario, but sexologists are allowable as a medical expense only in Quebec."

I wonder if the French are on to something. Maybe if you have a sex therapist you won't need a marriage therapist.

"What shall I tell Karl?"

"Tell him to move to Quebec."

• • •

My parents are driving to Florida for a week's vacation that night and have asked me to stay at the farm to take care of Dad's two horses while they're gone. In the light of everything that has happened over the last few days, I welcome the change of scenery.

But as I'm driving along the lake with Wanker, the sky darkens and the clouds look ominous. It may be mid-March, but winter is far from over. Dead groundhogs don't lie.

61

SURE ENOUGH, THERE'S another snowstorm that night, but the ploughs are out in full force Monday morning and I make it to work despite the slippery roads. I've slept well and feel a bit better about the whole situation with Rusty. Breaking if off, I am certain, was the right thing to do. At least I'm not waiting by the phone anymore.

Cindy, however, is not so fortunate.

"I hate men, I hate men, I hate men," she chants, hunting me down at the photocopier.

"Internet Dave was supposed to call me Saturday morning so we could spend the day together. I waited all day and he finally called around five. He said there'd been an emergency at work, but he promised to call me on Sunday. I waited all day Sunday, and he still hasn't called. He ruined my entire weekend."

I put a hand on her shoulder.

"We are on a mission. As soon as tax season is over, we're dumping these losers and only dating men who treat us right and appreciate us."

By Tuesday I'm having misgivings about babysitting Dad's horses. At any other time of the year it would be fine, but with so much work to do at the office it's exhausting coming home and having to feed them and clean out their stalls. Plus, the snow just keeps falling, which makes for a treacherous drive home on the peninsula.

On Wednesday morning my car gets stuck at the end of my parents' long driveway. I dig myself out, but it takes forever and I'm late for work. I skip darts that night because:

a) I need to get back to the farm to do the chores and let Wanker out, and
b) I haven't spoken to Rusty since my angry phone call Saturday night and don't want to face him or his friends at the bar.

By the time I get out to the farm after work our neighbor has ploughed the driveway.

It doesn't snow nearly as much that night, so Thursday morning I think, "No problem; I'll just gun it when I get to the drifts at the end of the driveway." I'm almost to the ditch when I get stuck in a big drift that must have blown in during the night. One of Dad's trail-riding buddies happens to be driving by. He digs out my car and promises to come back in the afternoon to plough the driveway yet again.

Thank god for the charity of country neighbours. I'll be relieved when Mom and Dad return, so I can go home where my driveway is short and five minutes from my office.

In an effort to get caught up I grab a quick dinner in town and work until ten. On the way back to the farm I'm so exhausted I almost cause an accident: I'm driving down

County Road 17A in the dark, lost in my thoughts, when I realize I'm about to pass the driveway. I throw on my brakes and swerve in just in time, cutting off the car behind me, which, as luck would have it, turns out to be a police car.

The officer makes a u turn and pulls into the lane behind me.

Uh, oh, I think as he walks toward me.

I roll down my window and he looks into my puffy eyes.

"Have you been drinking?"

He has curly brown hair and dark-brown eyes.

"No, I'm an accountant. I'm just tired from staying late at the office every night to prepare tax returns."

"Make sure you slow down and signal next time."

Am I imagining things or do I see the hint of a smile? He doesn't give me a ticket.

When I go out Friday night to feed the horses I see they've chewed up the wooden boards Dad used to build a separating wall between them. The pile of timber is strewn over the barn floor, and both horses are together in one large stall. They must have been restless after being cooped up all winter and attempted to eat their way to freedom. I must admit I've employed the same strategy myself.

I also find a large metal pole lying on the floor of the stall, which may or may not have been used to keep the barn roof propped up. I reassemble the boards, put the metal pole back in place and get the horses separated. So far they're behaving, but I hope there's no more structural damage to the barn before Dad gets home on Sunday.

• • •

I have a hair appointment Saturday in Owen Sound at 9:30 and plan to go directly to the office afterward. I get up early and work out, which turns out to be redundant.

I'm just starting the chores when I discover the water valve in the barn and all the outdoor taps have frozen. This means I'll have to haul five-gallon buckets of water up the stairs from the basement of the house to the barn. When I'm finally finished, I back my car into a snowbank and have to shovel for half an hour to get it out. My parent's driveway is the equivalent of five city driveways. To get out on the road I wait until there's no traffic coming and gun it out the lane as fast as I can. When the drifts get too deep I swerve onto the lawn.

I make it onto the road. The drive down Range Road, which has yet to be touched by a plough, is harrowing.

I get to my hair appointment in the nick of time. It just goes to show that there is no force in nature greater than the bond between a woman and her hairdresser.

That afternoon Shelly, at home looking after the kids while Steve's at an auto show in New Orleans, sends me an email.

> To: Jane@FACK.ca
> From: CrazyMom@home.ca
> Steve had better get home soon; the kids are wearing me out. I don't know why they call it morning sickness when it lasts all day. Steve has an appointment Tuesday at the doctor.
> My diet is going well. I have this great recipe. You warm up a tortilla then add some refried beans, top it off with no-fat sour cream and salsa

and roll it up. The whole thing only has about 125 calories, and two are very filling.

I heard you are having a tough time reliving *The Country Life*. Too bad there weren't any single neighbours to dig you out.

To: CrazyMom@home.ca

How did you know I'd be here?

We must be doing something wrong. Why are we looking after things so people can be in the sunny south? I'm thinking we should be at the beach and other people should be looking after our things.

I just walked into one of the manager's offices, and he kindly informed me that I had a post-it note stuck to my bum. I pulled it off. It said "Left off here."

Does this stuff happen to other people or is it just me?

To: Jane@FACK.ca

You can't go to Florida, because accountants aren't allowed to leave the country during tax season. When an accountant hands her passport to the customs officer at the US border between March and April an alarm goes off and they detain you in a holding cell until a Revenue Canada Agent comes to collect you and escort you back into the country.

PS: I knew you'd be at work BECAUSE YOU ARE ALWAYS THERE!!!!!!!

On Sunday I prepare tax returns, do my laundry and clean Mom and Dad's house, the barn and my office. I do the chores and am relieved to be able to move Wanker and all my clothes and things back home. Sunday night Dad calls from Kentucky to say they're stuck in a snowstorm and can't get back, so I return to the farm for two more nights.

62

I'M THRILLED TO be back to civilization and my comfy little house.

I go to darts for the first time since breaking up with Rusty. He keeps his word and isn't there. His friends in the bar are polite but distant. Fun Donnie asks me where Rusty is.

As I'm leaving Paula says, "So I hear you and Rusty are on the outs."

"Does everyone at BG Kids think I am a complete bitch now?"

She gives me an understanding smile. "Never try to teach a pig to sing, Jane; it won't work, and it just annoys the pig."

Back home I call Rusty and apologize.

"Sorry for breaking up with you on the phone last Saturday; I was just drunk and frustrated."

"I completely understand, and you had every right to be upset. It's just that I've been burned too many times before. I'm not normal."

I can't disagree on that one.

"I just wanted to apologize and make sure you were okay." Why is it I cannot stay mad at him?

I invite Kristen over for coffee. She's the one person I can discuss sex with. I tell her all about Rusty and how he'd shared our intimate details with his bar buddies. Why had he come on so strong and then thrown on the brakes?

"There is nothing wrong with you, and you weren't 'too fast,'" Kirsten reassures me. "I think you should date Alex."

"You just like him because he's a Conservative; you didn't see him at the FACK open house dressed like Bozo the clown."

"Most single heterosexual males don't know how to dress themselves. He needs a woman like you in his life to give him fashion advice."

"I know Rusty was all wrong for me, but there was a powerful attraction between us."

"Was he good in bed?"

"Not really. He had difficulties keeping his erection, and his penis was the size of my thumb. Beside his belly it looked like a pickle on a plate."

"A mini gherkin," Kristen giggles.

• • •

When I get home from work late Saturday afternoon there are no messages on my answering machine. I attempt to fill my ache with cold Cantonese noodles, some pink, purple and yellow jelly Easter bunny candies and a half-dozen iced raspberry Danishes as I curl up on the couch reading *Bridget Jones: The Edge of Reason* and listening to country-music videos on CMT.

Mom and Shell call. Both urge me to suck it up and call Alex. I break down and dial 555 373 ALEX and leave a message.

"Alex, it's Jane from Fielding Austin Cooper Keyes calling."

I hesitate. "I was just wondering if you wanted to get together for a drink or something. If you're interested, give me a call."

On Sunday morning I take a few hours off work to regroup. I don't have a clean dish in my cupboard and my laundry basket is overflowing onto my bedroom carpet. A bad smell emanates from the kitchen, where the entire contents of my fridge consist of a half-dozen cans of diet pop, a jar of olives and some mouldy broccoli.

After lunch the loneliness becomes unbearable. Sundays at the office, though, are always depressing. It's deathly quiet as I work.

At home there are still no calls from Alex or Rusty or anybody. I hate being alone in this lonely house. Tax season seems to stretch on forever.

Just when I think I can't sink any lower, Alex calls.

His voice is the pin that pops the dark depression balloon that's floated around me all weekend. He's at a friend's house and we talk for half an hour. He's going to call me back when he gets home.

I love politicians.

By the end of the evening my Alex dossier is filled. Other than his part-time hours as a city councillor, he doesn't appear to have a job. When pushed, he says he "speculates." He doesn't sleep. He likes to bike and hike and keeps busy

volunteering for the Cancer Society. He says that since neither of us are members of the Owen Sound Legion but we
both happened to be there on the night we met, fate must
have brought us together.

It sounds very romantic, but as I hang up I feel a disso-
nance—the feeling you get when your intuition is telling
you something is off but you're not sure exactly what it is.

I had starved myself and worked out like a fiend on
Sunday, and Monday I do the same, to compensate for my
Saturday-night excesses. It's my turn to work the meat raf-
fle on Friday, and I want to look good.

Alex and I have a date tonight at the Harb. I've figured
out his office is in the commercial building at the south end
of 1st Avenue, although for some reason he won't tell me
where he lives.

When I arrive he's at the bar with a man I've never seen
before. Alex introduces him as his friend Rob Johnston. Rob
is obnoxious and doesn't shut up for an hour and a half. I
barely get a chance to speak to Alex. His friend is rude, tells
gross stories and uses offensive language. After two hours
of this I tell Alex I'm leaving.

I can't figure out what's happening here. Who brings a
loudmouth like that on a first date? I still think Alex is sweet,
but there's something not right here. He's sporting a hor-
rendous comb-over and a wooly mauve sweater that looks
feminine and has seen better days. He chain-smokes the
entire time we're at the bar.

"You will be the one to make me quit, Jane," he says.

Monday night I get home late from auditing in Hanover.
Alex's left a voice message.

"Rob is not a great friend of mine. He was drunk and didn't know what he was saying. When will we be getting together again?"

After the disappointment of the previous night, there's no way I'm going through another horrible date with him. I call him back.

"Alex, you're a really nice guy, but I don't think we have anything in common."

"You're a really nice lady, Jane. You're too good for me."

It's such a sweet thing to say that it makes me wonder if I've done the right thing.

Now I feel bad about Alex and Rusty. I miss the feel of Rusty's bulky body wrapped around me.

• • •

Working on the audit out in Hanover, John and I take a break to have lunch at a Chinese restaurant. Our waitress is so thin you can see every bone in her face. Her eyes are huge hollows and her clothes hang on her. She gets to me. I bring my two days of starvation to an end when I go home and indulge in a monstrous binge.

Kristen, Dad, Shelly and Cindy call to see how I'm doing. I'm so lucky to have such supportive friends and family. I will get through this.

There's a television show on Monday nights I can really relate to, about a thirty-something lawyer desperately looking for love in all the wrong places. There are shows about doctors, lawyers and waitresses, but I've yet to see a show about accountants. On the rare occasion you do see an accountant in the movies or on television, it's always the stereotypical bespectacled bald male nerd. He's usually given a secondary role: the disappointing blind date or the anxious mafia accountant who gets sticky fingers and meets with an untimely accident.

At FACK, Larry and Sam spring to mind when contemplating the historic definition of bean counter. Sam wears flood pants so often Kim and I have nicknamed him High Pockets. But these two gentlemen are the exception rather than the rule. Over 50 per cent of today's accounting graduates are women and, although dark suits are still our uniform of choice, splashes of colour have started creeping in.

In my favourite lawyer show, the female lead puts all her energy into becoming a professional woman only to find she's sacrificed love and family life for her career. During this week's episode, her childhood sweetheart/soulmate dies suddenly.

His final words to her are "In the end, love is all that matters."

I have five weeks left until my birthday. I must find my soulmate before it's too late.

63

JOHN AND I finish the Hanover audit on Friday and we don't have to go back. I celebrate with a trip to Heritage Place Mall, where I find a great pair of jeans that fit perfectly, a new shirt and some miraculous instant-slimming ultra-firm control panties. I'm determined to look my best working the meat raffle tonight.

At work I can barely concentrate. I have a manicure on my lunch hour, then leave early to get dressed and do my make-up.

At the Frog my heart races as I spot Rusty. He's looking good in jeans and a green golf shirt. I know it can never work for us, but I'm still so crazy about him. Is it simply human nature to want the things we know are bad for us?

The guys in the bar introduce themselves and chat me up. Selling meat-raffle tickets really is the perfect way to meet men, unless, of course, you've got your eye on a vegetarian.

Gord is noticeably absent.

Halfway through my rounds I return to the bar to find Rusty alone.

"How've you been?" he asks quietly.

"Fine." I keep on counting.

I get into a rhythm and begin beating Paula back to the bar. She asks where I'm going afterward and I tell her I'm having dinner with Shelly. It's not true, but I need an excuse to get out of there.

When the last round's finished, I pay my tab and leave right away, stopping for some dog food and supplies before home. I've just shrugged out of my coat when the phone rings.

"Are you mad at me? I went to your house and you weren't there. What part of slowing down is it that you don't understand?"

Now it's my turn to be confused. Does Rusty think we're still a couple? Why would he just show up at my house after the meat raffle?

"No, I'm not mad at you. I'm fine. And slowing down means going slower."

He laughs.

Despite my Friday-night bravado, the rest of the weekend is terrible. I work all day Saturday and most of Sunday and spend both nights alone. On Sunday night I cannot stop crying. For two hours I just lie in my bed with tears streaming down my face.

I am quite certain I am going to die childless, unmarried and alone. I plan my funeral. There will be a closed casket with a spray of daisies and a small musical ensemble—perhaps a guitar, flute and oboe. For the hymn I want *I Come to the Garden Alone*, and I would also like a soloist to sing *Go Rest High on That Mountain*. Donations in my memory could be made to the Ontario Federation of Lonely Women or Accountants Anonymous.

It's a pity party of immense proportions.

I wake up Monday morning resolved to stop feeling sorry for myself, get off my butt and do something positive about my problems.

• • •

At work everyone is greeted with the following email:

To: Staff@FACK.ca, Partners@FACK.ca, Admin@ FACK.ca

From: PartnerFrank@FACK.ca

Good Morning, Everyone:

As of yesterday afternoon we have only processed 1,213 tax returns, which is 173 less than last year at this time. We generally produce approximately 3,200 returns by April 30th. This means we now have to average 88 tax returns per day to get them out on time.

We need you to make every effort humanly possible to complete and have your returns reviewed and in for processing ASAP. I am personally concerned that if we don't kick up our production a notch, we will get backed up and blocked at the end of the month. This causes disgruntled clients, bad tempers and many mistakes.

Thank you in advance for your anticipated cooperation,

Frank

"Can you believe that email from Frank?" Cindy says as she pops into my office. She's followed by Lori doing her weekly Monday-morning rounds.

"How am I supposed to 'kick it up a notch?'" I ask them. "I've worked every weekend since the middle of February."

"I know. FACK's turned into a sweatshop. In my head I can't stop humming Fantine's song from *Les Miserables*," Cindy says.

Lori puts her hand over heart and launches into a passionate rendition of "I Dreamed a Dream."

Cindy and I join her for the chorus of "One Day More," but we have to stop before we get rolling because we're laughing too hard.

On Wednesday Anne, who's off on her controversial maternity leave, brings her new baby boy to the office. She's dressed him in the little blue outfit I'd given her at the baby shower the Bitchin' FACK Goddesses had hosted for her.

The baby is sweet and beautiful and Anne looks great. She lets me hold him and I inhale his lovely baby smell, not wanting to give him back, until Anne informs me I'm not cradling his head properly.

Everyone comes and makes a big fuss over the baby— except Kim. She's still smarting over Anne's betrayal. Some hurts are just too big to get over.

That night at darts Rusty's Mustang is parked in its usual spot in front of the bar, a trusty steed waiting patiently outside his cowboy's favourite watering hole. I spot Rusty at the end of the bar and my heart thumps. He must have come here to see me, I think. I can't wait to finish the game so I can go talk to him.

He walks past me en route to the men's room but avoids eye contact. Then he starts his car from inside the bar. It seems to run forever, and he leaves without speaking to me.

My heart sinks; the evening drags. I leave before the game is even finished.

At home my growing insecurity gives way to desperation. Unable to control myself, I call Rusty. No one answers and I hang up.

Then I try Alex and get his answering service.

I call Rusty again. This time when his machine kicks in I hesitate then say, "I miss you. Give me a call."

Is this what holding Anne's baby does to me?

I can't get back with Rusty, though; there's no potential for a long-term relationship, and he doesn't even want sex anymore. What's in it for me?

I wish Alex and I had talked more on our 'date.' Why did he have to bring his rude friend along? Alex likes me and calls right away and doesn't play games. Isn't that what's important? The hideous clothes and flyaway hair can be fixed. This is a man who truly cares about me.

It's six-thirty Thursday evening and nobody has returned my calls. No doubt they've both figured out I'm mentally unstable.

I let Wanker out the next morning for some fresh air before work. When it's time for him to come in I open the back door and see him in my elderly neighbour's back yard, merrily digging up her flower bed. I call and call, but he's a dachshund on a mission. Ellen is going to put a contract out on me soon.

• • •

I hand the Meaford Mariners audit in to John for review and apologize for the bad shape of the file. Teary, I tell him I'm going through some personal problems and it's affected my work.

I'm going to allow myself to self-medicate with one final comfort-food feeding frenzy. Then I will diet, exercise, get caught up at work and pull myself together.

Cindy has been very supportive. After tax season we will start over with a fresh batch of new men. Until then I'm going to stay focused and stop behaving like a desperate love-starved lunatic.

I arrive home with a grocery bag full of junk food and notice that Alex has called. I return his call and get his machine.

Mom calls. She thinks Alex sounds like a much better match for me than Rusty. She has never witnessed his wind-blown comb-over, however.

Then one of the BG Kids meat-raffle-runner volunteers calls.

"Jane, can you help me out? I'm supposed to do the raffle tomorrow night but an emergency has come up and I can't make it. If you'll cover for me, I'll take one of your shifts."

I'm torn. The last thing I want is to see Rusty after he didn't return my desperate call on Wednesday night. But I need someone to cover me on May 24 so I can do the Big Walk for Cancer with Alex.

"Sure, can you cover me off for the last Friday in May?"

"Not a problem."

Which means that tomorrow night I'm going to have to face Rusty without Paula for backup.

Then Alex calls back. He sounds cautious.

"I should have asked that obnoxious guy from the bar to go away. I don't even know him. I think he must have had me mixed up with someone else."

"Oh. I thought he drove you over?"

We talk for almost two hours. Alex is a chess master, loves to read, jog and hike. He plays scrabble with an old lady in a nursing home and another old lady grows plants for him. Last winter he had a walk-on role in Owen Sound Little Theatre's production of the *Will Rogers Follies*.

Every once in a while, he sneaks in a question about me.

"I've never been married, Jane. Have you?"

"Nope."

"Do you want to have kids?"

"It might be getting a little late for that."

"Don't worry, Jane. My great aunt Lucinda had a baby when she was fifty." Given my current state, I find revelations like this incredibly comforting. Alex has won me over.

"Do you want to do something tomorrow night?" he asks.

"I have to sell meat-raffle tickets."

"Okay then."

"But I'm free on Saturday."

"What do you want to do?"

"I'm up for anything as long as your friend Rob doesn't come along."

"I'll call you Saturday and we'll decide then. No Robs, I promise."

I don't want to lead him on if there's no attraction. But he seems rather sweet in an off-the-wall kind of way. Or is my wishful thinking justifying his weirdness?

All of a sudden, the weekend is looking much more interesting than originally planned.

64

From: Cindy@FACK.ca
To: Jane@FACK.ca
Here are the minutes from the March 28 meeting of the Bitchin' FACK Goddesses (BFGs) that I promised you. Sorry you missed it.
Minutes: BITCH, BITCH, BITCH.
Motion to accept minutes: Cindy.
Seconded by: Lori.

I SPEND MOST of Friday going through my house with an electrician. After he safeties all the electrical outlets, my house is officially insured and I won't have to renovate my old electrical system, which is a huge relief.

Dean is upset with me, however, because he needed several last-minute changes to the Meaford Mariners financial statements and I wasn't there to make them. I go back to work after the electrician leaves but then can't stay late because I'm scheduled to work the meat raffle.

I wear a heather-grey Tshirt with an old pair of black jeans. I'm feeling good. It's Fun Donnie's wife, Jan, and me, Dickie and Rusty. Rusty looks tired and has red bumps on his nose.

The first round is slow. Then the place begins filling up. Gord comes in wearing a baseball cap. I wonder if he's attempting to cover up another bad dye job, but he looks cute regardless.

With tickets in hand I tap him on the back.

He turns to me and says, "So how does this work? I give you my money and then I can give you my meat?"

It feels as though he's slapped me.

My ears are burning with shame and I want to cry. I've liked him so much for so long. I've given up on the possibility of the two of us ever getting together, but I'm not prepared for such a crude, hurtful insult. Does he think he's being funny?

He keeps on talking but I'm in shock and stop listening. When I recover enough to speak, I mumble, "Okay, can we move this along" and hand him his tickets.

I let Jan wait on him for the rest of the night.

It's a small comfort that the other men are friendly and attentive for the most part. A shy guy sitting at the bar with a brush cut asks me what I drink.

Close to the end of the night Gord comes up and puts his arm around me. "I hope I didn't offend you, Jane."

How could anyone not be offended?

When Rusty and I have a rare moment alone I say to him, "I have a date tomorrow, Rusty. I just wanted to tell you in case you hear about it from someone else."

"I understand. We never had a commitment. Don't be going as fast as we did."

Then someone comes over to talk baseball-glory-days with Rusty, so I say good night and slip away.

I've been home for just a few minutes when Rusty calls. "I didn't understand your message the other night."

"I just miss you."

"I'll be over in half an hour."

"Okay, but absolutely no sex tonight."

He arrives freshly showered in track pants and a baseball shirt. For once we do everything right. He starts kissing me right away. We move to the couch and end up on the living room carpet. For an hour we just kiss, touch and talk.

"I just want to spend the night cuddling. We could keep our clothes on."

I can't believe I buy this.

When I get to bed he's naked under the blankets except for his underpants. It doesn't take him long to get me talked out of my clothes, too.

He's amazing. Sweet, tender, sexy. He barely takes his hands off me all night. A couple of times he asks about the guy I'm going out with tomorrow.

"Is it someone from your office? Is it the insurance guy? Maybe you'll fall in love with him and this will be the last time we'll ever be together."

"I'd rather be with you," I tell him honestly. I've never felt this close and connected to him when we were together.

He leaves around eight the next morning. I'm happy to work all day Saturday. The office is quiet and I need the solitude. All day I bask in the memory of our one perfect night together. I don't want to talk to anyone and pop the bubble.

From the sublime to the ridiculous, my night of passionate romance with Rusty is followed by my date with Alex.

We're supposed to meet at the Inn on the Bay for drinks. Doesn't anyone buy a girl dinner anymore?

He's late, so I walk into the bar by myself, which puts me in a bad mood before our date has even got started.

He arrives twenty minutes later wearing a black vinyl jacket zipped up to his chin. A big campaign button with "Alex" spelled out in bold letters dangles from the zipper. Mesmerizing, it swings like a pendulum just below his Adam's apple as he talks and smokes. It's quiet in the bar and I pray that nobody I know sees us together.

Over the next two hours I dig up the following facts on Alex:

He left a dream job at Bell because he was "bored." Then he lost all his money in a stock-market scheme in 1991. Other than his position on city council, he hasn't had a job since. He smokes when he's not getting any sex and he's been smoking continuously since 1985. By the way, did I want to help him quit smoking? He lives in his office and doesn't drive or own a car. He's walked the nine blocks to our date.

I feel bad about this and insist on giving him a ride home, but he refuses. As I'm about to get into my car he grabs me and gives me a deep French kiss, his tongue flapping in my mouth like a dying trout on a dock.

Icccccccccccccccccccckkkkkkkkkkkkk!!!!!

I drive home, brush my teeth and rinse with mouthwash four times. My skin crawls.

I decide to be done with men until April 30. I'm not going near Alex ever again. After last night I will always have fond memories of Rusty, but I realize there's no future for us.

65

THERE ARE TWO couches in the FACK office building; the couch on the second floor serves as a bed for staff forced to pull all-nighters in order to get files out on a deadline. There's also a couch in reception for clients to sit on, but in tax season it occasionally doubles as a makeshift bed. Larry has also been known to sleep in his car in the parking lot rather than drive back to Chatsworth exhausted.

Sometimes I wonder what it would be like to work in an office where the doors get locked at 5 p.m. and everybody just goes home. With three weeks to go until the end of April, we're all tired and cranky and getting on each other's nerves.

Larry's doctor prescribes sleeping pills for him every tax season. He uses them on those nights when he only has time for three or four hours of sleep and doesn't want to waste precious minutes tossing and turning.

My tossing and turning, however, has more to do with Rusty than with work. At the office I can't stop reliving our last perfect night together. Whoever said "It's better to have loved and lost than never to have loved at all" had no idea what they were talking about. At night I can't stop crying. Why do I always end up alone?

Alex has called seventeen times. Every day when he's walking through town, stopping at different houses for food and conversation, he borrows the host's phone to call me. Each time he calls, a different name appears on my call display. It's like he's trying to trick me into answering.

After call number eighteen I decide I'd better talk to him and end things for good. But I keep getting his answering service, and it would be cruel to leave a break-up message.

• • •

Cindy is on cloud nine because Dave came over to her place Tuesday night. He bought a boat and hopes they will be spending lots of time on it this summer. She invited him over for pizza and a movie this weekend.

Rusty calls tonight. God, his voice sounds good on the phone. He gives me the "I'm not looking for a commitment and you're a great lady and I hope we can always be friends" speech.

"I'm not mad at you. You were honest about not wanting a commitment from the beginning, so I'm okay with that. I am looking for a commitment, but you're not the type of guy I'm wanting to have a commitment with."

"I really hope things went well on your date Saturday night."

"They didn't."

"That's too bad." He pauses. "I can't make a commitment."

Why does he feel the need to keep telling me this?

"Don't worry, I had a good time. Promise me it will always be our secret." Now I'm the one being ridiculous. How can it be "our secret" when he's already shared every intimate detail of our relationship with fifty of his best friends at a bar?

"It will."

I don't know how I stay so calm when my heart is breaking. The chemistry between us is just so powerful.

I need to take some time and regroup now. I have wonderful, supportive friends. They will help me get through this. I won't give up. I've had to work hard for everything good I've received in my life. Perhaps the same is true of finding love.

Alex calls me at seven-thirty Friday morning. "I wanted to be the first to wish you a happy birthday," he says.

"You're definitely the first, Alex. My birthday's not until May."

"Yes."

"Alex, it's April 14."

"Oh."

This is a man who makes important political decisions for our city.

"Maybe we'll get together sometime."

"Maybe." I'm running late and have to go.

I make it through a long, desolate weekend. Saturday finds me feeling frantic. I think about going to a party where I'd heard Chet's band is playing, asking Dad to fix me up with one of his coworkers, but mostly I'm just dying to call Rusty.

I pull myself together. I know the combination of my fortieth birthday less than three weeks away is driving me to desperation, but I must stay focused and get a grip. I'll deal with it all when tax season is over. I just have to keep treading water until then.

• • •

Cindy is in love.

She and Dave have been together every day for an entire week. For Easter he gave her a flip phone and a coffee-table book about cats. She gave him a tray of Cadbury chocolate eggs and navy socks with a nautical motif. How in love do you have to be to give each other Easter presents? In addition to seeing each other every night they now call each other from work several times a day. Her tiny kidney-shaped phone is perpetually glued to her head so that the Martianesque silver antenna appears to be growing out of her ear. Had Dave given her a matching phone for the other side they would look like giant silver earrings. I'm happy for her, but nothing is worse than being around the newly madly in love when your own heart is breaking.

In an effort to distract myself I turn on the radio. I hear the DJ announce that forty-two-year-old Madonna is pregnant with a son. This gives me new hope. If the material girl can have a baby at forty-two, so can I.

And then I have a brilliant idea.

Meet Your Soulmate has a whole chapter devoted to personal ads. My first impulse on reading this chapter when Shelly gave me the book last year had been "Personal ads are for losers. In a million years I would never do this."

But the more I think about it, the more it makes sense. And I can't possibly do worse than the guys I've dated recently.

I'm considering putting an ad in the *Kitchener Record*. I could access a much bigger single-adult male population, and nobody in Owen Sound would know about it. I'll tell Shelly and Kristen what I'm doing for safety purposes, but I will swear them to secrecy.

It sounds crazy, but just thinking about this new venture has my confidence flooding back. I'll no longer be at the mercy of the dwindling pool of Grey County single men. I'll be proactive and choose who I want from the hundreds of responses my personal ad is sure to generate. My desperate panic over turning forty without a boyfriend is slipping away.

66

AFTER MISSING TWO weeks in a row, I return to darts with renewed determination. I'm terrified of seeing Rusty, plus a pimple has popped up on my eyelid again and I'm not feeling my best.

To add to my stress level, I get stuck in a traffic jam at the corner of 3rd Avenue East and 10th Street, an unusual occurrence when it's not tourist season and the Platers aren't playing. Then I realize there's been a car accident, caused by someone who'd run a red light.

I assume an ambulance has already left the scene by the time traffic gets moving again and I see the mangled car. I'm not usually superstitious, but I shudder when I remember that this intersection is referred to as Damnation Corners. Years ago it had been home to four bars, one on each corner.

I finally pull in to the Frog parking lot and am relieved not to see Rusty's car anywhere.

Crew Cut Man, who'd bought me a beer at the last meat raffle, is perched at the bar. We exchanged hello's as I walk to the darts table. It's a busy night. We have fifteen people playing and the bar is packed.

I sit with Bonnie and Paula when they come in a little later. I wonder how I can get to know more about Crew Cut Guy. What would *Meeting Your Soulmate* advise me to do?

"Can you send that man at the bar a drink from me?" I ask our waitress. "Tell him I never got a chance to thank him for the drink he sent me at the meat raffle last Friday."

Normally I would never have the confidence to pull this off. But I've doubled out twice in a row and my mojo has come roaring back.

Mr. Crew Cut responds by sending me a delicious shooter called a slippery nipple. I raise it to toast him and he comes right over.

His name is Bruce. In his early fifties, he's an electrician who's worked at Bruce Nuclear for most of his adult life. Enough with the fifties guys already, I think. When I take out my personal ad, I'd better put an age limit on it.

"Thanks for buying me a beer the other night. I thought I should return the favour," I say.

"I sent you the drink because you sold me the winning meat-raffle ticket."

"Oh, right."

I'd thought he'd sent me the drink because he was interested. With the air hissing out of my confidence balloon, I feel somewhat stupid now.

It's about then I notice everyone in the bar appears to be giving us their undivided attention. Bonnie and Terry, in particular, have their arms folded across their chests and are frowning at me like school marms on detention duty.

This really irks me. I'm pretty certain they are the ones who spearheaded the negativity campaign against Rusty and me. Why can't they just leave us alone? If things had been allowed to progress naturally between us, maybe we'd still be together.

Bruce seems like a nice man, but I don't feel any chemistry developing, and he's too old for me. He lives out near Allenford but would like to move into town when he retires. He has four children, all of whom have grown up and moved out. That's the conundrum of dating a fifty-something guy. The advantage is that their kids are grown, so you're not required to live with and/or finance them; the disadvantage is that these guys don't want to have any more.

I discover that Bruce is a widower; his wife died suddenly from an aneurysm four years ago. They had a wonderful life together and he misses her terribly. He loves his kids. They've all been very supportive except for his youngest, who has a serious drug problem. Bruce is finding it difficult to deal with this on his own and has been drinking too much himself.

"Do you want to go out with me sometime?" he asks.

Oh god. I don't want to hurt his feelings after everything he's just told me. But leading him on would be worse, I think, and I'm running out of time.

"I'm sorry. I'm seeing somebody."

It doesn't feel like a lie; my heart still belongs to Rusty. We shake hands and he leaves.

I go back to darts, where Paula and I are on a roll. She just doesn't want to go home, so I play three more games with her, Bart and Jimmy, the bar owner. We'd win a game and she'd say, "Okay, this is the World Series," and we'd play another.

I finally leave around midnight. Mother Nature must have been feeling her oats that night, as she's sent the softest dusting of powdery snow. Even in Georgian Bay, it's unusual to have snow in the middle of April. It's a clear night, the falling flakes like downy feathers sprinkled over everything.

And then I see it. Arriving at my car I stop dead in my tracks.

Illuminated by the floodlight of an overhead street lamp for all to see, someone has taken a snow brush and sketched a gigantic set of boobs on the hood of my car.

Who on earth would do something like this?

The disapproving looks I got all night from Bonnie and Terry spring to mind. I'm sure Rusty told them everything that went on between us.

How did this happen? For years my reputation has been immaculate. And after seven years of enforced sexual abstinence, I'd been concerned my virginity had managed to restore itself. One indiscreet move and suddenly I'm the Whore of Corkscrew City.

Perhaps bars are not the best place to meet men, despite cheerful shows about everyone knowing your name. And do I really want a partner who drinks and smokes constantly, like the Frog's patrons do? The idea of taking out a personal ad is more appealing by the minute.

67

I REALIZE I'M not the only one feeling the pain the next morning when a decidedly dejected Cindy walks into my office. It's surprising to see her looking so sad after she's been overflowing with happiness these last few weeks.

"Oh, no," I say, on red alert. "What's wrong? Is everything okay with you and David?"

"It's not David. He's been wonderful," she sniffs. "It's Ken. He sent me this awful email this morning. He accused me of talking too much with the staff and then fudging my timesheets by billing the time to clients."

"Really? He said that?"

"Yes. Basically he's accusing me of lying, and I couldn't believe he'd put something like that in an email without even coming to me to talk about it first. I went to his office to discuss it and he was horrible. He said 'We don't come to work to socialize, Cindy. We're here to make money.'"

"But everybody needs to take a break now and then. It's good for morale, and taking a break actually makes you more productive."

"That's what I said, and that if we worked someplace where they had a union they'd have to give us breaks."

I'm worried for her now. A unionized chartered accounting firm is simply unheard of, and the fact that Cindy'd uttered the 'U' word in partner Ken's presence is a problem. I sincerely hope she's not about to vanish into thin air like Jimmy Hoffa or end up at the bottom of Georgian Bay.

"How did that go over?"

"Oh my god. He was so mad. He gave me a big lecture." Striking a pose, she put her hands on her hips and recounts Ken's diatribe.

"We don't make anything here, Cindy. We don't make widgets or hula hoops or mouse traps. The only product that we as partners have to sell is YOUR TIME. Your charge-out rate is a hundred dollars an hour. Every time you stop to pee, it costs me $14.89. When you gossip and take breaks, it wastes everyone's money."

"He was never like this when we were Montgomery Lawrence. He used to be so good to work for. Ever since the merger he's been nasty." Cindy's mortified and teary-eyed for the rest of the day. In an effort to cheer her up, Kim buys her flowers and I take her out for lunch.

On Saturday afternoon I allow myself a two-hour break from preparing tax returns to play in a darts tournament that Paula has organized at the Legion. Paula, Bonnie, Terry, Big Dickie's wife, Janet, and I were there to represent the Wednesday-night Barking Frog League.

I'm not that keen to attend. It's a ladies' tournament, so it doesn't fit with my meet-a-man mandate. But Paula has spent a lot of time organizing it, and I feel I really should go.

Dart tournaments, I soon discover, consist mostly of sitting around drinking and eating and waiting for your turn.

Paula is my partner for the first game and we lose to the pair who eventually win the whole tournament. I get a few high scores in our first two games and we advance to the next round. Then we get smoked.

It's a long, uncomfortable couple of hours. I get the distinct feeling most of the women don't like me, Terry especially. A stony frown is constantly on her face. When we get thrown together for the second game I say, "Hey, how's it going?"

She glares at me, harrumphs, turns her back and stalks off without answering.

Why am I wasting my time on these people? If they are this petty and mean, I don't need them in my life.

After the tournament we adjourn to the Frog for dinner. Relief floods over me when I notice Rusty's car isn't parked out front.

But he's already inside at the long table with the rest of the competitors. "See my new car." He points proudly to the new Grand Am in his regular parking space.

I preferred the Mustang.

I sit between Paula and Marty with Rusty across from me. Marty's a lot of fun, and we joke around. The first time we met I thought Marty was just a young guy, but he's actually forty-four. He's been married for three years and is madly in love with his wife. He said after he turned forty he wanted to find someone and settle down.

Too bad I hadn't known him then.

I buy a pop then hear Rusty tell the waitress, "One more round and I'll have my tab."

Wanting to beat him out the door, I pay my own tab and leave.

When I get back home Rusty's left two messages for me to call him.

"Are you mad at me, Jane?"

"No, I'm just trying to act normal around you."

"I miss talking to you. I liked talking to you a lot."

"I miss talking to you, too."

"It's our age difference that really bothers me. You're only ten years older than my son."

"And I'm uncomfortable with all your baggage."

"I've only been married once and I lived with someone once, but that was a long time ago. How did your date go?"

"Not well. This week Bruce from the bar asked me out. He works at Bruce Nuclear, too. Do you know him?"

"Yeah, I went to school with him. I could come over. I have to golf in the morning; could you wake me up at seven?"

"I have to work in the morning, too."

"But it's Sunday."

"There are no Sundays in tax season."

"It probably wouldn't work, then. Neither of us would get any sleep."

"Good night, Rusty."

After he hangs up, I re-listen to the messages he'd left, relishing the sound of his voice on the line.

Enough already. It's time to leave the bar scene behind. Darts league and meat raffles are almost finished, and then I won't have to see Rusty again.

Why does this make me so sad?

Sunday morning I'm at the office bright and early for what I hope will be my second-last working weekend of the year. I boot up my computer and can't believe how many emails have come in since yesterday. I take one lousy Saturday afternoon off for a darts tournament and my Inbox overfloweth. Who needs to reach me so badly on a Saturday afternoon?

I began wading through them.

> From: KarlBrayer@medicalarts.com
> Re: Eat my pumpkin Peter Peter
> Dear Ms Parker:
> I have called Joe Cooper and lodged a complaint regarding your recent unprofessional and inappropriate behaviour. I have no further use for your services and am requesting that my accounting work be transferred to another accountant immediately.
> Regards,
> Dr. K. Brayer, MD

Holy crap. What have I done to upset Karl this time? Part of me thinks I should worry I'll be in trouble with the partners while another part jumps for joy at the thought of never having to work with Old Doc Brayer ever again.

The next emails are even stranger.

> From CrazyMom@home.ca
> Re: Little Boy Blue come blow me horny
> Thanks a lot, Jane. Steve read your email last night and got all turned on and I had to have sex with him. It's all your fault.
> Shelly

From: jimcatherine@telephone.ca
Re: The Cock Doth Crow to let you know
    If you be wise, it's time to rise
Hi Sweetie:

    I got your email and I'm speaking for both myself and your father when I say we're really starting to worry about you. I know you're stressed over turning forty and you feel like a failure because you never got married, but we don't think it's normal for you to be spending so much time at work. Maybe it's time to think about getting some counselling? There's no shame in it, honey. Lots of normal people get therapy.

    I was speaking with my friend Beatrice, who works in the parks and recreation department, and she has a son who is a social worker down at the health unit. She says he's very nice and he's also single, so if he's unable to help you with your emotional problems maybe you two could date? Either way, I think it sounds like a WIN WIN!
Love,
Mom

From: AlexCouncillor@cityowensound.ca
Re: Goldy rocks a Bare Naked Threesome
Hello Jane!

    I am so excited that you sent me this email. After our last date I thought you were not interested in having relations with me. I will call you tonight.
Yours truly,
Alex

PS: I am certainly open to the possibility of a threesome if you know of someone who might want to join us. I am certain that my good friend Rob Johnston, who you met on our first date, could be enticed.

From: JakeGoodson@Drake.ca
Re: Little Jake Horny will plumb your pie
    Party at my place Saturday night, Jane. We'll rub a dub dub in my new hot tub.
Kisses,
Jakey

Oh my god. What the hell is going on here?

Do I live in such a small town that even my clients have heard gossip about me? Is my ruined reputation the cause of these bizarre emails? But what about the ones from Mom and Shelly? How would anyone get access to my email?

I sit there staring at the screen, blinking for a few minutes. Several people are at the office already, but I'm not sure who to discuss this with. Then I get the familiar "You've got mail" beep. There's a new message from managing partner Dean.

Surely, this is the one where I get fired. Can you fire someone in an email? No, it's probably an email summoning me to his office so he can fire me there. Either way, I am terrified to open it.

From: PartnerDean@FACK.ca
To: Staff@FACK.ca
Subject: Porn Virus

Please be advised that we have contracted a new computer virus called "The Worm." This virus arrives as a message with a nursery rhyme in the subject line. The message body contains what appears to be an attachment called "Pics4You.exe." If you click on the file and open it, the worm loads into your computer's memory and attaches itself to the first 100 listings in your email address book. It then emails your client a link to a porn site known as The Naughty Nursery's Rhymin' Hymens.

We are working on the problem and hope it will be fixed soon. In the meantime, please remember never to open an email from an unknown source and never click on any attachments. If any such email comes into your Inbox, delete it immediately, then go into your Deleted box and delete it again.

Thank you for your co-operation in this delicate matter.

Best Regards,
Dean

68

SHELLY GOT MARRIED in 1988.

After four years of dating, Steve, the eldest and most likeable son of a Meaford family auto-dealership dynasty, proposed when Shelly put a deposit on a diamond ring and informed him she had picked out her own Valentine's Day present this year. Their relationship, which had consisted of two months of romantic bliss followed by forty-four months of continuous turmoil, kicked into high gear.

The months that lead up to the wedding were a tense time for all of us, and I was grateful to be living in Toronto, away from the unfolding drama. Tempestuous at the best of times, Shelly had morphed into Bridezilla on the warpath. She ditched her lifelong best friend as maid of honour and replaced her with a new college chum. She tore a strip off Mom and me when we mentioned we'd seen a wedding dress we liked in the window of Angie's shop, and she hid all her shower gifts, thwarting Mom's fantasy trousseau tea. When my parents, who'd paid for the entire two-hundred-plus–people extravaganza, drew the line at footing the bill for Owen Sound's premier photographer to capture the blessed event on film, Shelly flew into a rage and did not speak to anyone for the nine days leading up to the wedding.

Which actually turned out to be a blessing in disguise.

Shelly's engagement generated an abundance of pitying looks in my direction. The question on everyone's lips was "Jane, does it bother you that your younger sister is getting married first?" Even worse was the well-intentioned "Don't worry, Jane. Your day will come."

In actuality, it didn't bother me that Shelly was getting married first. Steve was a great guy, and I was happy for her. I wanted to finish my degree, get my accounting designation and have a career, whereas Shelly, who'd always loathed gainful employment, was happy to stay home and have babies. I continued to take comfort in my comfortable relationship with Carl. Even though I steadfastly refused to move in with him, we'd been together for so long it felt like we were married. We were the fabled old shoe.

The one thing missing from my life was exercise. Working at the store all day and attending classes and studying in the evenings left little time or energy for working out. This, in combination with Carl's and my great love of food and entertainment, had me packing on the pounds. I found myself closing in on 175 pounds—a heavy load for my petite frame to carry. But Carl said he loved me just the way I was. We didn't have to go far or do much; everything we needed was right there.

Shelley's new maid of honour picked out the teeniest micro-mini bridesmaid dress I'd ever seen. Coming home one weekend to try it on, I discovered its tiny skirt covered approximately 63 per cent of my burgeoning size-18 thighs.

"Just think. You won't have to pay to get it shortened to wear after the wedding," Shelley said as I looked at myself dubiously in the mirror. I wondered how the priest would react to a gaggle of nearly naked bridesmaids in the sanctity of his church.

If the wedding wasn't enough to seal the deal, Shelly's getting pregnant shortly after the honeymoon certainly did. She stayed home with Madison for five years then got pregnant with Billy.

Our family life was altered dramatically as its focus shifted to the newly minted grandchildren. My parents set up a crib in Shelly's old room, bought a minivan, two car seats and a dresser chock full of kids' clothes. For the better part of the next two decades they would babysit a child almost every weekend, taking the kids to gymnastics, hockey practice, birthday parties, movies, Christmas concerts, swimming lessons, soccer practice, baseball, go kart racing and the orthodontist. When Steve and Shelly needed a vacation, their kids vacationed with my dad, now officially referred to as Grandpa James.

Being beaten down the aisle didn't bother me until I raced home from Toronto to meet my new niece. Holding tiny Maddie in my arms, something inside me stirred. For the first time in five years, I stopped to think about where my relationship with Carl might be headed.

I had one year left of university, then two years of study before I wrote my final accountancy exams. We'd never talked about having kids, but Carl was such an easy-going guy, I knew he would make a great dad.

It would happen when the time was right. I was sure of it.

69

STILL INCREDULOUS OVER the porn virus, I walk down the hall to get Cindy's take on it. She has some shocking news of her own.

"David and I have moved to the next level." She is as giddy as a schoolgirl. "You won't believe this, but he brought up the subject of marriage last night."

"Oh my god—he proposed."

"He didn't quite propose, but we discussed it and we both think it's a good idea."

"Oh, Cindy. I'm so happy for you." I give her a big hug.

"I'm not supposed to tell anyone yet, but I'm sure it won't be a secret for long."

That night I have dinner at Norma Jean's with Shelly.

"Everyone at the Barking Frog is talking about me and what a slut I am. It's making me feel bad about myself."

"Seriously, they're talking about you?"

"For forty years I've had this squeaky-clean reputation. I was Jane, shy virgin accountant ice princess. One romp with Rusty and I'm nominated for the Hosebag of the Year award."

"It's time for you to stop hanging out there. Have you heard from Mark White lately?"

Why is she bringing up Mark? We've been friends for twenty-five years. Surely if something were going to happen between us it would have shown up on the radar by now.

I take her advice about the Frog and brief Kim on the situation—how Bonnie and Terry have poisoned Rusty against me and are treating me like pond scum. She says she understands and promises to keep her ears open for me.

• • •

It's Monday, and one week remains of what feels like the longest tax season of my career. It also means I have one week left before my dreaded fortieth birthday. My mission to find my soulmate, unless some miracle occurs in the next seven days, has failed. Feeling stressed and exhausted, I make an appointment with my doctor.

"Your body is stressed and exhausted," Dr. Peters tells me. "Have you ever had a mammogram?"

"No."

Why is he asking me this? He's only been my doctor for the last eight years.

"Maybe you'd better have one."

"Is this because I'm turning forty this year?"

"Well, yes, but I didn't want to say anything."

He writes out a prescription for antidepressants.

Work is busy. New Moon Farms, one of Larry's clients, is dumped on me. It's not a bad job, but I can't deal with Larry on top of everything else right now.

On Wednesday it finally warms up, although it's grey and rainy. The last of the snow has washed away. I'm grateful for the gloomy weather. There's nothing worse than working around the clock indoors when the sun is shining down on everyone but you.

Working lots and avoiding social interaction, I miss the wrap-up party for my darts league. Kim tracks me down at the office and reams me out for not going.

She's right, of course. I should have at least gone to say goodbye to everyone. Bonnie and Terry have been awful, but Paula, Fun Donnie and several other teammates have been so nice; I should have put my problems aside to see them. But I just couldn't bear seeing Rusty again.

There'll be no way to avoid him on Friday night, when I have to work the meat raffle, though.

Will I get through it without some creep making a rude comment? I don't think I can handle one more glare from Terry. I want to look good, but not sexy. I'll try to keep a low profile.

And I absolutely must not sleep with Rusty again.

Anne calls to ask if I'll go to the movies with her on Thursday night. She needs to get out of the house for a while. The baby is wonderful, she says, but it would be nice to have some adult conversation.

We see an amazing movie called *Me, Myself, I*. It's about a woman who rejected a proposal from the man who turned out to be the love of her life. Instead she has an exciting, award-winning career as a journalist. On the eve of her thirtieth birthday, she's feeling lonely and regretting her choice.

I could totally relate.

Afterward we go for coffee. I tell Anne about my problems with Rusty; she tells me about her problems with Kim.

"I feel bad about the way I handled things. I thought Kim
was having problems at home and maybe if she talked to
Sam it would help. Instead, Kim feels betrayed that I went
to Sam behind her back."

I thought about the times Anne had dumped entire
audits on my shoulders and put her feet up while I did all
the work. In the eleventh hour, when things weren't going
according to plan, she'd look for a junior to blame instead of
taking responsibility for her team.

"Have you apologized to Kim for not reaching out to her
first?"

"No, and I'm not going to."

At work Friday morning I overhear half of a phone conversation Kim is having.

"No, she said she would still go."

There's some mumbling I can't make out, then "Goodbye,
Rusty."

Great. Everyone is talking about me, but no one is talking to me. I'll go tomorrow and stay calm and cool, do my
thing and get out of there.

My summer is all planned. I'm going to meet a nice man
from Kitchener through the personal ads. I feel fit, confident, and ready to move on. No more boozers in bars.

I call Shelly and offer her two hundred dollars to take my
place selling meat-raffle tickets on Friday.

She refuses.

70

IN 1989 I took Carl to my ten-year West Hill high school reunion.

It wasn't the first time Carl had met my family. I'd brought him home for various family functions and weekends over the years, and they'd occasionally visited us in Toronto. For the most part he got along fine with everyone, although Shelly complained that he was whiney and had to have everything his way.

I was dreading the reunion. Still feeling grossly overweight, I worried that no one would recognize me. And of course there was the possibility that Kyle and Chris would be there.

I found a somewhat-forgiving navy jersey dress and had my hair done in a French braid.

My classmates seemed to have accomplished so much in ten years. They'd married, got their degrees, bought houses, established careers and had children. Still single and several months away from graduating, I felt like a loser with no accomplishments to speak of.

The girl who'd always been "the smart one" was now a doctor. Another classmate had just been through her second divorce and was engaged again. Ten years go by fast, but a lot can happen.

Kyle and Angie made quite an entrance. Angie had recently given birth to their third baby but still looked fabulous. She had actually brought the infant with her; he dangled in a shiny black satin sling that matched her strapless gown, a most precious jewel around her neck. She nursed him at our table.

Sitting beside her, I felt dowdy but did my best to be a good sport. I dutifully cradled Kyle Junior while Kyle and Angie danced.

Chris's arrival also caused a bit of a stir.

He wore a soft pair of tan suede pants tucked into short leather boots with a navy silk shirt. His curls were cropped short at the sides with a faux mohawk highlighted with soft purple streaks down the centre. A short pheasant feather dangled from his right ear. I'd never seen him look more beautiful. One glance and I was transported back to the eleventh grade and falling in love with him all over again.

Chris had made a pact to kiss every woman in the room that night, and I waited nervously for it to be my turn.

I was heading back from delivering a screaming Kyle Junior to Angie on the dance floor when he slipped his arms around me and planted a soft one on my cheek.

"Hey," I said. I couldn't stop smiling. "You can't know how much I've missed your beautiful face. How are you doing? Are you still living in Montreal? Are you a famous artist yet?"

"I'm still in Montreal, but I'm a famous waiter. I guess I'm not exactly living our dream. It's just that I can make a lot more money in tips than I do selling my art."

"But are you still working as an artist?"

"Yes. I have a very supportive partner and I paint every chance I get."

When I'd heard several years before that Christopher was gay, it hadn't surprised me. I think on some subconscious level I'd known it for a long time; I'd just never wanted to accept it. I had no problem with homosexuality. People are who they are. The real problem was accepting that Chris could never be mine.

"You look good, Chris. Are you happy?"

"I am, Jane. I really am."

"So, who is this supportive partner? Did you bring him tonight?"

"No, my parents are still having a little trouble adjusting to the whole homosexual thing, but they're getting used to the idea. I know they will eventually."

"Maybe I could meet him someday."

"I'd like that, Jane. You will always be my first love, and I love those times we spent together, you know. I wish we could have stayed friends."

"Me, too. Maybe it's not too late."

I'd meant to introduce him to Carl, but Chris was feeling tired and wanted to go home. Maybe the four of us could get together sometime after I finished school, I thought. I vowed to get back in touch with Christopher once we were settled. Before he left, we exchanged addresses and phone numbers.

Watching him walk away, I felt something that had been dormant for a long time begin to wake up. Christopher Graham, I realized, was the great love of my life. I remembered that feeling, of knowing with pure certainty that he was the one I wanted and no one else would ever come close.

I liked Carl a lot and I had been tentatively trying to tell myself I loved him. If we got married we'd have children and a comfortable lifestyle. And maybe that was enough. I should feel lucky to have such an opportunity; it was much more than some people ever got.

It took me eight months to find the courage to break up with him.

71

ON THE LAST Friday night of tax season, I brace myself for the meat raffle.

Everything starts off okay. I wear jeans and a Tshirt with little blue flowers on it. I even make a point of wearing my garnet ring. *Meeting Your Soulmate* advises single women not to wear rings on any of their fingers. Apparently some men are unable to determine which finger is "that finger" and get confused.

It's a slow night. With the arrival of warm weather, people would rather be outdoors.

Two old friends of mine from West Hill, Michelle 'The Murph' Murphy, who teaches Grade 1, and Jamie McKinley, who'd become a nurse, are seated at the bar. Waiting for the place to fill up enough to start the raffles, I have a drink with them.

"You're looking a little tired, Jane," Murph says. "Your buddy Paula told me you work too much."

"Well, it's tax season. It goes with the territory."

"You must make a ton of money working all that overtime."

"I don't get paid for it. I'm on salary."

"Seriously? You work all those hours and don't get paid for them?"

"I know. I always think if I was a mechanic and a bunch of cars came into my shop on Friday night, my boss wouldn't say, 'Hey the client needs these fixed ASAP. You're all going to stay here and work on them for free.'"

Jamie is looking at me like I'm nuts, but Murph nods.

"I know what you mean. I'm expected to put in all these extra hours marking report cards and doing extracurricular activities on my own time."

"But you do that because you're passionate about your kids," Jamie says.

"And you get the whole summer off," I add.

"And *she* has a great pension and makes twice as much money as you," Murph chimes in.

"Okay, this is not helping," I say.

"We're not the only ones." Michelle looks at Jamie. "You work lots of overtime, too."

"I do it to save lives," Jamie says.

"And you get paid double time and a half," Michelle says.

"Yes, but that doesn't mean I don't care deeply about what I'm doing. I'm passionate about saving lives."

"Why do you do it, Jane?" they ask in unison.

I think about it for a while.

"Because I'm passionate about paying my rent."

"Okay, passionate accountant," Paula calls out to me from the meat cooler. "Tie your money apron on. It's show time."

Over at the raffle station Big Dickie is shooting elastics at unsuspecting patrons. I chuckle when he catches nasty Maurice in the back of the head. He smiles when he sees me and reminds me of my first night when I'd stuck a bunch of change in my pockets and couldn't balance my cash.

"If the cash doesn't balance tonight, I'm going to have to strip-search you."

Off to sell tickets, I make a point of being polite but not flirtatious. I'm thrilled to see Fun Donnie shooting pool and run over to give him a hug. There seems to be a lot of newbies at the Frog and no sign of Gord.

Rusty and Dickie keep ordering drinks and I try to pace myself. I haven't eaten dinner, though, and Rusty orders a blue lagoon in honour of my birthday on Monday.

And that's when it hits me. I'm going to be forty on Monday. At least this horrible tax season will finally be over. But holy shit—forty.

When we finish, Paula asks if I want to go out for dinner and I think, Perfect. I'll grab a bite with Paula and then Rusty won't be able to call me when I get home, like he always does.

I freshen up and pay my tab. Then Paula drops the bomb. "Do you want to ride over with me or Rusty?"

There's no way to back out gracefully. Paula drives me to the casino.

We settle at a table in the downstairs bar. Paula gets herself a hot dog and fries. Rusty comes in and buys yet another round of drinks. Then I buy a round.

A really good band comes on and I sit between Paula and Rusty watching them. Suddenly his musky smell and close proximity, combined with work stress and beer and the big birthday, are too much for me. I reach under the table and gently rub my hand against his leg. Just a little bit, and I only do it twice.

Paula excuses herself to go to the washroom and Rusty immediately reverts to the powerful, passionate kisses he does so well.

"Do you want to go back to my place?" he whispers, his breath hot in my ear.

The sound of Paula clearing her throat jolts me back to reality.

"Okay, guys. I'm going to take off and do some gambling."

Rusty takes my hand and leads me to his car.

72

RUSTY LIVES IN a townhouse four blocks from me. I'd always been curious to see what it's like. Looking around the place, it's obvious why he wouldn't want to bring a woman here.

His living room serves as a storage shed for several of his son's bicycles, his kitchen sink overflows with dirty dishes and there are auto parts on the kitchen table. The bathroom should be cordoned off as a toxic-waste area.

A king-size bed takes up almost the entire bedroom. No need for dressers—his clothes are just strewn about haphazardly.

After some lovely incident-free sex, Rusty insists on falling asleep with me in his arms. As much as I love the idea of this romantic gesture, in practice I simply can't sleep snuggled up with my special someone.

Attempting to oblige, I cuddle up beside him, breathing in his bulky warmth. But eventually restlessness overcomes me and I have to adjust my position. He wakes up, pulls me back into his arms and barks, "Jane, go to sleep."

It dawns on me, then. I've been fighting the feelings I have for Rusty for way too long. I'm in love with him, and, in the end, that's all that matters.

This is it: we're back together for good this time. Sure we have our problems, but you can't fight chemistry like ours. If it hadn't been for his meddling friends, we probably would have officially become a couple months ago. Maybe I will introduce him to my family on my birthday.

We both have to get up early Saturday morning, me for my last working weekend at the office, Rusty for an early tee-off time. He drives me back to the Frog. My car looks lonely after being abandoned all night in the empty parking lot.

The fact that everyone must have seen it there doesn't bother me at all. This was no one-night stand. Rusty and I are back together for good. I have a certified boyfriend and will not, as I have feared for so many months, have to turn forty all alone.

Memories of the night before wrap themselves around me like a soft blanket.

At work I'm in pretty good shape, despite the panic-infused mayhem that grips our office as the personal-tax-return filing deadline rushes to meet us. I prepare a couple of returns for some last-minute clients who've just realized it's April 29. Then I call John and ask if anybody in the office needs help to get their work done before Monday night. Since April 30 falls on a Sunday, the Canada Revenue Agency has extended its deadline to Monday, May 1, which means I'll actually have to work on my birthday.

Larry, who slept at the office again, is slumped in his chair looking rumpled and snoring softly. "It's life, Jim, but not as we know it," Frank declares as he slams a stack of freshly reviewed returns on Larry's desk. Larry startles awake and bumps his head on his desk lamp. A thin line of his drool drops onto one of the tax returns.

Every year Dr. Brayer waits until the very end of April to bring in the information we need to prepare his year-end financial statements. Since he's a sole proprietor, his entire year-end has to be done in order to file his personal tax return. Since I'm caught up, John assigns the job to me. Dr. Brayer still records all his transactions manually in a columnar ledger book. The columns don't balance, many of the details are missing, and everything is handwritten in the same chicken scratch the doctor uses when he scribbles out prescriptions. I used to feel sorry for the pharmacists who had to decipher them. Now the race is on for me to decode an entire year's worth of transactions, get the year-end finished and finalize his tax return in the next forty-eight hours, all while working on last-minute changes, clearing taxes queries and fielding questions from unhappy clients. I put my nose to the grindstone and get everything finished by Sunday night.

I fall into bed, exhausted but relieved it's almost over. I'm a little surprised when I get home and there's no message on my answering machine from Rusty. But, then, he knows how crazy-busy I am this last weekend. Maybe he's just being thoughtful and doesn't want to disturb me.

When I wake up the next morning, it's official. I am forty.

I don't feel any different. Yes, I'm tired, but who wouldn't be after working nine weeks in a row with only Easter Sunday off? I know not a lot of things will happen today. My family celebration will be next weekend. I do a mental inventory check for a potential midlife crisis but don't feel anything out of the ordinary coming on.

At work the Happy Birthday banner has been hung over my desk and someone has left a card on my chair. The front reads

An Ode to 40

40 is good, 40 is grace
With 40 comes crow's feet and lines on you face
40 is wonderful, 40 is cool
40 is flatulence followed by drool

40 is fun, 40 is fine At 40 fertility starts to decline.

The inside of the card reads, "I'd continue, but it doesn't get any better."

Everyone in the office has signed the card and offered a few words of wisdom. Kim has written "I hope the next forty years are even more fun than the first, because in the end all we have are our memories."

I hand the card over to Cindy, who gives me my first birthday hug of the day. "Technically that's not correct. Your fertility actually starts to decline at thirty-five."

"Thanks for clarifying."

Still, I don't feel too bad. With all my rush taxes done, I try to get back to my regular year-end work, but I'm too tired and antsy to focus. My thoughts continually drift to Rusty. Maybe he'll take me out for dinner and we'll swing by the tax party after.

Alex emails me happy birthday wishes on the correct day this time. Mom, Shelly and Kristen call to wish me a happy birthday. "Where is your new beau taking you for dinner tonight, Jane?" Mom asks.

"I'm not sure. He's surprising me."

Shelly puts Billy on the phone.

"Hello, Billy."

"Is this Aunt Jane?"

"Yes."

"Where's Nana?"

"Nana doesn't live with me, Bill. She lives with Grampa."

"Who do you live with?"

I've explained to Billy a dozen times that I live alone, but he refuses to accept this concept and continues to believe that, since I'm not married, I must still live with my parents.

"I live with Wanker."

"Okay, bye."

"Billy, say happy birthday," Shelly says in the background.

"Happy birthday, Aunt Jane. I love you."

"I love you too, Bill."

For once, he and my father are not the only men who do.

Cindy takes me out for lunch. We split a cheesecake and each get a free butter-ripple shooter.

I think of the goal I'd set to find my soulmate and how lucky I am to have finally found him. I've come in just under the wire.

"Just think: a year ago we were single and alone and now we've both met 'the one,'" I say.

Looking over her menu, she gazes at me dreamily. "David and I have so much in common. Would you believe we both don't like liver?"

"You don't say," I say with what I hope is the proper degree of incredulity.

"I'm going to move back east with him when his contract in Owen Sound is finished."

"That's awesome, Cindy. You deserve the best."

When I haven't heard from Rusty by two o'clock, I call and leave a message telling him where the tax party will be; I'm not sure how to reach him at work.

Everyone keeps telling me how tired I look, which is basically code for "You look like crap." I wonder if it's because I'm now over forty or because I've worked sixty of the last sixty-one days.

Around three in the afternoon I'm about to slink out the door and rejoin the world of tax-free bliss when everybody decides they need something from me and they need it immediately. A tax return, which I'd prepared nine weeks ago and has been sitting on the floor of Dean's office waiting for review, gets changed three times.

Frank finds a mistake I made on an estate return, which normally would only have been prepared by Katie.

Joe gives me a return to fix and rerun that I hadn't even prepared.

A board member from Hanover calls demanding answers regarding a change I made on the Hanover financial statements audit two months ago.

And still no call from Rusty.

To stop myself from crying at work, I flee to my office and attempt to hole up there until the storm has passed.

"That's it, captain. She'll not take anymore," Frank mutters as I shuffle past him.

Kim follows and gives me a hug.

"Incoming," John shouts as he barges into my office with his arms full of files. He sees my teary face.

"She's not taking any more crap," Kim informs him. "We're all backed up with crap."

"You've reached new levels of crap concentration," John quips.

"Okay, enough with the toilet humour," I say, unable to hold back a smile.

"Are you okay?" John sits on the ancient case our client Thistle Funeral Home has been using to transfer their records to us for over two decades. "I was going to tell you about this new client I just met with, but it can wait until Wednesday if you need a break."

Just then the ancient box snaps under his weight and he falls butt backward on the floor.

"You did that on purpose, to make me feel better," I sniff.

It's just after five when I wrap up my last-minute questions. Before heading to the tax party I slip home to take Wanker for a quick walk around the block and check my answering machine. My heart races when I see it flashing, but it's only Nana calling to wish me a happy birthday.

I call Rusty's place again but hang up when I get his machine. One message is enough; two sounds desperate. Surely he'll be home from work soon.

Almost everyone is at the tax party except for Joe and John, whose wives have been looking after the kids on their own for two months straight and will not tolerate one more night. The office admin ladies were the last to arrive, as they had been busy assembling returns and assisting with client pick-up to the very end.

Conspicuously absent is Frank. After having successfully guided us through tax season without Katie, no one
deserves a party more, but he'd disappeared late that afternoon and his whereabouts remain unknown.

Cindy's infamous new boyfriend, Dave, accompanies
her to the tax party. From what I've heard about internet
dating, it's mainly a medium where sociopaths and nerdy
weirdos lacking in social skills stalk potential victims online.
But Dave strikes me as quiet, sensitive and intelligent. Most
importantly, he treats Cindy like a queen.

I keep checking the front door, waiting for Rusty to
arrive. Maybe he'll bring a birthday cake or a bouquet of
flowers. But as the time ticks away I'm forced to accept
that he's not going to make an appearance. Kim, who knows
I've been expecting him, keeps hugging me and putting her
hand on my shoulder for support.

At eleven-thirty Dean loads thirty-seven tax returns into
the back of his minivan and drives them downtown to the
post office, where he waits in line with several accountants
from other local firms. The post office stays open until midnight to accommodate the last-minute returns that need
to be postmarked May 1 to avoid Revenue Canada's hefty
penalties.

After Joe's departure everyone begins cueing up to say
goodnight. Having had several hours to sober up after my
last birthday drink, I say goodnight and drive home alone.

There are no messages on my answering machine. And I
realize my worst fear has been realized; I have turned forty
alone.

73

IN SEPTEMBER OF 1990, a decade after I'd started that first fashion course in Toronto, I wrote and passed my final accountancy exam.

I was officially certifiable.

After the years of working, studying and writing exams, my graduation was anticlimactic. I was certainly relieved to be done with all the studying, but for years I'd imagined my problems would magically disappear upon graduation. I was surprised when the loss of a definitive goal to work toward left me feeling adrift and unsure about my next steps.

My social life was in shambles. I'd broken up with Carl a year ago and, although a suitable mourning period for that relationship had passed, I'd yet to meet anyone who piqued my interest. My dear friend Kristen had moved back home to Owen Sound after I'd helped her husband, Evan, get a job as a mechanic at my brother-in-law Steve's auto dealership. Most of the new staff at Unique Boutique were younger than me, and partying with twenty-somethings and sharing close living quarters with a gaggle of roommates had lost its appeal.

I knew I needed a change. I just didn't have a clue what I wanted.

In April of 1991, one month before my thirty-first birthday, Mom phoned my apartment.

"Jane, I just read in the *Sun Times* that Christopher Graham passed away. You were always so fond of him, I thought you should know."

It had been two years since I'd seen Chris at the reunion. I thought of the feathers in his hair, the mischievous grin on his face as he kissed every girl in the room. I tried to hold that image of him in my head, so happy and beautiful and free.

My mother's words refused to register in my brain. It couldn't be true. The man who'd been the embodiment of love and laughter had left this world forever. I lay down on my single narrow bed and cried like a woman who'd stored up her tears for years.

It took a while before I could piece together the details of Christopher's death. My parents hadn't heard that he'd been sick. I found out later that he'd returned home, where his mom looked after him during his last few weeks. By the time my mother saw his obituary in the paper, the funeral was over. Mom eventually heard through the grapevine that, like so many young men coming out in the early eighties, he'd contracted AIDS before anyone really knew what it was or how to protect themselves.

I woke up the next morning with a calm certainty. I called home and was surprised when Shelly answered my parent's phone.

"What is it?" She sounded annoyed, and I realized I was calling during Oprah. I heard a toddler laughing in the background.

"I want to come home." Although she was the last person I'd ever look to for help or sympathy, I couldn't contain my sobs.

But her voice softened. I couldn't believe my ears when she immediately came to my rescue.

"I can pick you up this afternoon," she said without hesitation. "I'll get Steve to borrow one of the trailers from his shop. Have all your stuff packed up and ready to go. I'll tell Mom and Dad to get your room ready."

74

THE EUPHORIA THAT normally floods over me when tax season wraps up for another year is nowhere to be found.

It's just another day, I tell myself. I go to bed anxious to escape this day of hurt and disappointment. My recurring dream of desperately searching for a crying baby in an empty house returns. In a panic, I race again from room to empty room. Only this time, when I throw open the last door at the end of the hallway I'm standing balanced on the ledge of a rocky mountain cliff. The view is spectacular, but I'm paralyzed with fear and can't move. Then Wanker appears a few feet above me on the mountainside. When I reach up to rescue him he snarls; it's not Wanker at all but a mountain goat with a bearded pointy chin. The beast rushes toward me and rams me with his curled horns. My feet slide backward down the mountain on the crunchy gravel, and I grab at everything within my reach—tree roots, grass, rocks—in an attempt to regain my balance. But it's no use. I can't get my feet back under me. I'm still scrambling when the goat turns on me again, his deep-brown eyes changing to glowing red embers. Attempting to step out of his way I fall backward off the mountain. I kick my legs and flail my arms, but nothing stops me. Free-falling now, I spin in the air as the village below rushes up to meet me. Seconds before I hit the ground I wake up trembling and sweating.

I lie there for some time, staring at the ceiling, only partially released from the dream world. I remember the breathtaking view from the top of the mountain. I think about babies and grapple with the realization that in all like-lihood I will never have one. I cry and cry until I finally drift off, wondering what it would be like to fall asleep and never wake up.

• • •

I wake up angry.

In accordance with tradition, I've taken May 2 off. It gives me time to assess the situation and regroup. I remember with bitterness how excited I'd been a year ago, launching my plan to meet the man of my dreams and finally start my family. And with Rusty, I'd thought I'd found him.

How could I have been so stupid?

I'd left my car overnight at the bar, for god's sake. Rusty probably didn't call me because he'd been at the Frog all weekend bragging about Friday's exploits. How could I have let him humiliate and use me like that again?

As a matter of pride, I'd never succumbed to what I'd always thought of as the degradation of a one-night stand. Now Rusty has made me the butt of his sordid joke. How could I have let him treat me so badly?

You are not a victim, the angry voice in my head tells me. You deserve so much better than this. You deserve a real relationship—not some idiot who wants to sleep with you once a month with no strings attached and then ruin your reputation.

With renewed determination I sit down and write my first-ever personal ad:

> I am a professional single fit female who is a non-smoker. I've never been married and have no children, other than one very spoiled wiener dog.
>
> My interests include hiking, biking, reading, music, working out and walking my dog. I'm looking for an employed single male between the ages of 36 and 50 with a great sense of humour.
>
> A decent mustache is also an asset.

Placing my personal ad is much easier than I expect.

You call the phone number in the paper and set up a voice mailbox, where your message is recorded. To stay anonymous, you make up a name. Men call in, listen to your message and, if interested, leave a voice message for you to call their voicemail. You can chat with someone without ever revealing who you are, what your real phone number is, or where you live.

In my first voicemail I say I live in Owen Sound. I decide this is a bad idea and redo it.

I change it to "north of Kitchener." If I leave it as Owen Sound, I'd eliminate the whole pool of Kitchener men and severely limit my options. There can't be any decent single men left in Owen Sound. I've turned over every rock. If there are any good ones left, I'd have found them by now.

Plus, if I tell the truth people might recognize me.

I put my personal ad in the *Kitchener Record* and then call thirty or forty times to see if any men have read my ad and left a message.

They haven't.

I call five or six men's mailboxes and leave messages saying I'm interested.

Already I'm starting to feel better.

Instead of waiting at home by the phone, I'm being pro-active and taking charge of my life. Thinking about it gives me a warm feeling, and for the first time I feel some relief that the most horrible of single birthdays is over with. I've made it through and I'm still fighting. And, for all I know, Mr. Right may be listening to my voicemail right now.

If Cindy can find someone, so can I. I can't wait to see the look on Rusty's face when I introduce him to my new boyfriend.

As if magically conjured by my thoughts, Cindy calls, bubbling with excitement.

"David gave me a ring."

"Oh my god—you're engaged."

"No, it's not an engagement ring. It's a 'Honey, I love you' ring."

"You lucky thing. Rusty wouldn't give me a napkin ring."

"It's time you turfed that loser."

I think about how happy Cindy is and how well Dave treats her. I seriously consider internet dating. I've already taken the plunge and put myself out there with a personal ad; advertising on a second medium might increase my chances.

The only problem is that I don't have a computer at home and there's no way I'll do it at work and risk having the partners find out what I'm up to.

I call Kristen.

She invites me over for lunch and we have a riot drinking wine while filling out my profile and scanning my picture into three different dating websites. By the time we finish our cake I am signed up on PlanetUltimate, Lavalife and Quest.

It's a beautiful day and I decide to get out of the house so that all those men who are listening to my personal ad or viewing my online dating profile will have some time to contact me. I put Wank in the car and we drive north along the coast of the peninsula to Colpoy's Bay, where the rocky beach with the view of Whitecloud Island lifts my spirits.

Once we leave Owen Sound, Wanker realizes we are on a road trip. He hops from foot to foot, then stands on his short back legs and bounces up and down in a vain attempt to see out the window. I try to keep him on the passenger's seat but he constantly climbs all over me.

When we get to the trail Wanker rushes ahead up the old stone steps into the woods. The long stems of wild grass and Queen Anne's lace sway in the breeze. The water is choppy, and in the distance the insect-like buzz of motor boats harmonizes with the rhythmic slap of their bottoms hitting the waves. A lone Canada goose wades in the surf and hisses malevolently at Wanker, who gives it a wide berth. Geese normally mate for life; I wonder how this one managed to get separated from its gaggle. Perhaps his wife is hiding on a nest out of sight while he takes on the job of warding off strangers.

It gets darker as we hike farther into the woods. The trees are taller here, and the heavy canopy of newly budding leaves blocks some of the sun's rays. There's less grass with all the peninsula rock, but the forest floor is covered in ferns and moss. We stop for a rest at Skinner's Bluff, looking out to the east.

Dachshunds are bred to scent, chase and flush out vermin and other underground quarry; the German word "dachshund" means "badger dog." True to his heritage, Wanker is in his glory, exploring every nook and cranny, sticking his snout as far up every hole as it will go. His straight skinny tail is a rubber antenna waving back and forth like a metronome set to presto.

"If you were bred to hunt rats, Wanker, how come you couldn't sniff Rusty out?" I muse.

He lets out a gleeful yip and charges ahead as I mull over the activities of the last four days. A buzzing sound up ahead barely penetrates my subconscious. At first I think it's just the boats again, but it really sounds more like a baby's rattle. I remember my nightmare of the empty house and the crying baby. Have I sunk so low that my nightmares have come to haunt me in broad daylight?

But I hear it again and think, No, that was real.

I glance about in search of Wanker.

He's ten feet to my left, fervently digging into a hole like he's going for China. There must be something in there. I can't make out if it's just a rock or a rodent, so I move closer.

And that's when I see the rattler. It's about two feet long, thick bodied, with dark blotches outlined in white against its grey abdomen. It has a wide triangular head with a white

stripe across it. But it's the distinctive sectioned rattle at
the end of the tail that gives it away.

Wanker is crazed. He runs up to the snake, lets out a
bark, peels back to me and repeats this frenzied cycle. It
feels like we are caught in a slow-motion time-lapse photo-
graph. I call him away but he won't stop. Run, bark, repeat;
run, bark, repeat.

The snake remains motionless.

"No, Wanker," I scream. And then I am frozen, unable to
do anything except watch in fear.

Massasauga rattlesnakes are shy creatures that
haven't earned their scary reputation. There've been only
two known deaths from Massasauga bites in Ontario, and
both of those involved people who didn't seek treatment.
Most injuries occur when people misguidedly attempt to
handle them.

This snake is trapped and, with Wanker refusing to leave
it be, it cannot retreat. I watch in horror as its mouth opens
wide, hovers for a moment, then strikes, its fangs sink-
ing deep into the top of Wanker's silky head. He lets out a
mournful yelp and the snake, finally free, slithers quickly
away into the ferns.

I run to Wanker and scoop up his quivering body. He's
shaking, drooling and his eyes look wide and disbelieving.
There's blood everywhere, and already I can see his head
starting to swell. He's whimpering and breathing hard.

"Oh, Wanker, don't leave me now," I mumble into his vel-
vety fur. I take off my hoodie and wrap him in it, holding him
close to me as I run for the car, tripping and stumbling along
the rocky trail as my eyes fill with tears. I have to get him to
the vet before it's too late.

I pick up the cell phone I carry in the car for emergencies. I know the hospitals in Georgian Bay carry anti-venom, but what do you do for a dog? I call my regular vet in Owen Sound, who directs me to a clinic in nearby Wiarton that carries anti-venom for pets.

I step on the gas to get there as quickly as I can, trying to keep Wanker comfortable on my lap. When I arrive at the clinic, a vet takes him into an examining room immediately.

I tell her what's happened, although, from all the swelling in Wanker's head, it's pretty obvious.

"When dogs are bitten on the head, it's critical because of the speed with which the venom can impair the dog's respiratory system," she tells me. "It's especially dangerous with small dogs, since the swelling can encompass a massive part of their head."

"Will he make it?" I'm trying to keep it together but my lips twitch, giving me away.

"It's too soon to tell. I'm going to try fluid therapy to restore his blood pressure and inject epinephrine to treat the allergic reaction and swelling."

I spend the rest of the day at the clinic, holding Wanker, stroking him gently, and waiting. What would I do without my best friend?

By eight o'clock he appears to be stabilized and out of danger, but the vet recommends I leave him there overnight in case complications arise. When I get home the house feels empty without a dog to greet me. Edith Wharton said it so well: "My little dog, a heartbeat at my feet."

There's a message on my machine from Kim. She's sorry she didn't buy me a drink for my birthday yesterday. Do I feel like grabbing a quick one tonight?

I call her back. "Oh my god, Kim. I've had the worst day ever."

"Sounds like you could use some company," she says. "Where would you like to go?"

"Anywhere but the Barking Frog."

75

KIM AND I meet up at the Coach Inn pub, where we sit at the bar drinking lots of beer and listening to a cool cover band doing classic rock from the seventies and eighties.

I tell her about Wanker and how scared I'd been to almost lose him, and before I know it we are both in tears. She shares some stories about her life. She hadn't married George until 1992, after she'd had both of her kids with him. She's starting to go through menopause and she talks about that. Somehow she gets around to talking about her old boyfriends.

She wants to know about me, and I talk about Christopher and Kyle and Carl.

I tell her about Sean and we both laugh.

"I thought you were never going to tell me about him. We dated for three years when I was in university. I was madly in love and wanted desperately to marry him. But he wasn't the settling-down kind. All the time I was dating him he never told me he'd fathered a child. And then he went and married that bimbo."

This aroused my curiosity. Sean had never told me much about his ex-wife. "Which bimbo would that be?"

"I can't think of her name; I'm having a meno-memory moment. But you know who I mean—Rusty's wife."

Now it was my turn to be confused.

"Rusty's not married."

"Suzanne. That's her name—Suzanne. She was Rusty's first wife; she left him to marry Sean."

The beer I'm hoisting to my lips stops its course midflight.

"Wait a minute. Sean's ex-wife and Rusty's ex-wife are the same person?"

"Yes, it was quite the scandal back in the day. Sean and Rusty were good friends; they both played for the King Farms ball team. Then Suzanne ran off with Sean when the boys were just little. Three and six, I think."

The bar started spinning.

"Oh my god, Kim. I slept with both of them."

"You've really got to start dating outside this town."

"In the last seven years I've only been intimate with two men, and it turns out both of them were married to the same woman. How can that be a coincidence?"

The pain of my last encounter with Rusty, which I'd pushed to a back burner during Wanker's crisis, begins to steam, bubble and spew out over everything once again.

"He's talked about me all over the Frog, you know; I don't ever want to go back there."

"Rusty does love to talk, and I hadn't realized how much he's been drinking. With him it's sometimes hard to tell."

Rusty and Sean were married to the same woman? My brain goes into spin cycle; my thoughts are tumbling. How has this happened? Has the dating pool in Owen Sound shrunk so small you can't date one guy without the two of them being connected somehow?

Had Rusty known about me and Sean before we'd even gotten together? Was it a revenge thing? Rusty's wife had left him for Sean, after all.

Then another dumbfounding thought occurs to me. Rusty has the smallest penis I've ever seen, while Sean could have made a career as a stunt double for porn stars. Perhaps size really does matter.

At least to Rusty's ex-wife.

76

I CALL THE vet's office as soon as it opens the next morning. Wanker is responding well to treatment. There's still some swelling, but he's doing much better and is expected to make a full recovery.

Hugely relieved, I leave for the office in a positive frame of mind.

At work my focus shifts to the client files that came in during the last few weeks of April and were set aside until tax season was over. Many of them are difficult, messy files I hadn't wanted to get into until I had the time to concentrate on them. Some files slide through the process smoothly; others pass like kidney stones, creating intense abdominal pain as they pass through one's system.

Kristen calls with some news. "I've just had an Alex sighting. He's walking down 2nd Avenue in a dress shirt, tie and bucket hat."

"Well, spring must be officially here. The robins have returned, the Chi-Cheemaun has sailed and Alex's wearing his bucket hat."

"How is Wanker doing?"

"He came through like a trooper. I'm going out to get him after work tonight."

The office is abnormally quiet today. Cindy and most of the tax department took the week off, Katie is still on sick leave, several staff are out of the office on audits that started this week, and nobody's seen Frank since Monday night.

Joe is away and one of his clients, Stockett Construction, keeps calling John to get copies of their financial statements, which the bank demands by the end of the day. I'd cleared the queries on this job two weeks ago but Joe had never gotten around to signing off on the financial statements, and now John and I can't find the files. They've disappeared into the black hole that is Joe's office.

John and I have no choice but to pull on our hip boots and wade in after them. We meet at the door to Joe's big corner office, pushing it open as purposely as a cop on the trail of a potentially armed perp. John finds the phone number of Stockett's banker in one of the files. To write it down I grab Joe's pen from the gold and marble Platers' commemorative pen-holder on his desk, and it breaks right off.

We look at each other in horror.

"We're in trouble now," I say to John. "Wait 'til Dad gets home."

Fifteen minutes before the last courier is scheduled to leave, Joe swans into the office and signs off on Stockett's financial statements without so much as a glance at the queries. The file is closed for another year.

Back in my office I get a call from Emily, a sixty-six-year-old woman whose tax return I'd prepared back in March.

"Hi, Jane. My refund came in the mail today."

"That's good. Was it for the amount we'd calculated?"

"Yes, but for some reason the cheque was made payable to the estate of Emily B. Starr. When I took it to the bank they wouldn't cash it."

"You're not dead, are you, Emily?"

"No, I'm perfectly healthy."

"Okay, let me call Revenue Canada and see if I can find out what happened. I'll call you right back."

I get Emily's file from the file room and check over her return. I don't see anything wrong or unusual. I call Revenue Canada.

"She's dead," the agent confirms.

"It must have been sudden. I just talked to her five minutes ago."

The agent does not appreciate my sense of humour. "I can't discuss her file with you any further, Ms Parker. As soon as a taxpayer passes away, your authorization as her accountant is automatically revoked."

I call Emily back with the sad news. "You're going to have to call the CRA and convince them you're still walking among us. Just tell them the rumours of your death have been greatly exaggerated."

I don't think she got it.

I slip home for lunch, grabbing my mail at the front door. I open it with the same knife I'm using to make a sandwich. Searching for the mustard, I glance at my phone bill and do a double take. It's for $652.19. Apparently I'm being charged by the minute for all the calls I make to check on my personal ad. Add this to the hefty invoice I'd get for Wanker's emergency vet services, and I know that, once again, there'll be way too much month left over at the end of the money.

I can't stop beating myself up over this. My mini midlife crisis has come with a big price tag. Calling to check the personal ads has cost me over five hundred dollars. And if I'd had my head on straight yesterday, I'd have kept Wanker on a leash and out of danger. I'd had my head so far up my butt, dwelling on my problems, I hadn't paid attention to what was going on around me.

I take a deep breath.

It's time to calm down, take a break, get my ducks in order. No more bars or meat raffles, or dating men who have the same ex-wife. I'm going to stay home, work on my house, read some good books and try to make some sense of it all. Nothing else is going to happen to me for the rest of the month, at least.

I'm getting off this ride.

I chuck my lunch into a paper bag and drive toward the office, stopping to eat at a little park a few blocks away. So what if I'm forty, broke and single? The sun is shining, tax season is over, I have friends and family who love me, I finally lost that last ten pounds, and my little dog is coming home.

I watch a group of young girls playing double Dutch on the tarmac. Their hands expertly turn the long pink rubber skipping ropes in perfect rhythm. A girl at each end holds the handles as a third dashes into the centre and starts skipping. The rope-turners chant in time to the beat of the ropes hitting the pavement:

> I wrote a letter to my love
> And on the way I dropped it.
> A little doggie picked it up
> And put it in his pocket.

He won't bite you
And he won't bite me
But he'll bite the one who's got it.
So drop it, so drop it...

The school bell startles me, and the girls abruptly drop their ropes and run to classes. I reluctantly saunter back to my car, considering playing hooky on this gorgeous afternoon, but I remember the files piled high on my desk and return to the office.

It's too quiet with just John and I working upstairs, so I reach over to turn my radio on.

At the exact moment I push the On button the sound of screams erupt from the main floor. At first I think it's just from the radio, but then everything gets quiet and I freeze, my fingertips resting lightly above my computer keyboard. My ears strain to hear what's going on below, but all I can hear is the rush of blood from my heart, which seems to be beating at a highly agitated rate. Another scream cuts through the air, and then I hear a gunshot.

I look desperately around my office. There's no fire escape and no way out of the building without going downstairs. I briefly consider jumping out a window but worry that the fall will kill me.

The screams from the first floor stop, the front door bangs closed and an unearthly silence descends. I say a prayer that whoever caused this commotion has fled, but I hear footsteps. Someone is coming upstairs.

Trying to stay calm I flip off the desk lamp and radio and hide under my desk. If he thinks there's no one in my office, maybe he'll just walk on by. The sound of the footsteps on the stairs is light; whoever it is is humming to himself in a tuneless monotone. Too late, I remember that my computer is still running.

I'm trembling and trying not to make a sound, but my heart feels like it's beating loud enough to be detected miles away. Will anyone hear it and come to rescue me? My mind is racing. Scattered images pop into my consciousness. It's like I've emptied my old photo albums into a pile and my brain is randomly shuffling through them, picking out snap-shots from various time periods.

I'm filled with desperate thoughts. I don't want my life to be over yet; there are still so many things I want to do. Fall in love, have a baby, do something to leave this world just a little bit better than when I entered it.

In a moment of clarity unlike any I've ever experienced, I realize my life is perfect and amazing and wonderful. I know instantly that everything I want is within my grasp and always has been. All I have to do is stop waiting for the world to grant me permission.

I pray that I will live long enough to experience it all.

There's a slam as my office door hits the wall. I sense that the man with the gun is standing in my office, and I hold my breath. There's a moment of silence, and I pray that he's left. A bead of sweat drips off the bridge of my nose and lands in one perfect drop on the hardwood floor. More silence fol-lows, and hope bubbles up inside me; maybe he's moved on. I drop my chin to my chest and peer out from under the desk. Directly in front of me are Frank's battered brown topsiders. He's wearing one brown sock and one blue, and both sets of laces are undone. The shoes proceed around the corner of the desk and stop directly in front of me.

The muzzle of a gleaming mahogany hunting rifle lowers and points at my forehead. I look up at Frank, but there's no trace of recognition on his face.

I open my mouth to speak, but nothing comes out. I hear two clicks, like the sound of a key turning in a lock, then the roar of the gunshot, followed by an intense pain just below my chest. A second bullet rips through an overstuffed tax envelope sitting on the corner of my desk. It bursts open, sending dozens of T slips airborne. They flutter in formation like white, pink and blue butterflies before they come to rest ever so gently in a heap on the floor.

I'm going to have to sort those slips again, or else Frank will give me more fuck-up sheets. I watch a large red drop plop down on the pile. Another drop follows, and another. I watch in stunned silence as my blood fans out, rendering the receipts illegible.

In the movies when the heroine faints, it's always done so romantically. When I think of fainting I picture Scarlett O'Hara swooning with one hand pressed dramatically against her forehead, petticoats aflounce, as she falls back into Rhett's arms. My last thought is, How did I get the flu so fast? I think I'm going to be sick.

I get a warm feeling when I realize I'll get to take the rest of the day off.

Everything goes black.

77

I'M NOT TOLD until several days later that Frank had shot me and then John before he turned the gun on himself.

When Frank pulled the trigger for the final time there were no bullets left. Undaunted, he ran the length of the second floor hallway as quickly as his scrawny legs could, launching himself at the big picture window at the north end. He'd envisioned his body pierced by a thousand shards of glass, bones snapping when they hit the ground, like the printer he'd tossed from the second floor sixteen years earlier. But Frank's slight body simply bounced off the leaded glass, falling backward with a thud to the floor. One of Owen Sound's finest emerged from the shadows to pounce on him, securing him with handcuffs before pushing him outside to the waiting squad car. With Frank looking stunned and subdued, the cop hollered at the paramedics to go in and tend to John and me as quickly as possible.

Cindy's in the hospital room when I wake up. Sitting beside my bed talking to Internet Dave on her flip phone, she doesn't notice my blinking eyes until I try to sit up. This startles her so much she screams and drops her phone, which spins like a top on the hospital floor. Too dumbfounded to retrieve it she keeps repeating "You're awake, you're awake." I open my mouth to utter agreement but my throat is so parched that all that comes out is a croak. Cindy runs to find a nurse, who sprints to my bedside. She takes my vital signs, then Cindy hugs me and the nurse hugs me. Cindy picks up her phone and dials my mom and dad.

Kristen, who'd been looking after Wanker, smuggles him into the hospital for a visit. He's still wearing a doggie 'cone of shame' to stop him from worrying his snakebite wound. He looks like a walking wiener dog satellite dish. When he sees me he goes ballistic and attempts a heroic leap from the floor to my lap. His short legs aren't strong enough; he misses his mark and his cone gets stuck between the bars of my bed. He's wedged in so tight I can't get him out. He dangles, howling and kicking his feet like he's peddling a bicycle, until a nurse finally frees him. She places his quivering body in my arms.

They tell me I've been unconscious for four days but am recovering nicely from a gunshot wound to the abdomen. I'm wobbly on my feet, but my appetite has returned in full force and all bodily systems seem to be up and running. Since I'm used to working out every day, I feel bloated and weak from lying motionless for so long. I'm anxious to be active and feeling like my old self again.

John was not so lucky. Frank's last bullet pierced his chest at close range, and he died within minutes. The paramedics did their best to resuscitate him, but it was too late.

I think about John and how much I liked working for him. I remember how he used to go home at five every night to have dinner with his kids, read them stories, tuck them into bed and then come back to the office again and work late into the night. Now his children will wait forever for a father who is never coming home.

Frank suffered a mild concussion from hitting his head on the lead-glass window. He is undergoing psychiatric assessment at the Central North Correctional Centre in Penetanguishene and will most likely plead not guilty by reason of insanity. Frank had also fired shots at two administrative staff members working on the main floor. Betty fainted and Fiona didn't stop running until she'd reached the Owen Sound police station, which, luckily, is just around the corner from us. Joe had heard the noise, locked his office door and escaped out the first-floor window; he walked to Shoppers Drug Mart and called 911.

On the day of John's funeral, every flag in Owen Sound was flown at half mast. Dean broke down and closed the office for the first time in years. But only for one day, of course. Everyone knows that death and taxes are the only certainties in life.

With John, Frank and me out of commission, FACK found itself severely understaffed. This led the partners to ask Katie, who was responding well to chemo, if she would consider coming back to work between treatments.

She declined.

• • •

They want to keep me in the hospital for several more days, but I'm itching to go home as soon as possible. When you get a second chance to stop screwing up your life, you don't want to miss one minute of it. I'd thought turning forty was the end of the world; now I see it as a new beginning.

On my last day in hospital Paula stops by for a visit.

"I knew you wouldn't leave me to do our last meat raffle on my own, Jane," she says, leaning in for a hug.

We chat amicably for a while, enjoying the spring sunshine streaming in through my window.

"You know how I told you I'm retiring from Haven House at the end of the year."

"There you go rubbing it in again, Paula. You've always loved your job so much; don't you think you'll miss it?"

"I'm planning to volunteer there for the part of the year when I'm not travelling. I'd like to go someplace warm for the winter. At the board meeting last Thursday, they asked if I was ready to start training my replacement, and I told them she was recuperating from a nasty gunshot wound but she'd probably be ready to start sometime in June or July. Do you think you'll be up and about by then?"

Dad and Mom drive me home, where there's a shiny new desktop computer on the desk in my den. I turn it on and realize they've had it set up for me. It's even got an internet-connection cable. My email Inbox is flooded with messages from the three dating websites I'd signed up for on Kristen's computer. I remember the two of us drinking wine and laughing as we answered all the questions. That seems like a lifetime ago.

Apparently over a hundred men on the internet already want to go out with me. I know many of them will be totally inappropriate, but hopefully none are psychopaths. Some will be basically like me: a single person who wants to connect with other single people and has found a convenient way to do so.

A quick scan of my Inbox allows me to estimate that I can go on two dates a week for the next two years. As a woman of forty who is gainfully employed, baggage-free, semi-attractive and has no prison record, my status has sky-rocketed from social pariah to Wonder Woman. Although I'd ticked off the box saying I wouldn't date anyone farther than 100 kilometres away, my potential suitors are scattered from Thunder Bay to Ottawa. And, as the number of people with the internet in their homes continues to climb, the population of online men available for dating will grow exponentially. The floodgates have opened; once again there are too many fish in the sea.

I don't have to bowl, curl, golf, drink, peddle meat, throw darts or do anything that doesn't interest me in order to meet men ever again. I can date outside Owen Sound but, if what I'm seeing on these websites is correct, there may actually be a few guys out there I just didn't know about.

I will never chase men again. The shoe's on the other foot; men are chasing me.

My life has been reclaimed. I can spend my time working out, cooking, reading, looking after my dog and my adorable little house, and dating. I've already signed up for an art class at Georgian College, and I can't wait to get started.

78

THE FLAG IN front of the office is still at half-mast when I return to clean out my desk and say goodbye to everyone. I can't keep from peeking into Frank's office as I walk down the hall to mine. It looks the same as it always did, with files piled high on every available surface. The ashtrays and coffee cups have been removed, but a faint odour of stale cigarette smoke lingers in the air.

Packing up my office doesn't take much time. There aren't a lot of things I want to take with me. I put the framed photos of Dad and me on horseback, Shelly and Steve surrounded by their brood, and Wanker as a puppy, into a cardboard box. I remove my diplomas from the wall, a stash of jujubes from my desk, a spare pair of shoes, an Owen Sound Platers hockey puck and a blue stress ball with the FACK logo on it. I take the plaque with my name on it from my door and toss it in the box as well.

I chuck my voluminous copy of the 1999 income tax act into the recycling bin.

Cindy has arranged for the BFGs to take me out for a goodbye lunch. Joining her are Kim, Fiona and Betty. Anne comes in from her maternity leave, and Elizabeth is able to take time out from packing for her elopement back to Banff with Brian. She invites Wanker and I to come out for a visit.

I don't think I'm going to cry, but when Katie arrives sporting a beautiful Pucci patterned headscarf instead of her vibrant strawberry curls, I feel my eyes tearing up.

"I won't miss tax season, but I'll sure miss you guys." I don't let anyone leave until I've coerced them all into visiting me at Haven House.

I've made plans to go on a date with Dana this evening. He's a social worker I met online and we've gone out a couple of times. I've yet to be struck by lightening with him, but he seems pleasant and intelligent enough. He'd called earlier that morning to say he had to paint his house this weekend; would it be okay if we went to the late show?

"Sure," I say. *I guess we're going to the movies.*

"Good. We're going to *The Perfect Storm*; it's on at 9:45."

For a social worker Dana seems somewhat autocratic.

Then Cindy phones.

"David just gave me a diamond. We're engaged. It's official."

"Oh my god. I'm so happy for you."

And I really am. Dave seems like a great guy and appears to be as head over heels in love as Cindy is. I know that marriages are a gamble and the odds these days are against you. But maturity brings with it the wisdom to make better choices. Because we know ourselves so well by now, we have a better sense of what is right for us. When you marry in your twenties, you don't know who either of you is going to be when you grow up. I think Dave and Cindy know themselves well enough to realize they're a perfect fit.

Cindy's engagement gives me renewed confidence that you can find love past the age of forty and you can meet good men on the internet. Maybe it will happen for me and maybe it won't, but I know one thing for sure: if I do happen to meet Mr. Right, he's going to have to like babies.

I keep busy with housework all day and have just finished mowing the front yard when the phone rings. By the time I get inside Kim has left a message. She sounds ripped. She's at the Barking Frog and wants me to call her on her cell phone. I know I can't go out because of my date with Dana, so I decide to call her tomorrow.

When I finish cutting the back yard I see she's left another message.

"Jane, you're pissing me off. It's twenty to eight. I'm still at the Frog, you big turkey. Love ya. Bye."

By now I'm running late and have to rush to get showered and dressed. I'm towelling off when there's a knock at my front door. I must have left it open, because I can hear Kim calling me from the kitchen.

"Hold on," I holler. "I'm just getting out of the shower and I'm naked. I'll be right there."

I pull a towel around me and go to meet her. Swaying in my kitchen is a very drunk Kim with a somewhat-sheepish Gord in tow.

"I've been golfing in a tournament since noon in the fuckin' 89-degree weather, and I need a beer to cool down."

I fetch her one of the Old Viennas I keep in my fridge just for her and get Gord a Canadian. "I'd love to come out with you guys, but I have a date coming to pick me up in half an hour."

On hearing this news, Gord looks embarrassed and incredibly cute. I hope he won't think Dana is my boyfriend. "Why don't you stay here and have a drink with me while I'm waiting? We're going to a movie; you two could come with us."

Kim is all for it but sober Gord just wants to get the hell out of there. He does everything he can to get Kim to leave, but she's in the mood to party.

When he finally manoeuvres her to the front door, she lingers to say goodbye with the screen door cracked open.

Always thrilled to meet new people, Wanker, who'd been prancing in circles around our unexpected guests since the impromptu kitchen party began, sees daylight through the open door and makes a break for freedom. Escaping to the front yard he gleefully runs back and forth with Kim stumbling drunkenly in his wake. I stand helpless on the front step, clinging to my towel and laughing until I cry.

She finally corrals the wanton wiener and deposits him back in the kitchen, both parties exhilarated and panting from the exertion. She hugs me goodbye twice and yells at Gord, "Kiss her! Kiss her already."

He dutifully pecks me on the cheek and leaves to drive Kim home to her husband.

My date with Dana is a definite departure from our earlier hijinks. It begins with an in-depth analysis of his allergies and medical history. He follows up with a long explanation of how he needs to wear a pager to the movies in case a social-worker emergency arises and he's called upon to prevent someone from committing suicide.

I think that if I have to listen to him for one moment longer I'm going to need counselling myself.

After paying for the movie he says, "Jane, can you buy the drinks and popcorn? I don't have enough cash on me."

I try to focus on the movie, but I keep picturing Gord in my kitchen.

79

WALKING INTO MY final meat raffle in old jeans and a clingy tree-leaf-print Tshirt, I've never felt more confident. I'm chatting with Cindy when Rusty comes over and begins pulling meat from the big silver chest. He sits down across from me.

I chat with Bart and hug Fun Donnie. Cindy is in heaven flaunting her diamond ring in front of Bart as she shows it to Jimmy the bar owner and announces her wedding date.

There aren't many people in the bar and ticket sales are slow. It's the first night of the Canada Day long weekend, and the weather is gorgeous.

At first Paula wants to sell one ticket at a time, but that takes forever so we switch to two. We end up letting people buy as many as they want just so we can get rid of them.

On my first round, idiot Maurice starts giving me a hard time, insisting he wants to buy one and a half tickets. I just walk away from him and never go back. His wife is so nice. Why do these arrogant guys always have a nice wife who is perpetually mortified by their asinine behaviour?

Bruce the electrician is in his usual spot at the bar, looking spiffy in a yellow Tshirt so bright it would glow in the dark.

I get down to business, remembering how nervous I used to be about doing the raffles. Tonight I'm as calm and collected as Cindy Crawford strutting on the catwalk. I don't chat much with Rusty, but all my anger toward him has evaporated. What does it matter now? He's part of another lifetime; I've moved on to a better place.

I sell a ticket to a handsome blue-eyed man at the bar who resembles a real-life Ken doll. He casually puts his arm around my waist.

"How much are the tickets?"

"A buck apiece."

"And how much for you?"

"I'm not for sale," I tell him, slipping away from his grasp. I sell him my last ticket, whip off my money apron and sit down with Kim and Cindy.

"How come you didn't sell me the winning ticket tonight?" Gord, who'd been playing pool in the back corner, suddenly materializes.

"I guess you're just not lucky," I grin.

"I demand an audit."

"You'll have to ask Kim; I don't do those anymore."

"Did you hear about that guy who got caught stealing one-point-seven million dollars from his employer last week? The company was audited by this big-eight accounting firm and they didn't even catch it."

"Well, one-point-seven million might seem like a lot to you and me, but in the audit of a huge corporation like the one he worked at, it wouldn't be considered material."

"What do you mean by 'material'?"

"Materiality is essentially accountant speak for 'Don't Sweat the Small Stuff.' The concept is that you don't need to identify mistakes that wouldn't make a difference to a reasonable user."

"What happens if the user isn't reasonable, and how on earth do you quantify such a thing?"

"We calculate an actual number; then, as we're working our way through the audit, we keep a running total of mistakes we didn't adjust on a sheet called the Schedule of Likely Aggregate Misstatements, or SLAM. If the sum total of the errors goes over the materiality threshold we've calculated, we have to fix them or we can't give a clean audit report."

"So, your date the other night. Did he get a clean audit report?"

"He wasn't material."

"I think you'd better add him to your Statement of Likely Aggregate Misstatements."

"He might just put me over my threshold."

Kim has another beer and calls George to come and pick her up. Thrilled to be finished with meat raffles forever, I say my goodbyes and leave the Frog with a happy sigh. I'm sure I'll be back every now and then, but it will be on my own terms. My status as a regular has long expired.

I'm just getting ready for bed when there's a knock at the door.

I freeze for a moment. I look out the window and see a familiar Grand Am in my driveway.

Rusty's standing on my porch. He looks good; he's just had his hair cut short and his eyes are clear and blue. Our eyes meet and he pushes his way in. I put Wanker down and Rusty's arms are immediately around me.

"I came to apologize."

"For what?" I feel the attraction between us firing up again, but I take his hand firmly and remove it from my waist.

"For everything."

That sexy, husky voice. Even in my new confident state, I'm going to have to summon up super powers to resist him.

"I miss you, Jane."

He casts out the line with the expertise of a veteran fly fisherman, and for once I see it for what it really is. It's worked so many times before. He waits patiently to see if I'll bite, ready to reel me in. But those days are gone. I am wise to his ways. I've let go of the hate and the hurt, but I won't make that mistake again.

"I had fun, Rusty. I'll always remember you fondly."

"Are you seeing somebody?"

I think of my datebook, full to bursting for the next several months.

"Yes, I kinda am."

"Then I guess this is goodbye."

I kiss him chastely on the cheek.

"When we first met you told me I didn't kiss like a grandfather."

"But you are a grandfather."

And he's gone.

80

IT'S MONDAY MORNING and I'm sitting at my make-shift desk just outside Paula's office at Haven House, 'shadowing' her, when Alex calls. I smile when I see his name on my call display.

He's won a bunch of free show tickets for the Hanover casino. To tempt me into attending one with him, he begins firing off the names of upcoming performers.

"Danny and the Juniors."

"Before my time."

"The Monkeys."

"Um, no."

"Tony Orlando."

Actually, I used to really dig the *Tony Orlando and Dawn* show. Are they still around? In the end, though, I have to decline. It wouldn't be right to accept poor Alex's tickets and not go with Alex.

"Alex, the day we did the Big Walk for Cancer I noticed that Evangeline, who works at the library, could not take her eyes off you. She's single and close to your age. I think she would really enjoy going to one of these shows with you."

"Well, she's a very nice lady. It's just that she dresses so frumpy all the time."

Apparently the pot will not date the kettle, but at least I've tried.

I leave work early for an afternoon appointment with Dr. Peters. He'd visited me several times while I was in the hospital. Today he has lots of questions about my recovery and checks that the wound is healing properly.

"You're recovering nicely, Jane. Do you have any concerns?"

"No, I'm feeling great. Will there be any long-term side effects?"

"It's unlikely. The bullet didn't hit any of your organs. You were extremely lucky."

He doesn't have to tell me.

I'm sure one day this feeling will wear off and I won't be thrilled by every brilliant sunset. Maybe I'll stop savouring every delicious morsel of food like it's my last and stop lingering over every conversation with a fellow friendly spirit. But right now, all I want is to enjoy the extraordinary gift of being vibrant, healthy and alive on this planet at the dawn of a millennium bursting with possibilities.

"On a side note, I was going to tell you that we got the results back from the mammogram I prescribed at your last check-up," Dr. Peters says, breaking into my reverie. "Are you still taking the anti-depressants I prescribed back in April?"

"No. They got me through tax season and turning forty, which was great. But I've stopped taking them, and I won't be needing a new prescription."

"What about tax season next year?"

"I'm working at Haven House now. Tax season 2000 was my last."

"Congratulations. How's it working out?"

"I love it. It has its share of stress, like every job, and some days are better than others, but I've never been happier."

"Is there anything else I can do for you today, Jane?"

I take a deep breath and look him straight in the eye. "I've decided to have a baby on my own, and I want to know what my options are."

He smiles.

"There are several options available to you, Jane, and there is an excellent fertility clinic not far from here. I can set up a referral for you. They'll contact you to make an appointment to come in for a consultation. Would you like me to initiate the process?"

"I'd like that very much, Dr. Peters."

On my way home I pick up two coffees and muffins from the drive-through and stop in for a visit with Mrs. Graham. She still lives in her big old house on 9th Street but is preparing to move to a retirement villa.

She looks happy to see me. We drink the coffees on her porch and chat for a bit. Mrs. Graham and I are both introverts. Chris must have inherited his gregarious nature from his dad. But we are both comfortable in our own stillness, bonded forever by the boy we loved so much.

"I've been going through my old things to get the house cleaned up and ready to put on the market, and I came across something I want you to have," she says, leading me to the dining room.

Propped on an easel is a large water colour painting. At its centre a petite girl stands on a limestone cliff overlooking Georgian Bay. She stands with her back to us, shiny blonde hair hanging down her back. Both hands are in her jeans pockets and she appears to be searching the Lake Huron horizon. She wears battered sneakers and a rumpled hoodie. It must be spring; the colours are varying shades of lush green against jagged grey rock melting into blue lake and sky.

For a few minutes I just stare at the picture with my hands in my pockets, like its subject. The painting has a mossy grey-green mat and one of those gold metal frames that were so popular in the eighties. On the back I notice Christopher's scribbled signature and the title: *Still Life Jane in Grey County.*

A tear slides down my cheek, and Mrs. Graham comes to stand beside me, her hand resting lightly on my forearm.

"He painted it when he was at McGill, Jane. I know he would have wanted you to have it."

"It's so beautiful."

"It's beautiful to see you smiling again."

After we say our goodbyes and I load the painting into my hatchback, I've just enough time to pick up a few groceries at Metro before I have to get home to let Wanker out.

At the grocery store, I push my cart up the frozen-foods section, where a curly-haired man reaches for a five-cheese tortellini frozen dinner at exactly the same time I do.

"You take it," he says, smiling.

"No, it's okay. You take it," I say, flashing him a big one right back.

"I insist."

So, I do. After all, they're on sale for $1.99 and life is just too short, I think, to fight over processed pasta.

I can't help noticing he's kind of cute and has a great moustache.

"Have I seen you around before? You look kind of familiar," I say.

"I'm a police officer. We met one night last winter when you cut me off driving home late from work. And I was at your office the day of the shooting. I tackled Frank Keyes and helped the paramedics load you on the stretcher. It's good to see you up and about. How are you feeling?"

"Much better, thank you."

"If you're really in the mood for pasta, why don't I take you to Kettles for dinner one night? Their home-baked lasagna is the best."

I write my phone number on the back of my shopping list and hand it to him.

"Aren't you going to need this?" he says, looking down at the list.

"Not anymore. I know exactly what I want." And nothing will stop me from getting it.

It's a beautiful evening, so after dinner I take Wanker down to the harbour for a walk. It's busy again with the tourists back in town. Now that June is almost over it stays light outside until shortly after nine.

I smile and nod at people as they pass. Wanker stops to sniff around the red belly of the Ancaster Tug, an ancient grey logging boat that's beached in a small garden by the water. A young boy asks if it's okay to pet my dog. I nod, and Wanker trots over and sits expectantly in front of him.

"He's so soft," the boy says to me, gingerly reaching to touch the velveteen fur.

"Don't worry. He loves kids; he won't hurt you."

He cuddles with Wanker for a few minutes before running to catch up with his parents, who are ambling towards the parking lot together. At the last minute he turns to wave and blow a kiss.

I breath in the scent of a late blooming crabapple tree and laugh at two seagulls squabbling over a discarded French frie. I nod to a bearded fisherman patiently reeling in his line and navigate carefully around an elderly couple walking hand in hand along the ancient path.

In the distance I can see the shores of Balmy Beach leading up to Sarawalk on the outskirts of the county where I grew up. In the west, a red tailed hawk flys in lazy circles above the tree covered crest of the escarpment.

Moments before the sun finally drops down to touch the water, the lights of the ancient grain elevators that guard the harbour's mouth light up. The lamps from the iron lampposts add to the glow, accenting the shadows of dark pine trees against a glowing orange sky. Warm waves of quiet joy, like the small ripples lapping against the steel harbour walls, wash over me. I feel the gentle tug of the leash in my hand and turn back onto the brick path by the water's edge.

I walk off into yet another glorious Lake Huron sunset.

Acknowlegments

SPECIAL THANKS TO writer/muse Betty Gibson Saunders for her help and encouragement over the course of this project. Also to Heather Saunders, for her positivity, inspiration and enduring friendship.

Thanks to copy editor Joanne Haskins of Think Communications for always knowing the right words; Sari Richter for her capitvating cover artwork and to the Trimatrix Management Consulting Inc. team for pulling it all together.

And most of all to my amazing husband, who's encouragement, support and hard work makes everything possible.

Made in the USA
San Bernardino, CA
28 February 2018